Scientific Soapmaking

Also by Kevin M. Dunn

Caveman Chemistry

Scientific Soapmaking

The Chemistry of the Cold Process

Kevin M. Dunn

Clavicula Press
Farmville, VA

Scientific Soapmaking: The Chemistry of the Cold Process
by Kevin M. Dunn

Clavicula Press

Farmville, VA
www.ClaviculaPress.com
ISBN 978-1-935652-09-0

Revision History
Revision 1.57   2010/03/16   HSMG Debut
Revision 1.67   2010/06/18   BCCE

Publisher's Cataloging-in-Publication Data

Dunn, Kevin M., 1958–.

Scientific soapmaking : the chemistry of the cold process /
Kevin M. Dunn.

xviii, 413 p., lc23 cm.

Includes bibliographical references and index.

ISBN 978-1-935652-09-0

1. Soap. I. Title.

TP991.D86 2010

668'.12–dc21   2010902850

Table of Contents

List of Tables

List of Figures

List of Examples

List of Equations

Foreword

by Marie Gale

MAKING soap is both an art and a science. It is the unlimited combination of the two that makes handcrafted soapmaking so appealing (and sometimes so challenging).

It was the art that appealed to me when I first started making soap. I found many books that had pictures of beautiful and creative soaps that inspired me on my own artistic quest. Like making a perfectly decorated cake, my objective was to create tantalizing soaps with my own unique blends of color, scent and shape, and the perfect "feel" of the soap.

With that goal in mind, I found a basic recipe in a book and started on my soapmaking journey. I did read the sections in the book that explained the basic chemistry of soap, but, honestly, all that chemistry didn't seem nearly as important as finding just the right blend of essential oils and learning which herbs would produce gentle colors and holistic benefits. After some successful soap batches within the narrow confines of my basic recipe, I started improvising. Shortly thereafter I had my first failed batch; not much later I found Dreaded Orange Spots on some of my first soaps. It was devastating.

That's when I realized that the true art of soap making is how to create a bar of soap that is tantalizing and pleasing to the senses—and to do it within the constraints of the science and chemistry of the process.

Not one to give up, it was back to the drawing board. What caused my batch to fail? Why were there Dreaded Orange Spots on some soaps, but not all? What could I do to eliminate the problems? I went back and re-read all the information I had about the chemistry of soapmaking. I found and read handcrafted soapmaking books, searched the Internet and joined numerous on-line soapmaking groups. Sadly, the available information was not only limited, it was often conflicting and sometimes just plain wrong.

Meanwhile, I continued to make soap, experimenting on my own with oil blends, temperatures, and mixing techniques. Looking for more reliable information, I found and purchased numerous "old" books on commercial soapmaking (1930 and before). There I found the chemistry I was looking for—but it was very advanced and, not having a firm science and chemistry background, I spent many hours looking up words and studying the materials. My soaps were good, and my understanding of the science was increasing, but I still felt like I was reinventing the wheel. The real chemistry and research for handcrafted soapmaking should be out there somewhere, shouldn't it?

Then, at the 2005 Annual Conference of the Handcrafted Soapmakers Guild, I attended Kevin Dunn's presentation on the "Dreaded Orange Spot." It was my "ah-ha" moment. Here was some actually researched and documented scientific data! In the subsequent years Kevin has presented his research into a number of different aspects of soapmaking, each time bringing proven data and filling in a piece of the scientific puzzle.

With the publication of *Scientific Soapmaking,* we who make handcrafted soap will finally have the true science and chemistry we need, presented in a way that is understandable even to those of us who didn't pay attention during science and chemistry classes.

Marie Gale

Past President, Handcrafted Soapmakers Guild

Author, *Soap & Cosmetic Labeling*

February 21, 2010

Introduction

CHEMISTRY is not widely viewed with admiration by the general public. Astronomy has the stars, twinkling suns of unimaginably distant planets from which, perhaps, alien stargazers peer into the night sky and ponder our existence as we ponder theirs. Biology has ornate birds and fragrant flowers and glow-in-the-dark creatures of the ocean depths. Paleontology has myriad monsters both large and small, emerging, thriving, and vanishing over eons that dwarf our conceptions of eternity. Archeology has mummies, skeletons, lost tombs, splendid treasures of ancient civilizations, and the romance of dust left undisturbed by the passage of time. These are the sciences that inspire fiction. By contrast, there is no quicker end to a cocktail-party conversation than to confess a passing acquaintance with the Periodic Table. It is no wonder, then, that students shun chemistry in favor of her more personable sisters.

Yet the past thirty years have seen a renaissance in a long-forgotten chemical craft. This resurgence of interest was led, not by educators or industrial chemists or government agencies, but by modern-day alchemists working in kitchen laboratories that hearken back to the very dawn of the science. Retorts and furnaces have been replaced by Pyrex measuring cups and microwave ovens, base metals by lard and tallow and olive oil. Their Philosopher's Stone *lyes* hidden on grocery-store shelves, accessible only to those who appreciate its terrible power. And their "gold," like that of their hermetic forbears, is considered the key to health and longevity.

Soapmaking is now a well-established cottage industry, successfully competing with multi-national giants whose products sell for a fraction of the price of **handcrafted soap.** The Internet hums with websites and forums and mailing lists devoted to teaching and outfitting hobbyists and entrepreneurs alike. There are many wonderful books, most of them by women without formal training in chemistry, that provide a veritable cornucopia of recipes for soaps of every description. What need is there for another book, particularly one penned by a man and a chemist? While my sex and profession are under-represented among practitioners of the craft, I am no less smitten by the soap bug, and it is with a sense of profound humility that I venture to add a few words to the soapmaking literature.

Within the soapmaking literature there are really two distinct genres. The older of the two serves the traditional **commodity** industry with an emphasis on the economical production of soap by the ton, and its readership is expected to have a background in chemistry and chemical engineering. The newer genre serves the emerging craft industry with an emphasis on the production of high-quality soaps by the pound, and its readership is familiar with the language and format of cookbooks. Though the processes used by the two industries are really quite different, many of the principles are the same. By selectively borrowing scientific techniques from the commodity literature, I believe that makers of handcrafted soap would be better able to resolve problems and improve the quality of the products they so love. If I can bridge the gap between the commodity and craft literatures, I will consider my time to have been well spent.

There is nothing wrong with making soap from a recipe. There is nothing wrong with testing your soap by simply washing your hands with it and deciding whether or not you like it better than your last batch. But for many soapmakers, the thrill of early success eventually succumbs to the frustration of the scent that faded, the bar that never quite hardened, and the dreaded orange spots that disfigured an otherwise perfect bar of heaven-on-earth. The scientific approach to handcrafted soapmaking differs from the cookbook approach simply in the following proposition: We can explore the complexities of soap by changing one variable at a time and objectively evaluating the results.

The systematic approach need not drain soapmaking of joy or adventure. It simply adds method to the madness of spending hours in loving labor to make a product that must compete with those available ready-made at any grocery store. You may continue to use your favorite recipes, employing the methods of this book to solve problems as they arise. You may from time to time throw caution to the wind, blending whatever oils you happen to have on hand just to see what will come of it. You may simply be interested in how one chemist faces the challenges imposed by nature on this fundamentally chemical craft. The systematic approach has deepened my appreciation for this nearly magical avocation and has provided structure to my own personal exploration of its wonders. Whether you be a rank amateur or an established entrepreneur, I hope that you will find something of value in these pages. And, perhaps along the way, you will find in chemistry a beauty largely unappreciated by the general public.

To the Handcrafted Soapmaker

Many of the makers of handcrafted soap I have met confess that they wish they had paid more attention to high school chemistry. The arcane formulas and exotic glassware, the indecipherable names and brown glass bottles of stink seemed boring, dangerous, or irrelevant at the time. But these folks now find themselves determined to learn concepts they vaguely remember resisting in their youth. If you are such a person, I have written this book for you. In my mind, it is the textbook for the chemistry course you now wish you had taken in high school or college. I hope you enjoy it.

To the Student

Many students are forced to consume chemistry because their elders feel that, like broccoli, it will be good for them. Small wonder that these students resist the experience with all the ferocity of a cat faced with the prospect of a pill. If you are being force-fed a chemistry course based on this book, I can certainly understand your lack of enthusiasm. I might try to convince you that chemistry is fascinating and useful, but I presume that you are smarter than my cat, who sees through my pitiful attempts to hide pills in lumps of cheese. Instead, let me suggest that you simply *pretend* that you might someday, under some as-yet unforeseen set of circumstances, consider owning your own soap company. Imagine that you'll want to know how to make intelligent decisions so that your business will thrive. Imagine that, unlike your competition, you will not have to wish you had paid more attention in chemistry class. If you can make that leap of the imagination, you'll find that the time will go faster, the work will make more sense, and your grade will be higher than it would have otherwise been.

To the Teacher

You can lead a horse to water but you can't make it drink. We chemistry teachers live this proverb every day, leading reluctant students to water for which they have not yet acquired a taste. If twenty years of teaching has taught me anything, it is that I cannot teach people what they don't want to know. Much of my energy, then, is dedicated to motivating students—helping them to understand that some of the things I want to teach them are worth knowing. Students who are motivated by a desire to make soap will find that every bit of chemical theory and practice in this book advances them toward that goal. If we teachers can simply convince students that soap is as interesting as it is useful, they will become thirsty for the water we have to offer.

A Little Haiku

In the beginning
Jackie Thompson called me up
For a soap lecture.

Thanks to Mike Lawson,
Columbus Foods gave us oil
To support our work.

Alex Santic and
Liz Rand scrutinized my words
And fixed my mistakes.

Please see the index—
Scientific soapmakers
Are former students.

Beverley Hines keeps
The soap laboratory
Stocked and organized.

Without my Sunshine
I would be lonely and sad.
Thank you, my Dearest.

Conventions Used in This Book

Words set in **boldface italics** appear in the *Glossary*. Citations marked with square brackets [ ] appear in the *References*. Important points throughout the book will be highlighted by the following admonitions:

Duckbar the Duck will provide suggestions and tips that may make your life easier.

Marvin the Mole will remark on important issues of record keeping and the use of the notebook.

Leo the Lye-on will point out information that, if neglected, might lead to the misunderstanding of procedures or fundamental concepts.

Chevreul the Chemist will stress information that, if neglected, might lead to the failure of an experiment, waste of materials, or production of soap that is unsafe for use.

If Chevreul had an accident this serious, it would result in property damage or personal injury.

Pronunciation Guide

The following words may seem difficult to pronounce if you have never seen them. They are fun to say, however, and their correct pronunciation signals others that you may actually know what they mean. Practice saying them now so that you do not stumble over them later [79].

Alkali	**al**-kuh-lahy
Alkane	**al**-keyn
Anhydrous	an-**hahy**-druhs
Anion	**an**-ahy-uhn
Cation	**kat**-ahy-uhn
Centipoise	**sen**-tuh-poiz
Deliquescent	del-i-**kwes**-uhnt
Electrolyte	i-**lek**-truh-lahyt
Ester	**es**-ter
Hygroscopic	hahy-gruh-**skop**-ik
Miscible	**mis**-uh-buhl
Moiety	**moi**-i-tee
Phenolphthalein	fee-nawl-**thal**-een
Saponification	suh-pon-if-i-**kay**-shun
Saponify	suh-**pon**-uh-fahy
Stoichiometric	stoi-kee-uh-**met**-trik
Stoichiometry	stoi-kee-**om**-i-tree
Titrate	**tahy**-treyt
Titration	tahy-**trey**-shun
Triacylglyceride	trahy-as-il-**glis**-uh-rahyd

Part I

Experimental Soaps

When I began working on this book, one soapmaker suggested as a title *Everything You Always Wanted to Know About Soap*. This is not that book. This is less a book of answers and more a book about how to formulate answerable questions. The key to answering many of these questions will reside in your ability to make single, carefully formulated bars of experimental soap. Many of these bars will be "bad," in the sense that you would not give them as gifts or sell them as merchandise. We'll consider them good, however, in the sense that they allow us to test hypotheses without wasting valuable materials. The answers we find can ultimately be applied to larger batches that may thereby be new, improved, or more consistent. Even if you are already used to making 10 or 25 or 50 pounds of soap at a time, Part I will equip you with new skills to help you work effectively at an experimental scale. These skills will be essential for the procedures introduced later in the book.

Whether you are a novice or a professional, by the end of Part I you will:

- be familiar with the equipment needed for making small batches of soap
- understand how to use an electronic balance to make measurements
- understand how to read a material safety data sheet
- understand all of the math needed for experimental soapmaking
- be familiar with the common oils and the properties they lend to soap
- understand how to use the alkali ratio to determine the quantity of lye needed to make soap from a blend of oils
- understand how to determine the quantity of raw soap needed to fill a particular mold

Chapter 1

Tools of the Trade

*T*RADITIONALLY, the kind of study you are about to undertake would require a fair amount of specialized and expensive equipment. Recent advances, however, have raised the quality and lowered the prices of tools that will prove invaluable to your investigations. The first of these is an electronic scale; the second is a dedicated soap oven to accelerate cure times and simulate aging. Laboratory equipment, chemicals, and oils are now available by mail order from companies with online catalogs. And the most important tool of the soapmaker is a notebook in which to keep records. With these inexpensive tools, you will be able to explore soapmaking at a very sophisticated level.

1.1 Electronic Balance

There are two words for the thing people use to weigh things. What cooks know as a *scale,* chemists know as a *balance.* Historically, these two words referred to different weighing devices. A scale was originally a device with a pointer attached to a spring; a balance was a lever with pans upon which you placed standard weights. Most people nowadays, however, use an electronic weighing apparatus still known as either a kitchen scale or a laboratory balance, depending on venue. The inner workings are now exactly the same and you can use either term interchangeably. The soapmaker will likely need two or three different balances: one for experimentation, one for production, and perhaps one for bridging the gap between small-scale experimentation and large-scale production.

In order to use the balance to best advantage, the soapmaker needs to become familiar with two terms that specify the capabilities of a balance: capacity and readability. The ***capaci-***

ty of a balance is the largest weight it can accurately register. A bathroom scale may have a capacity of several hundred pounds, a kitchen scale may hold a few pounds, and a jeweler's balance may buckle under the weight of a few ounces. The ***readability*** of a balance is the smallest increment it can display. The bathroom scale reads to the nearest pound, the kitchen scale to a tenth of an ounce, and the jeweler's balance to a thousandth of an ounce. Since most of the work in this book is at the experimental level, you will need a balance with a capacity of 200.00 g and a readability of 0.01 g. I will refer to this as a ***centigram*** balance.

Until recently, electronic centigram balances started at several hundred dollars, but in the past few years the cost has dropped below $100.[1] The MyWeigh iBalance 201 has all of the features needed for experimental work. It has a capacity of 200.00 g and a readability of 0.01 g. It runs on batteries and has an AC adapter. Many battery-operated balances have an auto-off feature to save the batteries, which is very inconvenient if the balance turns off in the middle of an experiment. The iBalance 201 has an auto-off feature that can be disabled so that it remains on until you turn it off. It comes with a calibration weight, has a backlit display for easy reading, and a stainless steel pan for easy cleaning. While this may sound like an advertisement for the iBalance 201, any balance with all or most of these features will be fine for experimental work.[2]

"Pocket balances" have become increasingly popular and inexpensive in recent years. I tried out several brands but found them all to be too delicate for soapmaking. The pans are small, and it is easy to spill liquids in such a way that it damages the balance. In addition, many of them have auto-off features that cannot be disabled. None of them have AC adapters and the batteries don't last very long. These balances are perfectly fine for weighing jewelry or other solid, non-corrosive materials, but

---

1. Prices are given in this book to give the reader some idea of the relative costs of items needed for the work. All prices are in US dollars as of 2007/2008.
2. In this book I will give example prices from specific vendors. While not an endorsement, this practice gives the reader an idea of what things cost. It also thanks those companies who have given me good service. www.OldWillKnottScales.com [26] sells the iBalance 201 for $98.90.

making soap with them has proven frustrating. That said, the Jennings JScale JS-200XV has many of the features we would like to have. It uses easily replaced AAA batteries and the auto-off feature can be defeated. For $30 more, however, you could have the iBalance 201 and that would be my recommendation.[3]

1.2 Soap Oven

The handcrafted soapmaking community consists of many diverse denominations, each with its own acronym. The fundamental division is between those who melt soap and those who make it. Melt-and-pour (MP) soap is specially formulated soap that can be melted, mixed with scents and colors, and poured into a wide variety of single-bar cavity molds. **Cold-process** (CP) soap is produced from precisely controlled mixtures of oil and lye. Scents and colors may be added to the raw soap, which is poured into molds that are either insulated or heated. The heat source chosen gives rise to the terms *microwave hot process* (MWHP), *crock pot hot process* (CPHP), or *cold process oven process* (CPOP), also known as the *in the mold hot process* (ITMHP).[4] In this book we'll use the CPOP for single test bars, and the cold process for larger batches.

Oil saponifies (becomes soap) faster at high temperature than at low temperature. Because the **saponification** reaction releases heat, it is often sufficient to simply insulate a large mold. The heat released warms the soap enough that the reaction proceeds apace. In this book, however, we'll be making small batches of soap for experimental purposes. The heat from the reaction is quickly dissipated in a small mold, and we would like to compensate by keeping the soap warm in another way.

There is nothing wrong with using a microwave oven or crock pot to make soap, but for experimental work we would like to control and monitor the temperature. For this reason I suggest using a dedicated "roaster oven," which looks

---

3. www.OldWillKnottScales.com [26] sells the JS-200XV for $69.90.
4. The term **hot process** (HP) leads to some confusion because it is used by the commodity and handcrafted industries to describe different processes. For commodity soap, it refers to a process in which oil is heated or boiled with an *excess* of lye. For handcrafted soap, it refers to cold process soap that has been heated during saponification.

Figure 1-1. The Soap Oven

something like a large crock pot for roasting chickens and turkeys. Crock pots usually have only high, medium, and low settings—you want an oven whose temperature you can set. Look for one whose temperature control starts at 65°C (150°F). Models change from year to year, but at the time of writing the Rival RO200 has all of the features we would like.[5] It includes a built-in timer and the temperature can be set digitally. In addition to the Rival, we use a General Electric 168962[6] and a separate appliance timer.[7] The roaster oven may be used for melting fats and oils and for maintaining a constant temperature during saponification.

Because the thermostats on these inexpensive ovens are not incredibly accurate, it is important to use a thermometer to control the temperature of your soap oven. You may use an oven thermometer or you may drill a small hole in the lid of the oven to accommodate a digital thermometer probe. An infrared thermometer is not ideal for this purpose because the actual oven

---

5. www.RivalProducts.com [31], 2008 price $40.
6. www.geHousewares.com [13], 2006 price $30.
7. www.SmartHome.com [38], 2046 programmable timer, 2008 price $17.

temperature may vary from place to place within the oven. If you use an infrared thermometer, place an Erlenmeyer flask of mineral oil in the oven and use its temperature as representative of the oven temperature. Whatever thermometer you use, measure the actual oven temperature and adjust the oven setting up or down to reach the target temperature.

In addition to a roaster oven, a microwave oven is a handy addition to the soap lab. It can be used for melting oils rapidly and for dissolving soap for analysis. In truth, the roaster oven can do these things as well, but the microwave oven is faster and, as inexpensive as they have become, a soapmaker will not regret the minor expense of having both ovens available.

1.3 Laboratory Supplies

Most of the work in this book can be performed without specialized glassware. We'll make use whenever possible of items available at local grocery or drug stores. There are some specialized items that, though not required, are inexpensive and useful enough that it is worth your time to get your hands on them.

- *Thermometer:* You will need a way to measure the temperature of caustic solutions and raw soap. You may use anything from an inexpensive stainless steel pocket thermometer to a digital thermometer with a stainless steel probe. At the top of the line is an infrared thermometer, which is used simply by pointing it at the item and pressing a button. The thermometer itself does not come into contact with the item.[8]

- *Dispensing or Dropping Bottles:* These bottles are capable of delivering one drop of liquid at a time. Two styles are included in the table and either of them is suitable for our work. You need at least five bottles of whichever style you prefer.

- *Transfer Pipets:* Transfer *pipets* look like one-piece plastic medicine droppers. They are chemically inert and come in a variety of sizes. You can get a box of 500 very inexpensively.

- *Bottles:* Because of the heat generated, it is generally recommended that lye should be mixed in a Pyrex glass container.

---

8. My infrared thermometer cost $49.99 from www.RadioShack.com [29].

Table 1-1. Laboratory Supplies

Description	Part Number	Price ($)
Pocket Thermometer	096-01864	6.75
Digital Thermometer	096-01740	18.25
Infrared Thermometer	096-93435	50.90
LDPE Dispensing Bottle, 125 mL	150-23736	1.95
LDPE Dispensing Bottle, 125 mL	150-24252	1.95
Transfer Pipets, 5.8 mL, 500/PK	132-24513	14.75
PP Wide Mouth Bottle, 125 mL	150-23847	0.90
PP Wide Mouth Bottle, 500 mL	150-23849	1.80
PP Wide Mouth Bottle, 1000 mL	150-23850	2.80
Erlenmeyer Flask, 125 mL, 12/PK	115-20155	17.00
Erlenmeyer Flask, 500 mL, 6/PK	115-20159	14.90
Watch Glass	115-20093	0.50
Evaporating Dish	117-32230	0.70
Glass Vials w/caps, 30 mL, 12/PK	115-27974	10.50
PP Powder Funnel, 95 mm	150-23402	2.50
Safety Goggles	180-11037	4.90
Eyewash Bottle w/Eyecup, 16 oz	180-50267	7.50
Eyewash Solution, 32 oz	180-11328	9.75
pH Paper Strips	113-33912	1.50
Nitrile Gloves, 100/PK	various sizes	7.95

www.Cynmar.com [9].

For lye storage, however, glass bottles are less than ideal because the lye will react with the glass over time. In addition, if you move into large-scale soapmaking you will find that large Pyrex containers are expensive, heavy, and of course, fragile. I am going to recommend that you mix and store your lye and other chemicals in polypropylene (PP, recycling code 5) plastic bottles, which are resistant to high temperatures. Not only are plastic bottles resistant to harsh chemicals, they are better than a measuring cup at containing lye fumes. We'll also use these bottles for weighing and storing oils and for making soap. You will need a dozen or more small (125 mL), three to six medium (500 mL) and four large (1000 mL) bottles. Bottles come in wide-mouth and narrow-mouth varieties. The wide-mouth bottles are easier to clean and can often times be loaded without the use of a funnel.

- *Erlenmeyer Flasks:* An **Erlenmeyer** flask has a wide bottom and a narrow mouth, making it perfect for mixing solutions by swirling them. We'll need at least three 125 mL flasks for measuring free alkali or acid and three 500 mL flasks for measuring saponification values. Though flasks are not expensive, an economizing soapmaker might reasonably substitute oven-safe Mason jars in any procedure that calls for an Erlenmeyer flask.

- *Watch Glasses:* A watch glass is a small curved dish that we'll use to cover Erlenmeyer flasks when they are in the oven. You will need three watch glasses if you want to measure saponification values.

- *Evaporating Dishes:* An evaporating dish is a porcelain dish intended for drying things. We'll use them to measure the moisture concentration of soap. If you have more than one dish, you can analyze several soaps simultaneously.

- *Vials:* Vials are always handy. Get them with Teflon cap liners, which will resist harsh chemicals.

- *Funnel:* A powder funnel has a wide neck that will allow chunks of material such as sodium hydroxide pellets to pass through. It may also be used to fill plastic bottles with the solutions you will prepare.

- *Safety Goggles:* Safety goggles are the most important piece of safety equipment for the soapmaker. The most serious hazard is the possibility that a drop of lye might be splashed in your eye with disastrous and life-changing consequences. Safety glasses or prescription glasses are acceptable alternatives for the less safety-conscious soapmaker, but goggles provide the most protection.

- *Eyewash Bottle:* With any luck you will never need this. It will sit on your workbench, waiting in anticipation of a careless moment that, hopefully, will never come. The bottle is designed to quickly wash an eye in case of an accident. Academic laboratories will have relatively expensive eyewash stations, but the solitary soapmaker can get by with an inexpensive eyewash bottle. If you do have an accident, you will be very glad to have spent the money on this. The eyewash solution is just sterile saline.

- *pH Paper Strips:* This is the modern version of litmus paper. When dipped into a solution, these paper strips change color according to the pH of the solution. Strips are available in narrow range or wide range varieties. If you get narrow range strips, we are most interested in the range 7–12. The wide range strips are cheaper, however, and are sufficient for our needs.

- *Gloves:* Dishwashing gloves are perfectly fine for making soap, but nitrile gloves are inexpensive and more resistant to harsh chemicals.

Most scientific supply companies sell the materials listed above, but many will not sell to the general public. Table 1-1 contains part numbers and prices for supplies that may be purchased from Cynmar Corporation, which sells to the general public. Their prices are very competitive and they have given me excellent service over the years.

1.4 Chemicals

There was a time in the not-too-distant past when it was possible to buy sodium hydroxide at the grocery store in the drain opener aisle. In the US, Red Devil Lye was a staple of the fledgling handcrafted soap industry for many years. Unfortunately, it was also a staple of the handcrafted methamphetamine industry, and in recent years sodium hydroxide has

Table 1-2. Chemicals

Description	Price ($/lb)		
	8 lb	32 lb	64 lb
FG Sodium Hydroxide	3.12	2.50	2.03
Technical Sodium Hydroxide	2.62	2.03	1.72
Potassium Hydroxide	3.75	2.50	2.34

www.AAA-Chemicals.com [1]

Prices in us$ per pound.

Description	Part Number	Price ($)
Phenolphthalein Powder, 25 g	*CHP-84768	4.90
1% Phenolphthalein Solution, 500 mL	*CHP-84785	10.17
Citric Acid, Anhydrous, 1 lb	†CIT-1	2.50
Tetrasodium EDTA, 1 lb	†EDTA-01	8.00
Rosemary Oleoresin Extract, 16 oz	†ROE-01	38.95
Beeswax, 1 lb	‡5041	12.00
Candelilla Wax, 1 lb	‡5061	14.00
Carnauba Wax, 1 lb	‡5071	10.00
Cinnamon Leaf Essential Oil, 16 oz	⌖702	19.50
Clove Bud Essential Oil, 16 oz	⌖704	24.25
Lavender Essential Oil, 16 oz	⌖707	39.25

*www.Cynmar.com [9]

†www.LotionCrafter.com [18]

‡www.EssentialWholesale.com [10]

⌖www.WholesaleSuppliesPlus.com [42]

disappeared from grocery and hardware stores. It is still available by mail order, but methamphetamine producers who value their privacy have taken to stealing it from soapmakers rather than having it shipped to their home laboratories. Sodium and potassium hydroxides are the most hazardous materials you will use in soapmaking. Not only will you have to pay shipping charges to get them, but you will have to lock them up to protect them from children and marauding drug dealers.

Table 1-2 gives prices for chemicals available from AAA Chemicals.[9] While the technical grade sodium hydroxide is good enough for making production soap, I recommend the food-grade (FG) material for experimental work.

In addition to sodium and potassium hydroxides you will need other chemicals to perform the tests and experiments in this book:

- *Phenolphthalein:* Phenolphthalein is an indicator that turns pink at high pH. It will be used for the analysis of starting materials and finished soaps. You may dissolve the dry powder in alcohol to make a 1% solution, or you may buy the solution pre-mixed.

- *Citric Acid:* Many acids would be suitable for the tests we need to perform. In an academic laboratory, potassium hydrogen phthalate is the primary standard for acid/base titrations, but it is not generally available to the public. Food-grade *anhydrous* citric acid, however, makes a very good acid standard, and it is available in high purity and low cost from the same firms that sell soapmaking supplies. Make sure that it is *anhydrous* citric acid by asking your vendor for the material safety data sheet. Anhydrous citric acid has a Chemical Abstracts registry number (CAS) 77-92-9.[10]

- *Tetrasodium* EDTA: A very small quantity of this material added to soap will prevent it from getting the "dreaded orange spots."

---

9.   www.AAA-Chemicals.com [1]. www.BoyerCorporation.com [2] also sells sodium and potassium hydroxides to soapmakers.
10. Another variety of citric acid is the *monohydrate,* with a variable moisture concentration that makes it unsuitable as a standard. It has a CAS number 5949-29-1 and is *not* the acid you want.

- ROE*:* This is a natural product preferred by some soapmakers for preventing the "dreaded orange spots."

- *Waxes:* Beeswax, candelilla wax, and carnauba wax may be used to protect sensitive essential oils from the caustic lye.

- *Essential Oils:* Essential oils are often used to add fragrance to soap. We'll explore the challenges of using clove and cinnamon oils, which cause raw soap to solidify more quickly than usual, a phenomenon known as "seizing." *Many* other essential oils are available at a wide range of prices. I have listed lavender as one of the more popular scents for soap.

1.5 Oils and Fats

All soaps are made from oils and fats. Our experimental work will lead us to explore the properties of soaps made from the **fixed oils** and fats listed in Table 1-3. The italicized oils are those that will be used as examples throughout this book. Some of these oils may be found at the grocery store or a local wholesaler. Since shipping charges tend to be rather high for large quantities of oil, it is worth your while finding a local source when possible. But for experimental soapmaking the quantities are small enough that the shipping charges will not break the bank.

1.6 Soap Molds

There are a huge variety of molds available for soapmaking. Experimental soaps can be made in disposable cups, food storage boxes, or other found items. A particularly convenient mold, however, is produced by the Upland Soap Factory.[11] These are wooden molds that disassemble easily and have a silicone liner that makes removal of the finished soap easy. Eight of these molds may be packed into the soap oven at the same time. At Hampden-Sydney we use these molds exclusively for our soap research.

---

11. www.UplandSoapFactory.com [41] sells a set of two mini molds for $24.95.

Table 1-3. Oils and Fats

Description	Price ($/lb)		
	7 lb	35 lb	50 lb
Lauric Oils			
Coconut Oil	1.80		1.01
Palm Kernel Oil	1.68		0.92
Palmitic Oils			
Lard (Pork Fat)			0.54
Palm Oil	1.62		0.85
Tallow (Beef Fat)			0.54
Oleic Oils			
Avocado Oil	2.52	2.28	
Olive Oil	1.96	1.84	
Peanut Oil		2.34	
Rice Bran Oil	1.63	1.68	
Ricinoleic Oils			
Castor Oil	2.00	1.53	
Linoleic Oils			
Corn Oil		0.71	
Cottonseed Oil	1.07	0.90	
Grape Seed Oil	2.23	1.76	
*Safflower Seed Oil**	1.74		
Sesame Seed Oil	2.60	2.35	
Soybean Oil		0.72	
Sunflower Seed Oil*	1.35	1.26	
Linolenic Oils			
Hempseed Oil	5.24		
Linseed Oil	2.07		
Walnut Oil	1.77	1.42	

Columbus Foods [7].

*Price is for high-oleic variety.

1.7 Desktop Scanner

An ordinary desktop scanner is extremely useful for analyzing soap samples. For one thing, it can measure color far more precisely than the human eye, and this makes it a powerful tool in studying the aging of soap. For another, the resolution of even an inexpensive scanner can usually be set to 1200 dots per inch, making it an excellent substitute for a microscope. This common piece of office equipment is thus a powerful tool for troubleshooting soap defects.

1.8 Notebook

So there you are, soaping up with the most luxurious bar of saponified heaven that has graced the planet since the days of Imperial Rome. Family, friends, and customers are clamoring for more. You make the same soap, to the best of your recollection, but it falls far short of the nirvana you visited with the previous bar. Was that avocado or apricot oil? Frustration and unhappiness certainly await you if you don't make regular use of the most important tool of the soapmaker: the notebook. It doesn't matter if you use the loose-leaf or spiral-bound variety. What matters is that you keep records of every batch you make so that you can learn from your mistakes and benefit from your triumphs. You can set up your notebook as you see fit, but I will tell you how I keep mine.

I use a standard "composition book," of the kind commonly sold for use in school. The pages are sewn in so that they cannot come out. I leave a few pages at the beginning for a table of contents. I start a new page for each batch of soap, no matter how large or small. This leaves me plenty of room for recording both the conditions of manufacture and the properties of the finished soap one week, one month, and even one year after it has left the mold. I make a habit of recording things in ink and when I make a mistake I draw a single line through it on the off chance that I might later decide that my "mistake" was correct after all; it would be nice to be able to read it. In future chapters, we'll talk about what things are worth recording, but for now, you must have a place to write things down so that you can get in the habit of keeping good records whenever you make soap.

1.9 The Soap Laboratory

An appropriate space for making soap will resemble a kitchen, with plenty of counter and storage space, a sink, a ventilation fan, and adequate electrical service. If possible, however, it should not be *the* kitchen, the place where food is prepared. Though many soapmakers begin their exploration in the kitchen using ordinary pots, pans, spoons, and scales, the serious soapmaker should move as quickly as possible to a workshop or laboratory space where equipment and supplies are unlikely to be used for food preparation. This need not involve a great deal of expense—an adequate laboratory requires only a six-foot countertop with a sink, ventilation fan, soap oven, and under-cabinet storage. A manufacturing facility would, of course, require more space.

At a minimum, you should have a drawer or cabinet in which sodium and potassium hydroxides may be stored separately from other chemicals. If possible, there should be separate drawers for acids, solvents, oils, and essential or fragrance oils. Keeping chemicals in separate polyethylene bins provides an additional level of protection against leakage. Cabinets should be equipped with child-proof locks and unsupervised access to the soap lab should be limited for children and pets.

We have a saying at Hampden-Sydney: "Think bad in the lab." We imagine the worst thing that could happen in a given procedure and prepare for that potential problem. In the soap laboratory, it would be hard to imagine a worse problem than splashing lye in the eyes. Your first line of defense is to wear safety glasses any time you are in the lab. Your second line of defense is to keep a filled eyewash bottle in a location that would be easy to find with one or both eyes closed. Your third line of defense is to keep a telephone similarly handy. At Hampden-Sydney, we allow advanced students to work at night and on weekends, but they must have a buddy—someone within shouting distance who can render assistance if it is needed. Working alone should be avoided if possible.

Another hazard for which you should be prepared is the possibility of fire. You should be aware that alcohol, essential oils, and fragrance oils are volatile,[12] and their vapors may be flammable. Consequently, sources of ignition such as space heaters, ranges, and ovens with open flames should be avoided. Fixed oils and fats may be flammable as well, and should be heated in a microwave oven, a roaster oven, or on a *laboratory* hotplate. If you must heat oils on a household range or hotplate, use a double-boiler with water in the lower pot. A chemical fire extinguisher should be kept in the vicinity of any heating appliance.

 Think bad in the lab—being prepared for catastrophes is the best way to avoid them.

---

12. Volatile substances readily vaporize at room temperature and their vapors may or may not be flammable. While some volatile substances (e.g., water) are odorless, every substance with an odor must be volatile to some degree, or else it would never get to your nose. A careful soapmaker will be on the lookout for possible ignition sources whenever fragrant chemicals are being handled.

Practice Problems

Answers to practice problems appear in Appendix A (page 335).

1. What hazards should be anticipated in making soap?

2. What are the capacity and readability of a scale or balance?

3. Why is an oven used for experimental cold-process soap?

4. Why does this chapter list prices, which are likely to be out of date by the time the book is published?

5. Why is it better to draw a line through a notebook error rather than erasing it?

6. What fire precautions are appropriate when making soap?

7. What kind of ventilation is appropriate to a soap laboratory?

8. How should chemicals be stored?

9. Why is the family kitchen an inadequate substitute for a dedicated soapmaking area?

10. What does it mean to "think bad in the lab"?

Chapter 2

Weights and Measures

*T*HE cook and the chemist place different requirements on their balances. The cook needs to know whether the turkey weighs 10 or 12 pounds; the chemist needs to know whether the sample of diethyl biglongnameate weighs 126 or 127 milligrams. The soapmaker lives somewhere in between. This chapter introduces important techniques for using a centigram balance. These techniques make it possible to accurately control the composition of single bars of soap. Without this control, we cannot be certain of the exact composition of our experimental soaps, rendering suspect any conclusions we might wish to draw from our experiments.

2.1 Units

In addition to the techniques for using the balance, we need to understand the various systems of units available for expressing weights. As we learn to convert from one unit to another, we'll find that the same methods will allow us to solve all of the mathematical problems in the work to come. If you were traumatized by math in high school, you may find the following method a little frightening at first. We won't be using calculus, algebra, or statistics. Just arithmetic. While the method may seem a little intimidating, I promise that once you master the math in this section you will be fully prepared for all of the math in subsequent chapters. More than that, you will be well prepared to solve the vast majority of numerical problems you will encounter in life. The method is known under a variety of names: *dimensional analysis, unit factor analysis,* or *factor label analysis,* but I'm going to refer to it as *hotdog analysis* for reasons that will shortly become apparent. All of the problems we'll need to solve are of the form, "How much of A is the same as a given amount of B?" For example, we might ask, "How many grams are the same as 12.34 pounds?"

In order to solve this problem we have to know something about pounds. You may know, for example, that there are 16 ounces in a pound or that there is a pound of sugar in a pound cake, but since the answer is in grams, we would do well to use the fact that there are 454 g in a pound. We can present the same information in a variety of ways. We could, for example, say that 454 g is the same as 1 pound. Another way of saying the same thing is that 454 g *equals* 1 lb. We can easily translate this sentence into an equation:

$$454 \text{ g} = 1 \text{ lb}$$

It is a curious fact that if you divide both sides of an equation by the same thing, the equation still holds true. In this case, let's divide both sides by 1 pound and see what happens.

$$\left(\frac{454 \text{ g}}{1 \text{ lb}} \right) = 1$$

The thing in parentheses, this thing that equals 1 is called a *unit factor* in most science books, but I'm going to call it a ***hotdog.*** For one thing, it looks kind of like a hotdog bun to me, with the numbers inside as the meat. For another, it should make the math a little less scary. After all, who's afraid of a little old hotdog?

There is another way to arrive at the same hotdog. We might very well say that there are 454 g *per* lb. Any time you have so many of one thing *per* so many of another thing, you can immediately write down a hotdog. The one thing goes in the top, the *per* turns into a horizontal line, and the other thing goes in the bottom. Before we get too far astray I should point out that "1 lb per 454 g" generates an equally valid hotdog. Can you write it down? Every valid hotdog is just as valid if you write it upside down.

"How many grams are the same as 12.34 pounds?" That was our original problem. The first step in hotdog analysis is to convert the sentence into an equation. The subject, in this case, "grams," comes first. The verb in the sentence is translated into an equal sign and the object, "12.34 pounds," follows it. We might just as well say, "How many grams *equals* 12.34 pounds?" So the first pass at solving the problem becomes:

$$? \text{ g} = 12.34 \text{ lb}$$

Another curious fact about equations is that if you multiply one side of an equation by 1, the equation still holds. 12.34 × 1 = 12.34, for example. Recall, however, that our hotdog *equals* 1, so we can multiply the right hand side of our equation by our hotdog and the equation still holds.

$$? \text{ g} = 12.34 \text{ lb} \left(\frac{454 \text{ g}}{1 \text{ lb}} \right)$$

Here we have *lb* in the top of the first term and in the bottom of the second. It is that third curious fact that when you have the same thing on the top and bottom of a fraction, they cancel. In this case, *lb* cancel, leaving *g* to the left of the equal sign and *g* on the right. When the un-canceled units are the same on the left and the right, all that remains is the arithmetic.

$$? \text{ g} = 12.34 \text{ lb} \left(\frac{454 \text{ g}}{1 \text{ lb}} \right)$$
$$= 5602 \text{ g}$$

Problem solved. 12.34 lb is the same as 5,602 g. I told you it would just be arithmetic!

Let's try one more example before moving on. How many grams are the same as 123.4 oz?

$$? \text{ g} = 123.4 \text{ oz} \left(\frac{1 \text{ lb}}{16 \text{ oz}} \right) \left(\frac{454 \text{ g}}{1 \text{ lb}} \right)$$
$$= 3501 \text{ g}$$

Note that we used two hotdogs in this equation. Where did they come from? We know there are 16 ounces per pound and 454 grams per pound. Each *per* gives us a hotdog. Remember that we can write either hotdog right-side up or upside down. We choose to write the first hotdog with *oz* on the bottom to cancel the *oz* after 123.4. We are then left with *lb* in the top of the first hotdog. We choose to write the second hotdog with *lb* in the bottom to cancel the *lb* in the top of the first hotdog. Just as in the first problem, this leaves the same units on the left and right of the equal sign, and it's just arithmetic after that. None of the math in this book is any harder than that. In fact, all of the math will work exactly the same way, one hotdog after another, canceling units on top and bottom, until finally the only un-canceled unit is the same as the unit of the answer.

2.2 Error and Uncertainty

Most people use the terms *error* and *uncertainty* interchangeably, but there is a subtle difference between them. Consider the weight of a hypothetical person visiting a friend. He goes to the bathroom and can't resist the temptation to step on the scale, which registers 185 pounds. "That's odd," he thinks, "I didn't think I weighed that much." When he gets home, he weighs himself and finds his weight to be 173 pounds. Which weight should he believe? Unless he has a way of calibrating his scale, he has no good reason to believe one over the other. But let's imagine that he has an item that is certified to weigh exactly 100 pounds. He puts it on his scale and adjusts a screw on the side of the scale until it reads 100 pounds. He then reweighs himself and finds his weight to be 180 pounds. The first two weights were in **error** by +5 and -7 pounds, respectively. The third weight would be considered more **accurate** than the previous two. What does it matter if the weight is off by a few pounds?

Consider for a moment how you would feel if you were weighing a baby and the scale registered 5 pounds off. It's one thing to think that a 180 pound man weighs 185 pounds; it's quite another to think that an 8 pound baby weighs 13 pounds! The second error seems somehow worse than the first. To express this, we often speak in terms of **relative error** and express it as a percentage.

So let's start with a question: "How many pounds of error are there for every 100 pounds of weight?" As usual, we convert this question into an equation, with the verb turning into the equal sign.

$$? \text{ lb error} = 100 \text{ lb weight}$$

We know that the first time our friend weighed himself, the scale registered 5 pounds of error *per* 180 pounds of weight.

$$? \text{ lb error} = 100 \; \cancel{\text{lb weight}} \left(\frac{5 \text{ lb error}}{180 \; \cancel{\text{lb weight}}} \right)$$
$$= 2.8 \text{ lb error}$$

We would say that the first time our friend weighed himself, the scale registered an error of 2.8 pounds *per* hundred. Another word for *hundred* is *cent* and we might very well call this 2.8 *per cent,* or 2.8%, for short.

$$\left(\frac{2.8 \text{ lb}}{100 \text{ lb}} \right) = 2.8\%$$
$$= .028$$

If the scale had made the same 5-pound error in weighing an 8 pound baby, the error would have been 63%. Thus the relative error confirms our instinct that it is somehow worse to make a 5-pound error on a small weight than on a large one.

Now suppose that our hypothetical person, still on the calibrated scale, picks up a toothbrush. The scale continues to read 180 pounds. Why? Because the toothbrush weighs less than a pound. Now it is certainly true that he weighs more with the toothbrush than without, but the scale is unable to register the difference. Even if the calibrated scale reads 180 pounds, all we can really say is that his weight is higher than 179 pounds and less than 181 pounds. We would say that the scale weighs to within ±1 pound of the actual weight, or that the **uncertainty** in this weight is ±1 pound. This translates into a **relative uncertainty** of ±1 pound *per* 180. We can once again ask, "How many pounds of uncertainty does the scale register *per cent?*"

$$? \text{ lb uncertainty} = 100 \; \cancel{lb\;weight}\left(\frac{\pm 1 \text{ lb uncertainty}}{180 \; \cancel{lb\;weight}}\right)$$

$$= \pm 0.6 \text{ lb uncertainty}$$

or

$$\left(\frac{\pm 0.6 \text{ lb}}{100 \text{ lb}}\right) = \pm 0.6\%$$

$$= \pm 0.006$$

The relative uncertainty is $\pm 0.6\%$. The phrase $\pm 0.6\%$ can be read, "plus or minus six tenths of a percent" or "give or take six tenths of a percent."

There is one more wrinkle on this hotdog before you can begin to talk like a scientist. When you are making careful measurements, it becomes inconvenient to talk about "half a percent" or "a third of a percent" or "six tenths of a percent." Instead, we take it one step further and ask "How many pounds of uncertainty does the scale register *per thousand?*"

$$? \text{ lb uncertainty} = 1000 \; \cancel{lb\;weight}\left(\frac{\pm 1 \text{ lb uncertainty}}{180 \; \cancel{lb\;weight}}\right)$$

$$= \pm 6 \text{ lb uncertainty}$$

or

$$\left(\frac{\pm 6 \text{ lb}}{1000 \text{ lb}}\right) = \pm 6 \text{ ppt}$$

$$= \pm 0.6\%$$

$$= \pm 0.006$$

A question phrased in this way gives its answer in ***parts per thousand,***[1] or *ppt*. To achieve relative uncertainties of ± 1 ppt, we need a scale with a sufficiently small readability, and this may depend on the chosen units.

While American cooks are most familiar with units of pounds and ounces, there are good reasons for the soapmaker to prefer units of grams. You might think that a chemist would have philosophical reasons for preferring the metric system, but when it comes to making soap, my preference is determined on strictly practical grounds. Consider a typical kitchen

---

1. Think of a ***percent*** as one part per hundred. A part per thousand is ten times smaller than a percent. 1 ppt = 0.1%; 1% = 10 ppt.

scale, the MyWeigh KD 7000, with a capacity of 15 pounds and a readability of 0.1 ounce. Suppose my soap recipe calls for 18 ounces of sodium hydroxide. I weigh out "exactly" 18.0 ounces, but even if the scale is accurately calibrated, I do not know the exact weight. All I know is that the sodium hydroxide weighs more than 17.9 ounces and less than 18.1 ounces. The sodium hydroxide might weigh 17.95 or 18.04 ounces, and I wouldn't know it because the balance does not read that extra digit. With a readability of 0.1 ounce and a weight of 18 ounces, the relative uncertainty in the weight amounts to ±0.6%. But if we switch the scale over to metric mode, the capacity is 7000 g and the readability is 1 g. The same soap recipe would call for 511 g of sodium hydroxide and with this mode I know the actual weight is somewhere between 510 and 512 g. With a readability of 1 g and a weight of 511 g, the relative uncertainty in the weight amounts to 0.2%. Bear in mind that we are using the same scale for both measurements. We may even be weighing the exact same object. But because a gram is smaller than a tenth of an ounce, the relative uncertainty of this scale is three times better in metric mode than in English mode.

With the question of units settled, we turn to technique. There are two situations in which you will need to weigh something. In the first case you simply want to know the weight, whatever it happens to be. In the second case you want to weigh out some predetermined amount. An analogous situation arises at the gas pump. Sometimes you want to fill the tank, however much gas that takes. Other times you want to hit some predetermined target, say, exactly twenty dollars worth. Careful attention to technique will allow you to handle both weighing situations with ease.

2.3 Weighing Analytically

Many times it is not important to hit a target weight exactly. In those instances it is sufficient to know the weight, whatever it happens to be. Suppose that we wish to weigh about 25 g of salt but that we want to know the weight to within ±0.01 g. In such a case I will instruct you to weigh 25.XX g of salt. I won't care that you hit this target weight exactly, but I will want you to record *all four digits* of whatever the weight turns out to be. This is known as weighing ***analytically.***

This isn't brain surgery, but careful attention to detail is required. Your focus here is to ensure that you know the exact weight of the material to within the limits imposed by your balance. You might imagine that this would be as simple as placing a flask onto the balance and pouring stuff into it. But oftentimes the flask itself will exceed the capacity of the balance, and if you use a balance with a larger capacity, it is likely to have worse readability. How are we to weigh a small amount of material into a large container? We weigh *from* the balance.

This procedure is entirely general, but for practice try weighing out 25.XX g of salt into an Erlenmeyer flask.

1. *Gather your materials:*
   - Goggles or glasses
   - A centigram balance
   - Salt
   - A 125 mL Erlenmeyer flask labeled A
   - A plastic cup labeled B
   - A plastic powder funnel
   - Your soapmaking notebook and a pen

2. *Arrange your workspace:* Note that flask A may exceed the capacity of the balance, so putting it onto the balance is not an option. Instead, we can use a lightweight, disposable plastic cup to hold the material being weighed. Place plastic *weighing cup* B onto the balance and flask A next to the balance. Put on your safety glasses. OK, it seems silly when you are just weighing salt, but you should get in the habit of doing so.

3. *Tare the balance:* Plastic cup B has a weight and you might be tempted to write it down so you can add 25 g to it. No need! The balance has a button on it marked *zero* or *tare.* If your balance has both buttons, press the tare button. The balance now reads 0.00 g, even though the cup is on its pan. Depending on emphasis, we may say either that we have tared the balance or that we have tared the cup.

4. *Fill the cup:* Pour the salt into cup B until the balance reads *between* 25 and 26 g. The exact weight does not matter, as

long as cup B contains more than 25 g. If you go over 26 g, you can simply pour some of the salt from the cup.

5. *Tare the balance:* Place the powder funnel *into the cup* and press the tare button so that the balance once again reads 0.00 g. We say that the funnel and cup are part of the *tare weight.*

6. *Weigh from the balance:* Place the powder funnel into the neck of the Erlenmeyer flask and pour all of the salt from cup B into flask A. Place the cup *and the funnel* back onto the balance. Don't worry that there may be a few crystals of salt left in the cup or on the funnel—they will be included in the tare weight. All of the salt is either in the cup, on the funnel, or in the flask. Whatever is not in the cup or on the funnel must now be in the flask. The balance registers a negative number that is equal and opposite to the weight of the salt delivered to the flask. This is the weight that should be recorded in your notebook.

 When weighing analytically, it is important to record all the digits of the weight but it is not important to hit the target weight exactly. The funnel and weighing cup are both part of the tare weight, and we weigh *from* the balance. Remember to tare the balance twice—once before filling the weighing cup and once before emptying it.

The procedure for weighing analytically may seem needlessly complicated at first glance. Why did I have you do it this way? One complication was that we weighed from the balance rather than onto it. We did this because the flask and its contents very often exceed the capacity of the balance. Weighing from the balance allows us to use a lightweight plastic cup and a more precise balance rather than switching to a less precise balance with higher capacity. Another complication was that we actually weighed the salt twice—once to get it between 25 and 26 g, and a second time to get the final weight. This was done to avoid weighing more than the desired amount. Yet another complication was that the funnel was part of the tare weight. If we had not done this, any small amount of salt left sticking to the funnel would have been unaccounted for. While this is not much of an issue with a free-flowing material like salt, it will be an issue for sticky materials like oils and soap shavings, and it

Example 2-1. Weighing Analytically

I wanted to weigh 25.XX g of salt into an Erlenmeyer flask. I placed a plastic cup onto the balance and tared it, added 25.28 g of salt to the cup, placed the powder funnel into the cup, and pressed the tare button again. I used the powder funnel to pour the contents of the cup into the flask, returning the cup and funnel to the balance, which now read -25.19 g. The actual weight delivered, 25.19 g, was smaller than the 25.28 g originally added to the cup because some small amount of salt clung to the cup and funnel. Because the cup, funnel, and clinging salt were all part of the tare weight, none of this mattered. 25.19 g were transferred to the flask and this was the number that I recorded in my notebook.

Because of the limitations of the balance, all I really know is that the actual weight of the salt was somewhere between 25.18 and 25.20 g. The relative uncertainty of this measurement was ±0.01 *per* 25.19, or ±0.4 ppt.

What would have happened if I had used a balance with a larger capacity in order to place the flask (rather than the cup) onto the balance? After taring the flask and pouring salt into it, the balance might have registered 25.2 g. I would have known that the actual weight was between 25.1 and 25.3 g and the relative uncertainty would have been ±0.1 *per* 25.2, or ±4 ppt. Weighing *from* the balance rather than *onto* it reduced our relative uncertainty by a factor of ten.

is just as well to be prepared for these from the start. The good news is that it takes far less time to *use* the analytical weighing procedure than to describe it. Practice it a few times, and it will soon become second nature. Once you are comfortable with weighing analytically, consider the situation in which it is important to hit the target weight as closely as possible.

2.4 Weighing Synthetically

Sometimes it is important to hit a target weight as closely as possible. This is known as weighing **synthetically.** Weighing synthetically is going to sound more complicated than weighing analytically, but it need not take much more time once you get the hang of it. There are some complications that arise from our desire to hit the target weight as closely as possible. To make our discussion more concrete, I will give the procedure first and then discuss the complications.

You can practice this procedure by weighing water into the Erlenmeyer flask from the previous procedure. Your goal is that the weight of the water should exactly equal the weight of the salt. The amount of water you desire to weigh is called the *target weight.*

1. *Gather your materials:*
   - Goggles or glasses
   - A centigram balance
   - Water
   - A medicine dropper or pipet
   - A 125 mL Erlenmeyer flask labeled A. This flask may already contain other materials.
   - A plastic cup labeled B
   - Your soapmaking notebook and a pen

2. *Arrange your workspace:* Place plastic cup B onto the balance and flask A next to the balance. Put on your safety glasses.

3. *Tare the balance:* Press the tare button. The empty cup is on the balance, which now reads 0.00 g.

4. *Fill the cup:* Pour water into cup B until the balance reads *more than* your target weight. In this example it might be

Example 2-2. Weighing Synthetically

I wanted to weigh 25.19 g of water into an Erlenmeyer flask that already contained 25.19 g of salt. I tared a plastic cup, added 37.58 g of water to it, and tared it again. I then used a pipet to transfer water from the cup to the flask until the balance read -24.25 g. The next portion of water in the pipet pushed the weight to -26.05 g so I returned water from the pipet to the cup, drop by drop, until the balance read -25.23 g. I was satisfied with that weight so I squirted the remaining water from the pipet into the flask, taking care to empty the pipet completely. I made an error of 0.04 g, but I was within 1 drop of my target weight. My relative error was 0.04 *per* 25.19, or +1.6 ppt.

---

29 or 35 or 47 g; it doesn't matter a bit as long as cup B has more than the required amount of water in it.

5. *Tare the balance:* Press the tare button. The filled cup is on the balance, which now reads 0.00 g.

6. *Weigh from the balance:* Use the pipet to suck up a little water from cup B and squirt it into flask A. The balance now reads a negative number, say -3.75 g. This is the amount of water you have removed from the cup. Use the pipet to transfer a second and a third portion of water from B to A. Eventually you will go past your target weight. Stop! You have passed your target but the water in the pipet is still pure water—it hasn't been anywhere yet. Return water from the pipet, drop by drop, *back into cup B* until the balance reads as close to your target weight as possible. If you are within ±0.05 g of the target then you are within 1 drop of the target. When you are satisfied, deliver the remaining water from the pipet to flask A. Now all of the water is either in cup B, flask A, or in the pipet. Since you know the weight of the water in the cup and the pipet is as close to empty as you can make it, the weight of water in the flask must be equal and opposite to the reading on the balance. Record in your notebook the weight of the water that you delivered to the flask.

When weighing synthetically, it is important to hit the target weight as closely as possible and to record all the digits of that weight. We use a pipet to deliver within 1 drop of the target weight and the pipet is not part of the tare weight. Remember to tare the weighing cup twice—once before filling it and once before using the pipet.

The procedure for weighing synthetically may seem even more complicated than that for weighing analytically. Some of the complications are the same for both procedures. The only real difference was that we removed the powder funnel and introduced the pipet. The pipet was *not* part of the tare weight because we needed to monitor the weight of the cup while the pipet was in use. This allowed us to transfer a known amount from the cup to the flask without the risk of overshooting the target weight. As long as the pipet is empty at the beginning and end of the procedure, all of the material will be either in the cup or in the flask and the weight registered by the balance is equal and opposite to the weight of the material transferred to the flask. One shortcoming of the synthetic procedure is that the pipet may not be *exactly* empty. The small amount of material remaining in the pipet results in a small error in the recorded weight. A type-A soapmaker might weigh the pipet before and after the procedure in order to account for the difference, but if you are careful to empty the pipet, the error is likely to be small. Another shortcoming of this procedure is that if the target weight is large, enhancing both accuracy and uncertainty, it will take forever to transfer the material with a pipet. This shortcoming is remedied in the next procedure.

2.5 Weighing in Two Portions

A pipet holds only about 4 g of water. If our goal is to transfer 100 g of material to an Erlenmeyer flask, that means about 20 trips from the cup to the flask. This would make the procedure boring, repetitive, and time-consuming. We can save time by combining the analytical and synthetic weighing procedures.

For practice, try transferring 100.00 g of water to an Erlenmeyer flask.

1. *Gather your materials:*
   - Goggles or glasses
   - A centigram balance
   - Water
   - A medicine dropper or pipet
   - A 125 mL Erlenmeyer flask labeled A
   - A plastic cup labeled B
   - A calculator
   - Your soapmaking notebook and a pen

2. *Arrange your workspace:* Place the plastic cup B onto the balance and flask A next to the balance. Put on your safety glasses.

   Your notebook should be opened to a new page with your pen at the ready. You will make a simple calculation during this procedures, and we don't want to confuse this calculation for an actual measurement. We therefore adopt the convention that the left-hand pages of the notebook are reserved for scratch work and preliminary calculations. The right-hand pages are reserved for observations and data.

3. *Analytically weigh the first portion:* Analytically weigh 9X.XX g of water from cup B into flask A using the procedure of Section 2.3. This is a quick and easy weight, the kind that brings a smile to your face. It could be anything from 90.00 g to 99.99 g, but whatever the weight turns out to be, record *all four digits* on a right-hand page of your notebook.

4. *Calculate the target for the second portion:* Subtract the weight of the first portion from the target weight. This will be the target weight for the second portion.

5. *Synthetically weigh the second portion:* This is the only one of the two weights that must be on target. Refill cup B and synthetically weigh water from cup B into flask A using the procedure of Section 2.4. You may or may not hit the target exactly, but you are trying to hit it to within 1 drop. Record the actual weight on the right-hand page of your notebook.

6. *Calculate the total weight delivered:* Simply add up the actual weights as recorded in your notebook. If you hit the second target weight to within 1 drop, your total weight should be within 0.05 g of the original target weight.

Example 2-3. Weighing in Two Portions

I wanted to transfer 100.00 g of water to an Erlenmeyer flask. I first transferred 92.73 g of water analytically and recorded this weight on a right-hand page of my notebook. Subtracting this from 100.00 g left me with a target of 7.27 g for the second portion of water, which I recorded on a left-hand page of my notebook:

100.00 - 92.73 = 7.27 g target weight

I *actually* transferred 7.25 g synthetically from the cup to the flask, and I recorded this on a right-hand page, right next to the weight of the first portion. Adding these two together gave a total weight of 99.98 g, which I recorded next to the other two actual weights:

92.73 g + 7.25 g = 99.98 g of water

The relative error in this measurement was -0.02 *per* 100, or -0.2 ppt.

If I had carelessly recorded 7.27 and 7.25 g on the same page, I might have been left to wonder at some future date which was the actual weight and which was the target weight. The difference between these two numbers is small, but if I have gone to all the trouble of making careful measurements, I would like to be certain which of the two numbers represents the actual weight.

Record calculations of target weights on a left-hand page of your notebook. Record actual weights on a right-hand page to avoid confusion later on.

2.6 Weighing in Three Portions

Now imagine that your goal is to synthetically weigh out 400.00 g of water but the capacity of your balance is only 200.00 g. At first blush you might be tempted to weigh 200.00 g twice. You would combine an analytical weight of 19X.XX with a synthetic weight to total 200.00 g and then repeat the process for another 200.00 g. You can save time, however, and can achieve the same results with only three weighings.

1. *Gather your materials:*
    - Goggles or glasses
    - A centigram balance
    - Water
    - A medicine dropper or pipet
    - A 500 mL polypropylene (PP) plastic bottle labeled A
    - A plastic cup labeled B
    - A calculator
    - Your soapmaking notebook and a pen

2. *Arrange your workspace:* Place the plastic cup B onto the balance and bottle A next to the balance. Put on your safety glasses.

3. *Analytically weigh the first portion:* Analytically weigh 19X.XX g of water from cup B into bottle A using the procedure of Section 2.3. Whatever the weight turns out to be, record *all five digits* on the right-hand page of your notebook.

4. *Analytically weigh the second portion:* Analytically weigh 19Y.YY g of water from cup B into bottle A. Record *all five digits* on the right-hand page of your notebook.

5. *Calculate the target for the third portion:* Subtract the weights of the first two portions from the original target weight. Record the target weight for the third portion on the left-hand page of your notebook.

6. *Synthetically weigh the third portion:* This is the only one of the three weights that must be on target. Refill cup B and

Example 2-4. Weighing in Three Portions

I wanted to transfer 400.00 g to a 500 mL bottle. I first transferred 191.82 g of water analytically. I then transferred 185.16 g analytically. I realized that it didn't really matter that the weight of the second portion was less than 190 g. I made the following calculation on a left-hand page of my notebook:

400.00 - 191.82 - 185.16 = 23.02 g target weight

I then transferred 22.99 g synthetically and recorded the total on a right-hand page of my notebook:

191.82 + 185.16 + 22.99 = 399.97 g of water

Because this was within 1 drop of my original target, I made a relative error of -0.03 *per* 400, or -0.08 ppt. The extreme accuracy of this measurement results from the fact that my target weight was much, much larger than the weight of a single drop of water.

---

synthetically weigh water from cup B into bottle A using the procedure of Section 2.4. You may or may not hit the target exactly, but you are trying to hit it to within 1 drop. Record the actual weight on the right-hand page of your notebook.

7. *Calculate the total weight delivered:* Simply add up all of the actual weights as recorded in your notebook and record the *actual* total weight on the right-hand page of your notebook.

Relative error and relative uncertainty provide us with an idea of how carefully a measurement has been made. Error results from a mistake of some kind, and in our work, the chief source of error will prove to be the difficulty of hitting a target weight to within 1 drop. Unlike error, uncertainty is an unavoidable part of any measurement, no matter how carefully it is made. It can be reduced by using better equipment (for example, a balance with a smaller readability), but it can never be eliminated. But the examples above have shown that the relative error and relative uncertainty of a weight can be made as small as we wish simply by ensuring that the target weight is much larger than the weight of a single drop (for relative error) or the readability of the balance (for relative uncertainty). In examples to come, we'll calculate relative errors and uncertainties in order to ensure that our procedures result in measurements that are as accurate as they can be.

Error results from a mistake. It may be avoided by taking sufficient care in making a measurement.

Uncertainty is an unavoidable part of any measurement. It may be reduced but it can never be eliminated.

Practice Problems

Answers to practice problems appear in Appendix A (page 335).

1. A balance has a capacity of 200 g. What is its capacity in ounces?

2. A balance has a capacity of 7 kilograms. What is its capacity in pounds?

3. How many minutes are there in a year?

4. A soap mold filled with 1.2 ducks of raw soap produces 11 bars of finished soap. How many ducks of raw soap are needed to produce 24 bars of soap using the same mold?

5. A mole of NaOH weighs 40 g and a mole of KOH weighs 56 g. 1000 g of an oil reacts with 144 g of NaOH. 1 mole of KOH reacts with the same amount of oil as 1 mole of NaOH. How many grams of KOH are needed to react with 100 g of the same oil?

6. Suppose you want to pump $10.00 worth of gasoline but slow reflexes result in an actual charge of $10.12. What are the relative error and uncertainty?

7. Suppose you want to weigh 10.00 g of water but overshoot the target by 1 drop, resulting in an actual weight of 10.05 g. What are the relative error and uncertainty?

8. Consider that in weighing a liquid you can hit the target weight to within 1 drop using a centigram balance. How large must a liquid weight be if you want the relative error to be within 1 ppt of the target?

9. You want to weigh 759 g of water. How far can you stray from the target and still be within ±1 ppt? What kind of readability do you need from your balance?

10. You have two balances: one with a capacity of 50 g and a readability of 0.01 g, and the other with a capacity of 7000 g and a readability of 1 g. If your goal is to weigh 5000 g of water, will you get better uncertainty using the first balance or the second?

Chapter 3

Material Safety

MATERIAL safety data sheets (MSDS) are your first line of defense in protecting yourself from the hazardous materials used in making soap. In the United States, MSDSs are required by the Occupational Safety and Health Administration (OSHA) [45] (Regulation 1910.1200g):

> Chemical manufacturers and importers shall obtain or develop a material safety data sheet for each hazardous chemical they produce or import. Employers shall have a material safety data sheet in the workplace for each hazardous chemical which they use.

If you have employees, you must keep MSDSs on file so that they may familiarize themselves with the hazardous properties of the materials you use in your business. Even if you are self-employed or a hobbyist, however, you should keep them on file for your own safety. Whenever you buy a chemical, you should ask the vendor for an MSDS. While they are also available on the Internet, your vendor should be able to provide you one for the actual material you are buying, whereas the sheet found on the Internet may be from a different manufacturer. Keep all of your sheets filed in a regular place so that anyone handling the materials may find them quickly and easily. You should also summarize your MSDSs in your notebook for quick access.

The MSDS is intended to summarize the hazardous properties of a material an employee is expected to handle. While it would be nice if it were written to be easily understood by a lay person, this is seldom the case. Let us examine the MSDSs of two substances, sodium chloride and sodium hydroxide. The similarities and differences will demonstrate the kinds of information available in an MSDS.

3.1 Sodium Chloride MSDS

In this section we'll consider an MSDS for sodium chloride, i.e., ordinary table salt. I created it by searching the Internet using the keywords MSDS and *7647-14-5* (the Chemical Abstracts Registry Number for sodium chloride). If you reproduce my search, you will find that there is a good deal of variation in the format and content of MSDSs. Some are very short and some are very long. All MSDSs, however, will contain the same sections. The sheet I have created is for illustrative purposes only—the one provided by your vendor may be more complete and specific to the chemicals you are actually using.

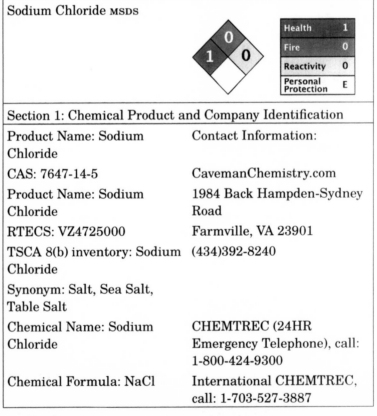

Sodium Chloride MSDS

Health	1
Fire	0
Reactivity	0
Personal Protection	E

Section 1: Chemical Product and Company Identification

Product Name: Sodium Chloride	Contact Information:
CAS: 7647-14-5	CavemanChemistry.com
Product Name: Sodium Chloride	1984 Back Hampden-Sydney Road
RTECS: VZ4725000	Farmville, VA 23901
TSCA 8(b) inventory: Sodium Chloride	(434)392-8240
Synonym: Salt, Sea Salt, Table Salt	
Chemical Name: Sodium Chloride	CHEMTREC (24HR Emergency Telephone), call: 1-800-424-9300
Chemical Formula: NaCl	International CHEMTREC, call: 1-703-527-3887

Section 1 of the MSDS tells us what the substance is and who produced it. The manufacturer bears the ultimate responsibility for the content of the MSDS. The MSDS should include an address and phone number so that you may contact the manufacturer for further information. In addition, it may include the phone number for a poison control hotline. Section 1 also contains the Chemical Abstracts registry number (CAS), which uniquely identifies the substance. While the name may have synonyms and the formula may be written in several different ways, the CAS number uniquely and unambiguously identifies the substance in question. The Registry of Toxic Effects of Chemical Substances (RTECS) is a database of information on toxic substances maintained by the Centers for Disease Control. The Toxic Substances Control Act (TSCA) inventory lists chemicals tracked by the Environmental Protection Agency. The Chemical Transportation Emergency Center (CHEMTREC) is a hotline for fire fighters, law enforcement, and other emergency responders to obtain critical information and assistance for emergency incidents involving chemicals and hazardous materials. At the top of the section I have included symbols for the NFPA and HMIS ratings, which will be discussed in Section 3.3.

Section 2: Composition and Information on Ingredients		
Name	CAS	% by Weight
Sodium Chloride	7647-14-5	100

Section 2 tells us that this sheet is for 100% sodium chloride. When one is searching online, it is easy to be misled by an MSDS for a material that merely *contains* the substance in question. Laundry bleach, for example, contains sodium chloride and you wouldn't want to confuse the hazardous properties of bleach with those of salt.

Section 3: Hazards Identification
Potential Acute Health Effects: Slightly hazardous in case of skin contact (irritant), of eye contact (irritant), of ingestion, and of inhalation.
Potential Chronic Health Effects:
Carcinogenic Effects: Not available.
Mutagenic Effects: Mutagenic for mammalian somatic cells. Mutagenic for bacteria and/or yeast.
Teratogenic Effects: Not available.
Repeated or prolonged exposure is not known to aggravate medical conditions.

Section 3 gives an overview of the hazardous properties, telling us, for example, that sodium chloride is an irritant. Acute effects are those that may occur shortly after exposure over a period of hours or days. Chronic effects are those that may occur after exposure of months or years. Carcinogenic effects would entail an increased risk of cancer, mutagenic effects would cause mutations to the DNA of cells, and teratogenic effects would cause birth defects.

Section 4: First Aid Measures
Eye Contact: Check for and remove any contact lenses. In case of contact, immediately flush eyes with plenty of water for at least 15 minutes. Cold water may be used. Get medical attention.
Skin Contact: Wash with soap and water. Cover the irritated skin with an emollient. Get medical attention if irritation develops. Cold water may be used.
Inhalation: If inhaled, remove to fresh air. If not breathing, give artificial respiration. If breathing is difficult, give oxygen. Get medical attention if symptoms appear.
Ingestion: Do *not* induce vomiting unless directed to do so by medical personnel. Never give anything by mouth to an unconscious person. Loosen tight clothing such as a collar, tie, belt or waistband. Get medical attention if symptoms appear.

The lesson here is that an MSDS makes everything appear to be hazardous, including ordinary table salt. The remainder of this chapter will help you to put warnings like these in perspective.

Section 5: Fire and Explosion Data
Flammability of the Product: Non-flammable.
Special Remarks on Fire Hazards: When heated to decomposition, it emits toxic fumes.
Special Remarks on Explosion Hazards: Electrolysis of sodium chloride in presence of nitrogenous compounds to produce chlorine may lead to formation of explosive nitrogen trichloride. Potentially explosive reaction with dichloromaleic anhydride + urea.

Section 6: Accidental Release Measures

Small Spill: Use appropriate tools to put the spilled solid in a convenient waste disposal container. Finish cleaning by spreading water on the contaminated surface and dispose of according to local and regional authority requirements.

Large Spill: Use a shovel to put the material into a convenient waste disposal container. Finish cleaning by spreading water on the contaminated surface and allow to evacuate through the sanitary system.

Section 7: Handling and Storage

Precautions: Keep locked up. Do not ingest. Do not breathe dust. Avoid contact with eyes. Wear suitable protective clothing. If ingested, seek medical advice immediately and show the container or the label. Keep away from incompatibles such as oxidizing agents, acids.

Storage: Keep container tightly closed. Keep container in a cool, well-ventilated area. Hygroscopic.

Section 8: Exposure Controls/Personal Protection

Engineering Controls: Use process enclosures, local exhaust ventilation, or other engineering controls to keep airborne levels below recommended exposure limits. If user operations generate dust, fume or mist, use ventilation to keep exposure to airborne contaminants below the exposure limit.

Personal Protection: Splash goggles. Lab coat. Dust respirator. Be sure to use an approved/certified respirator or equivalent. Gloves.

Personal Protection in Case of a Large Spill: Splash goggles. Full suit. Dust respirator. Boots. Gloves. A self contained breathing apparatus should be used to avoid inhalation of the product. Suggested protective clothing might not be sufficient; consult a specialist before handling this product.

Sections 5–8 might tempt you to purge your house of substances as hazardous as table salt. Remember that the intention of the MSDS is to give employees the information they need to handle materials in an industrial setting. This is not about protecting yourself from the salt shaker on the dining room ta-

ble. It's about people moving salt with bulldozers and forklifts.
Most soapmakers do not handle materials on such a large scale,
but as your business grows, these kinds of precautions will become more relevant to the protection of your employees.

Section 9: Physical and Chemical Properties
Physical state and appearance: Solid. (Solid crystalline powder.)
Odor: Slight.
Taste: Saline.
Molecular Weight: 58.44 g/mole
Color: White.
pH (1% soln/water): 7 [Neutral.]
Boiling Point: 1413°C (2575°F)
Melting Point: 801°C (1474°F)
Specific Gravity: 2.165 (Water = 1)
Solubility: Easily soluble in cold water, hot water. Soluble in glycerol and ammonia. Very slightly soluble in alcohol. Insoluble in hydrochloric acid.

Section 10: Stability and Reactivity Data
Stability: The product is stable.
Conditions of Instability: Incompatible materials, high temperatures.
Incompatibility with various substances: Reactive with oxidizing agents, metals, acids.
Corrosivity: Not considered to be corrosive for metals and glass.
Special Remarks on Reactivity: Hygroscopic. Reacts with most non-noble metals such as iron or steel, building materials (such as cement). Sodium chloride is rapidly attacked by bromine trifluoride. Violent reaction with lithium.

Section 10 may help you to decide whether different materials need to be stored separately from one another.

Section 11: Toxicological Information
Routes of Entry: Inhalation. Ingestion.
Toxicity to Animals: Acute oral toxicity (LD_{50}): 3000 mg/kg [Rat]. 4000 mg/kg [Mouse]. Acute dermal toxicity (LD_{50}): >10000 mg/kg [Rabbit]. Acute toxicity of the dust (LC_{50}): >42000 mg/m3 1 hours [Rat].
Chronic Effects on Humans: Mutagenic Effects: Mutagenic for mammalian somatic cells. Mutagenic for bacteria and/or yeast.
Other Toxic Effects on Humans: Slightly hazardous in case of skin contact (irritant), of ingestion, and of inhalation.
Special Remarks on Toxicity to Animals: Lowest Published Lethal Dose (LD_L) [Man] – Route: Oral; Dose: 1000 mg/kg
This section was originally two pages long. For complete information, consult the MSDS *provided by your vendor.*

Section 11 gives more details on toxic effects than given in Section 3. The details may appear frightening for such a common material as table salt. But in sufficiently large doses, just about any chemical can be dangerous. One clue to the relative hazard is the Lethal Dose 50% (LD_{50}), the dose required to kill 50% of a test population. This is a gruesome statistic, but it is the closest thing we have to an objective measure of how poisonous a substance is. Since it takes more to kill a big animal than a small one, it is expressed in milligrams of the substance in question per kilogram of body weight. It is also specific to the animals tested—in this case rats and mice.

To put these LD_{50}s in perspective, let's imagine what it would take to kill half a population of rats the size of human beings. 3000 mg is the same as 3 g and a 150 lb person weighs 68 kg. That means we could expect a dose of 204 g, or 0.5 lb to kill half of the individuals in this population of giant rat-men. I think you will agree that eating half a pound of salt would make a person very sick indeed. For comparison, the lowest published lethal dose (LD_L) in man is 1000 mg/kg, which for our example individual would be 68 g, or 2.3 oz. While smaller than half a pound, this is the dose required to kill only one, presumably weak individual, not half the population. It is also specific to humans, who may be able to tolerate less salt than rats.

What you should take away from this discussion is that the existence of an LD$_{50}$ or LD$_L$ for a substance does not automatically make it hazardous. Counterintuitively, a large number means that the material is relatively non-toxic, since it takes a larger dose to produce a harmful effect. Here we see that numbers like 1 g/kg or 1000 mg/kg denote the kind of substance that is routinely sprinkled on food without immediate harmful effects. When we look at sodium hydroxide in the next section, we'll see that its LD$_{50}$ is smaller than this, signifying that it is more poisonous than table salt.

Section 12: Ecological Information
Products of Biodegradation: Possibly hazardous short term degradation products are not likely. However, long term degradation products may arise.
Toxicity of the Products of Biodegradation: The product itself and its products of degradation are not toxic.

Section 13: Disposal Considerations
Waste Disposal: Waste must be disposed of in accordance with federal, state and local environmental control regulations.

Section 14: Transport Information
DOT Classification: Not a DOT controlled material (United States).

Section 15: Other Regulatory Information
TSCA 8(b) inventory: Sodium chloride
HMIS Health Hazard: 1 Fire Hazard: 0 Reactivity: 0 Personal Protection: E
NFPA Health: 1 Flammability: 0 Reactivity: 0

Section 15 may contain some of the most useful information on the entire sheet. Some sheets display the HMIS and NFPA ratings at the top, but most sheets do not. You will have to be on the lookout for these ratings, which will be discussed in Section 3.3.

Section 16: Other Information
Created: 05/21/2007. Last Updated: 05/21/2007.
The information above is believed to be accurate and represents the best information currently available to us. However, we make no warranty of merchantability or any other warranty, express or implied, with respect to such information, and we assume no liability resulting from its use. Users should make their own investigations to determine the suitability of the information for their particular purposes. In no event shall CavemanChemistry.com be liable for any claims, losses, or damages of any third party or for lost profits or any special, indirect, incidental, consequential or exemplary damages, howsoever arising, even if CavemanChemistry.com has been advised of the possibility of such damages.

Section 16 gives the date the MSDS was created and when it was last updated. It may also include references, a disclaimer, and any other information the manufacturer wishes to include.

The MSDS can seem rather daunting, even for a material as familiar as table salt. The manufacturer or importer has attempted to provide as much information as possible on every conceivable hazard that might arise in the workplace. The downside of such a comprehensive summary is that just about any material, no matter how innocuous, will appear to be a deadly poison. In the face of such information overload, how are we to distinguish truly dangerous materials from those that simply require common sense? For comparison, we now consider the MSDS for one of the most hazardous materials the soapmaker is likely to encounter—sodium hydroxide.

3.2 Sodium Hydroxide MSDS

As with the previous MSDS, this one has been compiled from several online sources for illustrative purposes. For your own safety you should rely on the sheet provided by your vendor. For the sake of brevity, I will comment only on those sections that differ significantly from the sheet for sodium chloride.

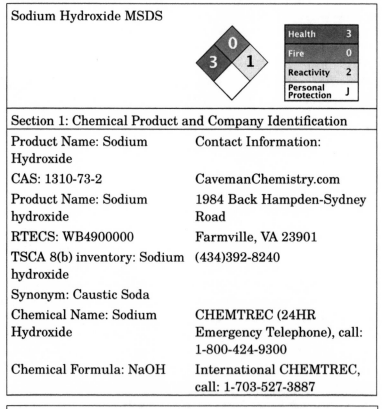

Sodium Hydroxide MSDS		Health	3
		Fire	0
		Reactivity	2
		Personal Protection	J

Section 1: Chemical Product and Company Identification	
Product Name: Sodium Hydroxide	Contact Information:
CAS: 1310-73-2	CavemanChemistry.com
Product Name: Sodium hydroxide	1984 Back Hampden-Sydney Road
RTECS: WB4900000	Farmville, VA 23901
TSCA 8(b) inventory: Sodium hydroxide	(434)392-8240
Synonym: Caustic Soda	
Chemical Name: Sodium Hydroxide	CHEMTREC (24HR Emergency Telephone), call: 1-800-424-9300
Chemical Formula: NaOH	International CHEMTREC, call: 1-703-527-3887

Section 2: Composition and Information on Ingredients		
Name	CAS	% by Weight
Sodium Hydroxide	1310-73-2	100

Section 3: Hazards Identification

Potential Acute Health Effects: Very hazardous in case of skin contact (corrosive, irritant, permeator), of eye contact (irritant, corrosive), of ingestion, and of inhalation. The amount of tissue damage depends on length of contact. Eye contact can result in corneal damage or blindness. Skin contact can produce inflammation and blistering. Inhalation of dust will produce irritation to gastrointestinal or respiratory tract, characterized by burning, sneezing and coughing. Severe over-exposure can produce lung damage, choking, unconsciousness or death. Inflammation of the eye is characterized by redness, watering, and itching. Skin inflammation is characterized by itching, scaling, reddening, or, occasionally, blistering.

Potential Chronic Health Effects:

Carcinogenic Effects: Not available.

Mutagenic Effects: Mutagenic for mammalian somatic cells.

Teratogenic Effects: Not available.

Developmental Toxicity: Not available.

The substance may be toxic to mucous membranes, upper respiratory tract, skin, eyes. Repeated or prolonged exposure to the substance can produce target organs damage. Repeated exposure of the eyes to a low level of dust can produce eye irritation. Repeated skin exposure can produce local skin destruction, or dermatitis. Repeated inhalation of dust can produce varying degree of respiratory irritation or lung damage.

While the chronic (long-term) effects of exposure to sodium hydroxide are comparable to those for sodium chloride, the acute (immediate) effects of exposure to sodium hydroxide are much more severe. Perhaps the most important line in the MSDS appears in Section 3: "Eye contact can result in corneal damage or blindness." If sodium hydroxide is going to hurt you, you aren't going to have to wait very long to find out about it.

Section 4: First Aid Measures

Eye Contact: Check for and remove any contact lenses. In case of contact, immediately flush eyes with plenty of water for at least 15 minutes. Cold water may be used. Get medical attention immediately.

Skin Contact: In case of contact, immediately flush skin with plenty of water for at least 15 minutes while removing contaminated clothing and shoes. Cover the irritated skin with an emollient. Cold water may be used. Wash clothing before reuse. Thoroughly clean shoes before reuse. Get medical attention immediately.

Serious Skin Contact: Wash with a disinfectant soap and cover the contaminated skin with an anti-bacterial cream. Seek medical attention.

Inhalation: If inhaled, remove to fresh air. If not breathing, give artificial respiration. If breathing is difficult, give oxygen. Get medical attention immediately.

Serious Inhalation: Evacuate the victim to a safe area as soon as possible. Loosen tight clothing such as a collar, tie, belt or waistband. If breathing is difficult, administer oxygen. If the victim is not breathing, perform mouth-to-mouth resuscitation. Warning: It may be hazardous to the person providing aid to give mouth-to-mouth resuscitation when the inhaled material is toxic, infectious or corrosive. Seek immediate medical attention.

Ingestion: Do *not* induce vomiting unless directed to do so by medical personnel. Never give anything by mouth to an unconscious person. If large quantities of this material are swallowed, call a physician immediately. Loosen tight clothing such as a collar, tie, belt or waistband.

The first aid measures described are more detailed and insistent than those for sodium chloride. It is particularly important to plan ahead for the possibility of eye contact. You do not want to be groping for the sink in an emergency. In an academic setting, each student should know how to use the eyewash station. In a business setting, an eyewash bottle should be kept within reach of the work area.

Section 5: Fire and Explosion Data

Flammability of the Product: Non-flammable.

Fire Hazards in Presence of Various Substances: metals

This section was originally more than one page long. For complete information, consult the MSDS *provided by your vendor.*

Section 6: Accidental Release Measures

Small Spill: Use appropriate tools to put the spilled solid in a convenient waste disposal container. If necessary: Neutralize the residue with a dilute solution of acetic acid.

Large Spill: Corrosive solid. Stop leak if without risk. Do not get water inside container. Do not touch spilled material. Use water spray to reduce vapors. Prevent entry into sewers, basements or confined areas; dike if needed. Call for assistance on disposal. Neutralize the residue with a dilute solution of acetic acid. Be careful that the product is not present at a concentration level above TLV. Check TLV on the MSDS and with local authorities.

Section 7: Handling and Storage

Precautions: Keep container dry. Do not breathe dust. Never add water to this product. In case of insufficient ventilation, wear suitable respiratory equipment. If you feel unwell, seek medical attention and show the label when possible. Avoid contact with skin and eyes. Keep away from incompatibles such as oxidizing agents, reducing agents, metals, acids, alkalis, moisture. Storage: Keep container tightly closed. Keep container in a cool, well-ventilated area. Hygroscopic. Deliquescent.

Hygroscopic means that the material absorbs moisture from the air. Note that it is spelled with a *g,* not a *d.* **Deliquescent** means that it will absorb so much water from the air that it dissolves in the absorbed water. If you leave a pile of sodium hydroxide on the counter, you may return to find a puddle of caustic liquid in its place.

Section 8: Exposure Controls/Personal Protection

Engineering Controls: Use process enclosures, local exhaust ventilation, or other engineering controls to keep airborne levels below recommended exposure limits. If user operations generate dust, fume or mist, use ventilation to keep exposure to airborne contaminants below the exposure limit.

Personal Protection: Splash goggles. Synthetic apron. Vapor and dust respirator. Be sure to use an approved/certified respirator or equivalent. Gloves.

Personal Protection in Case of a Large Spill: Splash goggles. Full suit. Vapor and dust respirator. Boots. Gloves. A self contained breathing apparatus should be used to avoid inhalation of the product. Suggested protective clothing might not be sufficient; consult a specialist before handling this product.

Exposure Limits: STEL: 2 (mg/m3) from ACGIH (TLV) [United States] TLV: 2 Ceil: 2 (mg/m3) from OSHA (PEL) [United States] Ceil: 2 (mg/m3) from NIOSH

The risk of eye and skin damage is much greater for sodium hydroxide than for sodium chloride. In addition, dust and fumes pose a significant risk to the lungs. If handling this material causes a worker to cough, the ventilation is not adequate and should be improved.

Section 9: Physical and Chemical Properties

Physical state and appearance: Solid. (Deliquescent solid.)

Odor: Odorless.

Taste: Extremely Bitter.

Molecular Weight: 40 g/mole

Color: White.

pH (1% soln/water): 13.5 [Basic.]

Boiling Point: 1388°C (2530°F)

Melting Point: 323°C (613°F)

Specific Gravity: 2.13 (Water = 1)

Solubility: Easily soluble in cold water.

Section 10: Stability and Reactivity Data

Stability: The product is stable.

Conditions of Instability: Incompatible materials, moisture, moist air.

Incompatibility with various substances: Highly reactive with metals. Reactive with oxidizing agents, reducing agents, acids, alkalis, moisture.

This section was originally two pages long. For complete information, consult the MSDS *provided by your vendor.*

Special Remarks on Corrosivity: Very caustic to aluminum and other metals in presence of moisture.

The final remark on aluminum is extremely important to the soapmaker. You should allow no aluminum utensils to come into contact with sodium hydroxide.

Section 11: Toxicological Information

Routes of Entry: Absorbed through skin. Dermal contact. Eye contact. Inhalation. Ingestion.

Toxicity to Animals: Acute oral toxicity (LD_{50}): 140–340 mg/kg [Rat]. Acute intra-peritoneal toxicity (LD_{50}): 40 mg/kg [Mouse]. Acute dermal toxicity (LD_{50}): 1350 mg/kg [Rabbit].

Chronic Effects on Humans: Mutagenic Effects: Mutagenic for mammalian somatic cells. May cause damage to the following organs: mucous membranes, upper respiratory tract, skin, eyes.

Other Toxic Effects on Humans: Extremely hazardous in case of inhalation (lung corrosive). Very hazardous in case of skin contact (corrosive, irritant, permeator), of eye contact (corrosive), and of ingestion.

Special Remarks on Toxicity to Animals: Lowest Published Lethal Dose: (LD_L) [Rabbit] – Route: Oral; Dose: 500 mg/kg.

Special Remarks on Chronic Effects on Humans: May affect genetic material. Investigation as a mutagen (cytogenetic analysis)

Note that the LD_{50} for sodium hydroxide is at least 10 times smaller than that for sodium chloride. In other words, it is 10 times more poisonous. Oral toxicity means it was fed to the animals. Intra-peritoneal toxicity means it was injected directly into the abdomen. Dermal toxicity means it was spread on the skin. Amazingly, the LD$_L$ for sodium hydroxide is only half as big as that for sodium chloride, making it only twice as poisonous. Rabbits, however, may tolerate sodium hydroxide more easily than rats or humans.

Section 12: Ecological Information
Products of Biodegradation: Possibly hazardous short term degradation products are not likely. However, long term degradation products may arise.
Toxicity of the Products of Biodegradation: The product itself and its products of degradation are not toxic.

Section 13: Disposal Considerations
Waste Disposal: Waste must be disposed of in accordance with federal, state and local environmental control regulations.

Section 14: Transport Information
DOT Classification: Class 8: Corrosive material
Identification: Sodium hydroxide, solid UNNA: 1823 PG: II

The DOT classification and UNNA number appear on trucks, rail cars, and shipping containers carrying hazardous materials. Placards bearing these codes allow emergency personnel to identify materials when accidents occur.

Section 15: Other Regulatory Information
HMIS Health Hazard: 3 Fire Hazard: 0 Reactivity: 2 Personal Protection: J
NFPA Health: 3 Flammability: 0 Reactivity: 1

The MSDS you get from your vendor may be even longer than this one, and it is easy to be intimidated by the sheer volume of technical information. While I do not wish to discourage you from reading and understanding every bit of this information, it is possible to get most of what you need to know from the NFPA or HMIS codes, which typically appear at the beginning or end of the MSDS. Section 3.3 will explain these codes, but first there are the usual disclaimers to finish out the MSDS.

Section 16: Other Information

Created: 05/21/2007. Last Updated: 05/21/2007.

The information above is believed to be accurate and represents the best information currently available to us. However, we make no warranty of merchantability or any other warranty, express or implied, with respect to such information, and we assume no liability resulting from its use. Users should make their own investigations to determine the suitability of the information for their particular purposes. In no event shall CavemanChemistry.com be liable for any claims, losses, or damages of any third party or for lost profits or any special, indirect, incidental, consequential or exemplary damages, howsoever arising, even if CavemanChemistry.com has been advised of the possibility of such damages.

3.3 NFPA and HMIS Ratings

While material safety data sheets are intended to give workers the information they need to handle materials safely, the sheer volume of material can be daunting. Wouldn't it be nice if there were a quick and easy way to get a general idea of the hazardous properties of a material without wading through six to ten pages of fine print? This kind of at-a-glance information would be particularly useful for someone in an emergency situation. A firefighter in a burning building, for example, does not have time to consult an MSDS before deciding whether to use water to douse the flames or to get the heck out of there before something blows up. To this end, the National Fire Protection Association (NFPA) developed a rating system to inform firefighters of the hazardous properties of materials at a glance.

The NFPA diamond is the most common hazard rating system in use. It consists of a diamond divided into color-coded quadrants, blue (left) for health, red (top) for flammability, yellow (right) for reactivity, and white (bottom) for special instructions. In each of these areas a material is rated on a scale from 0 (non-hazardous) to 4 (very hazardous). Table 3-1 shows the NFPA diamond for sodium hydroxide. Here we see that it has a

Table 3-1. NFPA and HMIS Ratings for NaOH

Health	3
Fire	0
Reactivity	2
Personal Protection	J

HMIS Personal Protection Codes

A Safety glasses

B Safety glasses, gloves

C Safety glasses, gloves, chemical apron

D Face shield, gloves, chemical apron

E Safety glasses, gloves, dust respirator

F Safety glasses, gloves, chemical apron, dust respirator

G Safety glasses, gloves, vapor respirator

H Splash goggles, gloves, chemical apron, vapor respirator

I Safety glasses, gloves, dust and vapor respirator

J Goggles, gloves, apron, dust and vapor respirator

K Air line hood or mask, gloves, full chemical suit, boots

X Ask Supervisor

rating of 3 for health, which makes it considerably hazardous, but not at the top of the scale. It has a rating of 0 for flammability, since it will not burn. It has a rating of 1 for reactivity. From the MSDS we can see that sodium hydroxide reacts with metals, among other things, but this level of detail is not available in the rating. There are several special ratings, but the most common are W, meaning that the material reacts violently with water, and OX, meaning that the material is an oxidizer. The presence of an oxidizer makes it nearly impossible to smother a fire. The major limitation of the NFPA diamond is that since its target audience is firefighters, the hazard ratings are appropriate for emergency situations involving fire.

To deal with safety in laboratories and manufacturing facilities, the National Paints and Coatings Association developed the Hazardous Materials Information System (HMIS). The HMIS symbol is rectangular but contains the same color codes as the NFPA diamond, blue (top) for health, red for fire, and yellow for reactivity. The numerical ratings follow the same order as the NFPA ratings, from 0 (non-hazardous) to 4 (very hazardous). The numerical values may differ slightly, however, since the level of hazard in the laboratory may be different from that in a fire. The white (bottom) area contains a code for the personal protection equipment recommended for the safe handling of the material.

In the model MSDSs for sodium chloride and sodium hydroxide, the NFPA and HMIS symbols appeared at the top of the sheet. More commonly, the ratings will be given as text rather than graphics in one of the later sections, for example, Sections 3, 15, or 16. In the model MSDSs, I included the ratings in Section 15. Manufacturers are not required, however, to include either of these rating systems.[1] If a sheet from your vendor does not contain one or the other, you can search online using the appropriate CAS number and the keywords NFPA or HMIS.

It is a very good idea to label your chemicals with either NFPA or HMIS rating symbols. Self-adhesive labels are readily available from laboratory and safety supply companies for a few cents each.[2] This is a very small price to pay for your own safety and that of your employees. With NFPA or HMIS graphics for ready reference and MSDSs for more detailed information, you should be well-prepared to handle any of the hazardous materials used in soapmaking.

---

1. J. T. Baker has developed the Saf-T-Label system using color codes similar to the NFPA and HMIS ratings. For more information, see reference [21].
2. www.Labelmaster.com [16] and SafetyEmporium.com [32] are two such companies.

Practice Problems

Answers to practice problems appear in Appendix A (page 335).

In the following problems, MSDSs may be found by searching the Internet using the keywords MSDS, NFPA, and the name of the materials in question.

1. Why should an employer keep MSDSs on file for access by employees?
2. What is the CAS registry number?
3. What statistic can be used to estimate the relative toxicities of materials?
4. Find an MSDS for citric acid. Is this material hygroscopic or deliquescent?
5. Find an MSDS for sodium chloride using the CAS number 7681-52-9 as one of your keywords. How does the information differ from that provided in this chapter?
6. Find an MSDS for sodium lauryl sulfate. What is the CAS number for this material?
7. Find an MSDS for phenolphthalein. Is this material flammable?
8. Find an MSDS for tetrasodium EDTA. How does the health hazard for this material compare to those for sodium chloride and sodium hydroxide?
9. Find MSDSs for ethanol and clove oil. Which of these materials is more toxic?
10. Find MSDSs for sodium lauryl sulfate and caffeine. Which of these materials is more toxic?

Chapter 4

Single-Oil Soaps

*M*AKING a batch of soap takes about an hour whether it consists of two pounds or twenty pounds. The oils must be melted, the sodium hydroxide and water weighed, the soap thoroughly mixed and poured into the mold. Labor costs can be minimized by producing batches as large as may be conveniently handled. While beginners make a few pounds of soap at a time, experienced soapmakers are able to mix and pour up to a hundred pounds of soap before it becomes too thick to get into the mold. But for experimental work it makes sense to go to the opposite extreme. By making a single bar of soap, techniques and formulas may be perfected without wasting expensive materials.

While scaling up to a hundred pounds is not as simple as using a bigger pot, scaling down to a hundred grams presents logistical challenges of its own. For one thing, we'll use our centigram balance to accurately weigh such small amounts. For another, a small batch is more easily mixed by shaking rather than by stirring. And while soap in a large mold retains enough heat to fuel the saponification reaction, small batches must be gently heated to simulate the warmth retained by a larger mold. If you are a beginning soapmaker, the following directions will give you an introduction to the soapmaking process. If you are an experienced soapmaker you may be tempted to skip to the next chapter, but I would encourage you to give the procedures of this chapter a try. The techniques developed here will prepare you for the more advanced experiments later in the book.

4.1 True Lyes

The goal of this procedure is to produce a solution of sodium hydroxide with a concentration of exactly 500 ppt (50%); this may very well be the most important procedure in the entire book. But don't worry—you are going to get plenty of practice making up this solution and before long you will be able to do it quickly and accurately. In this chapter you will also use it to make experimental quantities of soap. Before beginning the procedure we ought to explore the reason for using a solution rather than solid sodium hydroxide for the work to follow.

In common usage the words *caustic soda* and *lye* are often used as synonyms for *sodium hydroxide*. A more precise usage would reserve the word *lye* for a solution of sodium hydroxide in water. In this book, **lye** refers specifically to an aqueous sodium hydroxide solution with a concentration of 500 ppt, unless otherwise indicated.

Sodium hydroxide may come to you as granules, flakes, or pellets. Since flakes and pellets usually weigh more than drops, it would be difficult to hit a target weight exactly when weighing synthetically. Moreover, for many analytical tests, we would like to add chemicals in small increments, say, one drop at a time. Consequently, solutions are often more convenient than solids for weighing both synthetically and analytically. The following procedure will produce a sodium hydroxide solution that may be used for both synthetic and analytic work.

Most handcrafted soap books recommend that you make up your lye in a Pyrex measuring cup. While there is nothing particularly wrong with this practice, there are some advantages to using a plastic bottle for mixing lye. First, plastic is not as fragile as glass. Second, a bottle will contain the fumes and minimize the possibility of splashing lye around your workspace. Finally, large Pyrex containers are much more expensive than plastic ones, which will be a consideration for making larger batches of soap. The problem with plastic is that lye gets very hot as it is mixed and some plastics will be damaged by the temperatures, which may rise as high as 100°C (212°F). We'll use a polypropylene bottle, which is designed to withstand temperatures that high.

In this procedure we'll add NaOH and water in proportions that are as close to equal as possible. We are going to combine analytical and synthetic weights as in Section 2.5 (page 31), but we'll have to pay close attention to the order in which we weigh the NaOH and water. We'll analytically weigh the water first and then weigh the NaOH into it. Adding NaOH to water rather than water to NaOH helps to ensure that the NaOH dissolves quickly without clumping, and minimizes the production of harmful fumes. We'll ensure that the weight of NaOH is greater than that of the water and then synthetically weigh an additional portion of water until the weights of NaOH and water are as close to equal as possible. This will produce a solution with a concentration as close to 500 ppt as possible.

 The use of hard water should be avoided because dissolved minerals may contribute to the appearance of the **dreaded orange spots** (DOS), a defect that we'll revisit in Chapter 19. I recommend using distilled or de-ionized water for all of your soapmaking experiments. Water softeners and reverse osmosis purifiers produce water suitable for experimental work, but charcoal filters alone *do not* remove dissolved minerals. Please note that bottled "spring water" may contain undesirable dissolved minerals.

 Sodium hydroxide absorbs moisture from the air, so if we weigh 10 g of *wet* sodium hydroxide, part of what we are weighing is actually water. To get consistent results, store your sodium hydroxide in air-tight containers and avoid leaving them open for extended periods.

1. *Gather your materials:*
   - Goggles or glasses
   - An eyewash bottle
   - Gloves
   - A centigram balance
   - Distilled water
   - A 125 mL polypropylene (PP) plastic bottle labeled Water, with lid
   - Sodium hydroxide
   - A 125 mL polypropylene (PP) plastic bottle labeled NaOH, with lid
   - A 500 mL polypropylene (PP) plastic bottle labeled Lye, with lid
   - A pipet
   - A calculator
   - A powder funnel
   - Your soapmaking notebook and a pen

2. *Arrange your workspace:* Sodium hydroxide is an essential soapmaking material that can be handled safely, but it deserves your respect. Review the MSDS for sodium hydroxide before proceeding. You *must* wear safety goggles or glasses for eye protection and you *ought* to wear gloves. You also ought to have an eyewash bottle handy just in case a drop of lye should get past your goggles. You should make soap in an area with adequate ventilation, preferably under or near a ventilation fan.

   Your notebook should be opened to a new page with your pen at the ready.

3. *Fill the weighing bottles:* Our goal in this step is simply to ensure that there is more NaOH than water in their respective bottles. Since the bottles are the same size, we can assume that their empty weights are similar. Fill the NaOH bottle with NaOH and weigh the filled bottle without its lid. Fill the Water bottle, weigh it (no lid), and if it weighs more than the NaOH bottle, use the pipet to remove some water until the Water bottle weighs less than the NaOH bottle. Neither of these weights should be recorded in your notebook. All that matters is that the NaOH bottle is the heavier of the two.

4. *Weigh the first water portion:* Place the Water bottle and powder funnel onto the balance and press the tare button so that the balance reads 0.00 g. Use the funnel to empty the Water bottle into the Lye bottle. Place the Water bottle and funnel back onto the balance, which now reads -XXX.XX g, the exact weight of the water delivered. Whatever the actual weight is, record *all five digits on a right-hand page* of your notebook. Dry the powder funnel with a paper towel before proceeding to the next step.

5. *Weigh the NaOH:* Place the NaOH bottle and powder funnel onto the balance and press the tare button so that the balance reads 0.00 g. Use the funnel to empty the NaOH bottle into the Lye bottle. Place the NaOH bottle and funnel back onto the balance, which now reads -YYY.YY g, the exact weight of the NaOH delivered. Whatever the actual weight is, record *all five digits on a right-hand page* of your notebook.

6. *Calculate the target weight:* The weight of NaOH should be slightly larger than that of the water portion. You need a little more water. How much?

   YYY.YY - XXX.XX = WW.WW

   WW.WW is the target weight for the final water portion. To avoid confusing it with an actual weight, it should be recorded on a *left-hand page* of your notebook.

7. *Weigh the final water portion:* The remainder of the water is weighed synthetically, using the pipet rather than the funnel. Refill the `Water` bottle, place it onto the balance, and press the tare button. Use a pipet to transfer water to the `Lye` bottle until the balance reads -WW.WW g. Your goal is to hit this target weight to within 1 drop. Whatever the actual weight is, record *all five digits on a right-hand page* of your notebook.

8. *Mix the sodium hydroxide solution:* Screw the lid onto the bottle and, holding the bottle at the top, give it a gentle swirl. The solution will begin to get hot. Put the bottle down, loosen the lid to let off any pressure, and tighten it again. Then give the bottle another gentle swirl. Alternate loosening the lid, tightening it again, and gently swirling the solution until all of the sodium hydroxide has dissolved. Once all of the sodium hydroxide has dissolved, the solution will begin to cool.

   They say that a watched pot never boils. It must also be true that a watched bottle never cools. The good news is that you have all the time in the world and there is no need to watch the bottle cool. Go about your business. Read a good book. Stop and smell the flowers. The bottle will cool without your supervision. As the bottle cools, the pressure inside the bottle will actually drop. When the bottle can be picked up comfortably with your bare hands, loosen the lid one more time to let air back into the bottle.

9. *Calculate the actual concentration:* Calculate the total weight of the lye by adding the weights of NaOH and water as recorded on the right-hand page of your notebook. Divide the weight of NaOH by this total and multiply by 1000. You should get something close to 500 ppt. Whatever the actual

---

Example 4-1. Making Up a Little Lye

I wanted to make up some 500 ppt NaOH. I filled both weighing bottles, ensuring that the `NaOH` bottle was the heavier of the two. I analytically weighed 134.11 g of water and 147.40 g of NaOH into the `Lye` bottle:

Water (g)	Water (g)	NaOH (g)	Total (g)	Concentration (ppt)
134.11		147.40		

The arithmetic for the target weight was done on a left-hand page of my notebook:

147.40 - 134.11 = 13.29

I recorded the *actual* weight on a right-hand page. Then I divided the NaOH weight by the total weight and multiplied by 1000 to get the actual concentration:

Water (g)	Water (g)	NaOH (g)	Total (g)	Concentration (ppt)
134.11	13.34	147.40	294.85	499.92

In this case I overshot my target weight by 1 drop of water. If instead I had come up one drop short, the concentration would have been 500.08 ppt. As long as I get within 1 drop of the target weight, this procedure guarantees a concentration of 500.00 ± 0.08 ppt. This is close enough that in future calculations we'll assume that our lye is exactly 500 ppt.

---

number is, record it in your notebook and on the label of the `Lye` bottle.

10. *Cleanup:* Alkaline spills may be cleaned up with household vinegar. The only utensil that needs cleaning is the powder funnel, which may have a little bit of NaOH sticking to it. There is no need to empty or clean your labeled weighing bottles. Screw their lids on and put them in the cabinet with your sodium hydroxide, where you will find them the next time you need to make lye. Wipe down your balance and bring your notebook up to date.

Now you can remove your glasses, eyesight intact.

As long as we hit the water target weight to within 1 drop, we should always produce a lye with a concentration of 500.00±0.08 ppt. In all of our future calculations we'll presume that there is exactly 1 g of sodium hydroxide *per* 2 g of lye. Of course, that generates a pair of hotdogs, one upside down from the other. Can you write them down?

Never seal a container while its temperature is rising! You should tighten the cap on the lye bottle only briefly while you are mixing it. Once the temperature begins to fall, however, you should tighten the cap to protect the lye from absorbing atmospheric moisture.

You have made enough lye to produce about a dozen bars of experimental soap. When you need more lye, you may add it to the lye bottle without emptying the previous contents. After all, if you add 500 ppt NaOH to 500 ppt NaOH, its concentration remains 500 ppt. The more you practice making up the lye in this chapter, the more proficient you will become and the less time it will take.

It is important that the Lye bottle remain tightly sealed except during use. If left open, it will absorb moisture from the air, changing its concentration. If you leave the lid off of the Lye bottle for more than a few hours, I would suggest that you discard the lye and make up a fresh batch.[1]

4.2 Single-Oil Soaps

Most handcrafted soap is made from a blend of oils, each oil chosen to provide a specific quality to the finished soap. Before we can rationally blend oils, however, we must understand the properties of soaps made from the individual oils. There are six classes of oils and in this section we'll make a soap from each of them for comparison. We start with Castile soap.

---

1. Lye solution may be safely flushed down the drain with plenty of water.

4.2.1 Castile Soap

Castile soap has the well-deserved reputation of being a mild and luxurious soap. It is simply soap made from a single oil: olive oil. We'll take it as an exemplar of soaps made from the monounsaturated oils and will refer to them as *oleic* soaps, from the Latin word for olive oil, *oleum*. In this procedure you will get to practice your synthetic weighing techniques. Oil will be weighed into a polypropylene bottle, and lye will be weighed into the oil. The bottle will be vigorously shaken until the raw soap thickens, and then the soap will be poured into a mold. The soap will be kept in a warm oven for four hours to simulate the warmth that would be retained by a larger mold. When the soap is removed from the oven, it is fully saponified and ready for use. It will, however, continue to harden over the course of a few weeks as excess water evaporates.

Before we can make soap, we must determine the amount of lye to use with a given amount of oil. This is the most crucial decision you face as a soapmaker. If you use too much lye, the soap may contain un-reacted lye when the reaction is complete, rendering the soap too harsh for use. If too little lye is used, there will be unsaponified oil in the soap, wasting expensive material and leaving the soap less soapy than it would have otherwise been. The math is not difficult, and it follows the same format as all the math used in later chapters.

Key to this calculation is the **alkali ratio** (AR). The AR is the number of parts of alkali (NaOH or KOH) used to react with 1000 parts of oil, and it is expressed in parts per thousand.[2] The *part* in *parts per thousand* could be any unit of weight: milligrams, grams, ounces, pounds, or tons. As long as the same units are used for both the alkali and the oil, no unit conversion will be required.

Table 4-1 gives the recommended AR for olive oil as 131 ppt. If we want to make soap from 100.00 g of olive oil, the calculation goes like this:

---

2. Experienced soapmakers may already be familiar with the term *saponification value*, or SV. The SV is the amount of alkali required to saponify 1000 parts of oil *completely*. The AR is the amount of alkali *actually used* to react with 1000 parts of oil. For more information, see Appendix B (page 377).

Table 4-1. Recommended Alkali Ratios for NaOH

Description	AR		
	Ppt	Percent	Decimal
Lauric Oils			
Coconut Oil	176 ppt	17.6%	0.176
Palm Kernel Oil	163 ppt	16.3%	0.163
Palmitic Oils			
Lard (Pork Fat)	136 ppt	13.6%	0.136
Palm Oil	135 ppt	13.5%	0.135
Tallow (Beef Fat)	135 ppt	13.5%	0.135
Oleic Oils			
Avocado Oil	126 ppt	12.6%	0.126
Olive Oil	131 ppt	13.1%	0.131
Peanut Oil	133 ppt	13.3%	0.133
Rice Bran Oil	129 ppt	12.9%	0.129
Ricinoleic Oils			
Castor Oil	125 ppt	12.5%	0.125
Linoleic Oils			
Corn Oil	133 ppt	13.3%	0.133
Cottonseed Oil	134 ppt	13.4%	0.134
Grape Seed Oil	134 ppt	13.4%	0.134
Safflower Seed Oil	132 ppt	13.2%	0.132
Sesame Seed Oil	133 ppt	13.3%	0.133
Soybean Oil	134 ppt	13.4%	0.134
Sunflower Seed Oil	134 ppt	13.4%	0.134
Linolenic Oils			
Hempseed Oil	135 ppt	13.5%	0.135
Linseed Oil	134 ppt	13.4%	0.134
Walnut Oil	134 ppt	13.4%	0.134

Data derived from reference [80]. Fats and oils are listed alphabetically within families.

The italicised oils will be used in examples throughout the book.

$$? \text{ g Lye} = 100.00 \; \cancel{g \; oil} \left(\frac{131 \; \cancel{g \; NaOH}}{1000 \; \cancel{g \; oil}} \right) \left(\frac{1000 \text{ g Lye}}{500 \; \cancel{g \; NaOH}} \right)$$
$$= 26.20 \text{ g Lye}$$

The calculation works the same way in ounces:

$$? \text{ oz Lye} = 100.00 \; \cancel{oz \; oil} \left(\frac{131 \; \cancel{oz \; NaOH}}{1000 \; \cancel{oz \; oil}} \right) \left(\frac{1000 \text{ oz Lye}}{500 \; \cancel{oz \; NaOH}} \right)$$
$$= 26.20 \text{ oz Lye}$$

or in pounds:

$$? \text{ lb Lye} = 100.00 \; \cancel{lb \; oil} \left(\frac{131 \; \cancel{lb \; NaOH}}{1000 \; \cancel{lb \; oil}} \right) \left(\frac{1000 \text{ lb Lye}}{500 \; \cancel{lb \; NaOH}} \right)$$
$$= 26.20 \text{ lb Lye}$$

Returning to our experimental bar of soap, let's use 100.00 g of olive oil and 26.20 g of lye.

1. *Gather your materials:*
   - Goggles or glasses
   - An eyewash bottle
   - Gloves
   - A centigram balance
   - A 125 mL PP bottle labeled Lye
   - A 125 mL PP bottle labeled Olive Oil
   - A clean, dry 500 mL PP bottle labeled Soap, with lid
   - Two pipets labeled Lye and Oil
   - A thermometer
   - A soap oven (or microwave oven) and oven mitts
   - A single-bar soap mold
   - Your soapmaking notebook and a pen

2. *Arrange your workspace:* Sodium hydroxide is an essential soapmaking material that can be handled safely, but it deserves your respect. You *must* wear safety goggles or glasses for eye protection and you *ought* to wear gloves. You should make soap in an area with adequate ventilation, preferably near a ventilation fan. Your notebook should be opened to a new page with your pen at the ready. Record the name of the soap, the date, and the time that you begin.

3. *Preheat your oven:* Preheat your oven to 140°F or 60°C.[3]

4. *Heat the oil:* Pour about 90 g of olive oil into the Olive Oil bottle and heat it to a temperature of 43°C (109°F).[4] You may heat it in the soap oven while it preheats or you may use a microwave oven. If you use a microwave oven, set it for only 30 seconds at a time to avoid overheating the oil. While the oil is being heated, place the lid on the bottle but *do not tighten it.* Remove the lid and place it aside once the oil is hot.

5. *Weigh the olive oil:* Synthetically weigh 100.00 g of olive oil from the Olive Oil bottle into the Soap bottle using the procedure of Section 2.5 (page 31). Since the weighing bottle is smaller than the mouth of the Soap bottle, you do not need a funnel for the first (analytical) portion. Simply place the Olive Oil bottle onto the balance, make sure that it weighs less than 100.00 g, press the tare button, pour the entire contents into the Soap bottle, and return the Olive Oil bottle to the balance. Record *all four digits* of the weight in your notebook. Subtract this weight from 100.00 g to get the target weight for the second oil portion. Refill the Olive Oil bottle, place it onto the balance, press the tare button, and use the pipet to deliver the target weight of oil to the Soap bottle. Record the actual weight in your notebook and add it to the weight of the first oil portion. The total weight should be within ±0.05 g of 100.00 g.

6. *Weigh the lye:* Fill the Lye bottle about half-full with 500 ppt NaOH and synthetically weigh 26.20 g of lye from the Lye bottle into the Soap bottle. With this small quantity you are probably better off weighing in one portion as in Section 2.4 (page 29). Simply place the Lye bottle onto the balance, press the tare button, and use a pipet to transfer the target weight of lye to the Soap bottle. Whatever the actual

---

3. The exact temperature is not critical. Our goal is to simulate the warmth that would be retained in a larger mold. In such an environment, the soap temperature will usually exceed the oven temperature. If your oven cannot be set to 140°F, simply set it to its lowest setting.
4. As with the oven, the oil temperature is not critical. It should be warm enough to start the saponification reaction soon after the oil mixes with the lye.

weight is, record *all four digits* on a right-hand page of your notebook.

Screw the cap onto the Lye bottle and set it aside. The lye in the bottle can be used the next time you make soap. There is no need to empty it; simply refill it as needed.

7. *Mix the soap thoroughly:* The temperature of the oil/lye mixture should be somewhere in the vicinity of 38°C (100°F). Screw the lid onto the Soap bottle and give it a *vigorous* shake for 20–60 seconds. Your goal is to thoroughly mix the oily and watery components so that they form an emulsion. You should not be gentle; treat it like a can of spray paint. The oil and lye should emulsify to form a translucent liquid.

    Most soapmaking instructions tell you to pour the lye into a pot of oil and stir it with a spoon or stick blender. But in an opaque pot it's hard to see whether the mixture has separated. With this method, the status of the oil-lye mixture can be monitored through the translucent bottle. Furthermore, this method makes it unlikely that raw soap will splash all over your workspace. All I can say to experienced soapmakers is, "Try it; you may like it." Chapter 6 will adapt this technique to the production of larger batches of soap.

    When you first shake the bottle and set it down, the thin soap will quickly run off the walls of the bottle. But as you continue to shake the bottle, the soap will become thicker and creamier, and the raw soap will coat the inside walls of the bottle, a condition soapmakers call **trace.** Olive oil soap traces relatively slowly, so there is no hurry. The soap should be thick, like a milkshake or gravy, but pourable.[5] The most important consideration is that the ingredients are completely mixed.

8. *Pour:* Pour your soap into the mold. This part isn't rocket science; just be careful not to splash raw soap everywhere. Measure the pour temperature and record it on a right-hand page of your notebook.

---

5. If your soap becomes too thick to pour, all is not lost. You can place the soap bottle itself in the oven, but you will have to chop up the soap to get it out of the bottle.

9. *Bake:* Record the actual oven temperature in your notebook before placing the mold in the oven for 4 hours, after which time the soap should be fully saponified. At Hampden-Sydney, we use an appliance timer to turn the oven off after four hours. We take the soap out of the cool oven the next day.

10. *Cleanup:* Alkaline spills may be cleaned up with household vinegar. While your soap is baking, you can clean up your utensils. Wipe down your balance and put it away. Refill the `Olive Oil` and `Lye` bottles for your next soapmaking session. The raw soap in the `Soap` bottle will be easier to remove after saponification is complete; let it sit for a day before washing it with hot water.

11. *Cure:* Remove the soap from the mold. While the saponification reaction is complete, or nearly so, the soap will continue to harden over the next few weeks as excess water evaporates. Place the soap in an area where it can dry with adequate air circulation and weigh it weekly until the weight stops changing. Record the weights on a right-hand page of your notebook.

Congratulations! You have just produced what was for many years seen as the queen of soaps, Castile soap. In this book we'll use shorthand formulas for the soaps we make. This one will be called $Olive_{1000}Lye_{262}$, which gives the number of parts (grams, ounces, or pounds) of lye needed to react with 1000 parts of oil. Note that since this book will always assume that lye made from NaOH has a concentration of 500 ppt, the subscript for Lye is just double the AR. In addition to the formula, you may wish to copy out the entire procedure for this first soap as a bulleted list. Thereafter, you need only remark on variations from the standard method. Leave plenty of space, perhaps an entire page, for noting the properties of your soap, some of which may become evident only after the passage of some time. For now, though, let's systematically investigate some different common soapmaking oils.

The **soap formula** gives the relative amounts of each ingredient in parts per thousand parts of oil.

4.2.2 Palmitic Soaps

The soapmaking oils may be conveniently divided into several families. We are already familiar with olive oil, a member of the *oleic* family. Next we'll investigate the *palmitic* family, whose members include palm oil, tallow, and lard. Palm oil and tallow are generally available only from vendors of soapmaking supplies, but lard is universally available at grocery stores. All three oils are solids at room temperature except in warm climates or hot weather. The properties of the palmitic soaps are similar and you may choose to use any of the palmitic oils to make a representative bar of soap. Since the recommended AR for palm oil is 135 ppt, the soap formula is then $Palm_{1000}Lye_{270}$. While there is nothing wrong with this formula, the palmitic oils saponify more quickly than the oleic oils, and in order to give us time for thoroughly mixing the oil and lye we would like to slow the reaction down. We can do this by adding extra water: $Palm_{1000}Lye_{270}Aq_{135}$. To make a bar of palm oil soap, synthetically weigh 100.00 g of oil, 13.5 g of water, and 27.00 g of lye into a 500 mL bottle. If you make lard or tallow soap, be sure to use the appropriate alkali ratio.

The procedure for making palm oil soap is identical to that for olive oil soap except that the palm oil must be melted before it can be mixed with the lye.[6] While this may not sound like much of a complication, it bears some explanation. Palm oil from Columbus Foods, for example, comes in 7 lb (1 gallon) bottles, 50 lb pails, and 50 lb "no stir" cubes. Why "no stir"? Fats and oils are not pure compounds, but mixtures of different oils with different melting points. Palm oil is no exception. When melted palm oil cools, those oil components with the highest melting points start to solidify first and those with the lowest melting points solidify last. Columbus will make sure that the oil was thoroughly mixed when it was poured into the bottle or pail, but as it solidifies, the oil at the top of the container may have a different composition from that at the bottom. And soap made from oil at the top may be different from soap made from oil at the bottom.

---

6. In warm climates these oils may be liquids, in which case the procedure of Section 4.2.1 may be used. The only difference will be the weight of lye used.

The "no stir" cube, however, is stirred while cooling until it is solid, so that the oil is homogeneous. As long as your cube does not melt in transit or storage, the oil will be consistent from top to bottom. For this reason, Columbus only ships it during the cooler seasons. At Hampden-Sydney, we buy all of our palm oil as cubes and have never had a problem with them. The cube comes in a heavy cardboard box with a plastic liner. We simply scoop out what we need and get to work.

In bottles or pails, the entire container of palm oil must be melted and stirred before use. To melt a bottle, wrap it in an electric heating pad set to its lowest temperature. Palm oil melts at about 35°C (95°F), so you need only a gentle heat. You definitely don't want to melt the bottle, which is more likely to be polyethylene than polypropylene. Pails may be heated with a band heater, which wraps around the pail like a long, skinny heating pad.[7] Once melted, you can shake a bottle or stir a pail to mix the oil completely. In either bottles or pails, continue heating the palm oil until it is transparent and free of cloudiness, free-flowing, and similar in consistency to a liquid oil such as olive oil.

It would be quite wasteful if you were to melt an entire bottle or pail of oil for only one bar of soap! Let me suggest that, for experimental use, you completely melt and mix an entire container and then pour it into containers of convenient size. For experimental bars, pour the melted and mixed oil into 125 mL polypropylene bottles, enough for one bar of soap. You need not weigh the oil at this point—simply fill the bottle to the shoulder. For larger batches, of course, you can store the oil in larger bottles. From a 7 lb bottle, you can fill about thirty 125 mL (1-bar) bottles, seven 500 mL (4-bar) bottles, two 2000 mL (15-bar) bottles, one 1 gal polypropylene (PP) pitcher, or any combination of these. When you use any of these bottles, you must melt and mix the entire contents. Be sure to label each bottle with its contents.

---

7. www.SoapEquipment.com [43] sells a band heater, AC1178, for $107.50.

Once in smaller bottles, palm oil can be quickly melted in a microwave oven.[8] A 125 mL bottle of palm oil should be heated 30 seconds at a time for a couple of minutes until the temperature is 43°C (109°F). From there on, you can use the procedure of Section 4.2.1, having substituted the weight of lye that is appropriate for the oil you are using.

Whenever you break up a 7 lb bottle or 50 lb pail of solid oil, put aside a few 125 mL bottles for experimental purposes. Since liquid oils don't need to be melted, you need only one 125 mL bottle for each of the oils you use. Oil bottles may be refilled at your convenience without emptying or washing them as long as you refill them with the same kind of oil. Be sure to label each bottle and double-check the label before refilling.

The use of 125 mL oil bottles illustrates an important principle of chemical hygiene: *Always pour chemicals from a larger bottle into a smaller one, never the other way around.* If, for example, you were to accidentally pour olive oil into your 125 mL castor oil bottle, only the small bottle would be contaminated. Either you will notice your mistake and discard this small quantity of oil or you will make a single bar of mislabeled soap. If, on the other hand, you were to empty a 125 mL bottle of castor oil into a 7 lb bottle of olive oil, the entire bottle would be contaminated.

Never heat a sealed container! When heating an oil in a microwave or roaster oven, place the lid on the container but do not screw it on tight. A sealed container may explode if the contents overheat.

4.2.3 Lauric Soaps

Once you have introduced yourself to one of the palmitic soaps, it is time to explore the *lauric* family, whose members include coconut oil and palm kernel oil. Neither is commonly available from grocery stores, but coconut oil is available at some, and

---

8. Polypropylene bottles may also be heated in the soap oven while it is preheating. Polyethylene bottles may melt where they touch the sides of the oven.

it is well worth asking; the shipping charges on mail-order oil can easily be half the cost of the oil itself. In my area, Walmart has recently begun stocking LouAna Coconut Oil next to the lard. I have not found a local source for palm kernel oil and, like most soapmakers, I must order it by mail. Do not confuse palm kernel oil with palm oil. They have very different properties, for reasons that will become apparent in due time. Since the recommended AR for coconut oil is 176 ppt, the formula for coconut oil soap is $Coconut_{1000}Lye_{352}$. Like palm oil, coconut oil is a solid except in warm climates. Large bottles or pails should be melted, mixed, and packaged into smaller bottles for small-scale work. If you make up a few 125 mL bottles of each solid oil you own, you will always be ready to make experimental soap. Also like palm oil, coconut oil saponifies more rapidly than olive oil, and we add some extra water to slow it down. For now, make up a bar of $Coconut_{1000}Lye_{352}Aq_{176}$ using the procedure of Section 4.2.2. If you would rather use palm kernel oil, be sure to use the appropriate value of the AR.

4.2.4 Linoleic, Linolenic, and Ricinoleic Soaps

Your investigation is incomplete without an exploration of the *linoleic* family, whose members include sunflower, safflower oil, and grape seed oils. High-oleic (HO) varieties of sunflower and safflower oils are available and these belong to the oleic family. Walnut, hempseed, and linseed oils comprise the *linolenic* family. Make up one bar of soap from each family using the procedure of Section 4.2.1. If you wish to compare your results to mine, make one bar from safflower oil and the other from hempseed oil. Be sure to use the recommended alkali ratios for the oils you choose. These oils saponify slowly and no extra water is needed.

Your collection will not be complete without a soap made from the *ricinoleic* family, whose only member is castor oil, available in pharmacies in the first-aid section. As a base oil it is rather expensive, though it is frequently used as a minor soap ingredient, particularly for liquid soaps and transparent soaps. For now, make up a bar of soap from 100.00 g of castor oil using the formula, $Castor_{1000}Lye_{250}Aq_{250}$ and the procedure of Section 4.2.1.

4.3 Unmolding Soap

You should now be in possession of six very different soaps, one for each of the oil families.[9] It would be nice if I could tell you the properties of your soaps, how hard they are, how well they lather, and how gentle they are on the skin. But because oils are natural products they may differ from one another seasonally and geographically. And the composition of an oil may also depend on how it was processed. Olive oil, for example, is available in several grades: Pomace, Refined A, Refined B, Virgin, and Extra Virgin. My purpose here is not to explain what the various grades are, but to point out that there are different grades for most oils. Consequently, I have no way of knowing how similar your oils are to mine and cannot be certain that your soaps are the same as mine.

That said, let me tell you about my soaps for comparison with yours. Those I made from olive, palm, coconut, and castor oils were all solid bars when I removed them from the oven. I left them overnight and unmolded them the next day. The soaps made from safflower and hempseed oils, on the other hand, were still quite liquid even after their stint in the oven. They thickened over the course of a week, but even then they were very soft, and I had to mangle them somewhat to get them out of the molds. If your linoleic and linolenic soaps are still soft at this point, put them aside for the time being. I will assume from this point that you have four solid bars of soap for comparison with one another and that two of your soaps are still rather soft, perhaps still in their molds.

All four of my solid soaps were ready to be removed from their molds within 24 hours of mixing. But just as your oils may differ from mine, your molds may be of a different style or manufacturer from mine. You may even be using makeshift molds like disposable plastic cups. You will have to judge when the soaps are hard enough to be removed from the mold. When

---

9. In a classroom situation, each student may make one of the six soaps and work in groups to evaluate their properties.

they are ready, it should be possible to remove them from the molds without damaging them.

The solid soaps should be homogeneous—that is, they should be uniform in color and consistency. If a bar looks marbled or if it is a different color on the top than on the bottom, you may not have mixed the raw soap sufficiently before pouring it into the mold. One way to decide whether this was the case is to review the percent *yield,* which may be calculated by dividing the weight of the soap bar by the total weight of its ingredients. The percent yield tells you how much of the raw soap actually wound up in the mold. A high percent yield means that little soap was wasted, but it may also indicate that the soap was thin when poured, which might lead to separation problems. A low percent yield means the soap was thick when poured, but it may also reveal that good soap was needlessly wasted. A reasonable compromise would put percent yield in the neighborhood of 80–90%. If the percent yield for a soap that is marbled, mottled, or otherwise separated is greater than 90%, you should remake the soap, taking greater care to ensure that it is completely mixed before pouring it into the mold.

Another defect seen in soap is the appearance of air bubbles on the bottom and sides of the bar. These bubbles do not appear on the top or in the interior of the bar. A soap like this is perfectly fine for experimental testing and even for use, but you would not want to sell such a bar. Furthermore, an experimental bar with this defect may not realistically simulate a soap made in a large mold. While I don't yet understand the mechanism, I have found that bubbles are associated with high soap temperatures. If you have this problem, it would be a good idea to remake a bubbled soap using a lower oven temperature.

There is one property of soap that is more important than any other. If it is wrong, nothing else really matters—the soap will be too harsh for use and may even be dangerous. This property is alkalinity. In future chapters we'll develop increasingly sophisticated notions of alkalinity, but for now, alkalinity is what irritates your skin, burns your eyes, and stings your tongue.

4.4 The Tongue Test

Chemists have historically used taste as an important chemical property, even as late as the nineteenth century. Twentieth century chemists, however, became understandably wary of tasting things as the variety and potency of chemicals increased. As a twenty-first century chemist, I must advise caution in tasting substances that cannot be reasonably described as "food." But taste has served the soapmaker well in the past, and it continues to be used in the modern handcrafted soapmaking community as a way of evaluating alkalinity. When I say "taste," I don't mean by the spoonful, the dollop, or the dab. We taste things *cautiously.*

The tongue is the oldest chemical sensor we have and soapmakers have been using it for as long as there has been soap. So I'm going to teach you how to taste soap *carefully.* First, lick your finger. Then rub your wet finger over the surface of the soap to be tested. Then, imagining that your finger is covered with deadly poison, touch it delicately to the tip of your tongue. Perhaps you taste nothing, in which case you can taste more boldly a second time. Eventually, you will eventually taste something that tastes like fat, like soap, or like some-terrible-stinging-bitter-salty-something-that-you-would-prefer-never-to-taste-again. Bleaugh, splffft, hwauck, sptoo! Don't worry. Rinse your mouth out with water and remember that taste: the taste of ***alkali.***

If you are going to use the taste test, you have to know what alkali tastes like. I am assuming that your linoleic and linolenic soaps are the most alkaline of your soaps because the reaction between the oil and the lye is not yet complete. Try tasting these soaps and see whether they correspond to what I have described as alkaline. If so, that's the taste we would like to avoid in finished soap.

In comparison to these incompletely saponified soaps, finished bar soap is a pleasure. Lick, touch, taste. Try tasting each of your four solid soaps and rank them in comparison with the two liquid soaps. Now taste the top and bottom of each bar for comparison. Is one side more alkaline than the other? If your soap is marbled, do the areas of different color have different alkalinity? You have now calibrated your tongue, and if you are an occasional soapmaker, this may be the only method you need for testing soap alkalinity. We'll refer to a non-stinging, fully saponified soap as ***tongue neutral*** (TN).

There is an alternative to the tongue test for soapmakers who are uncomfortable with tasting soap. There are strips of paper called *pH Paper Strips*, which contain dyes that are sensitive to acid and alkali. Generally, they turn red in contact with acid and blue in contact with alkali, but the colors may vary by manufacturer. The strips will come with a chart translating color into pH. You can use these strips as a surrogate tongue. Simply dampen the strip with water, touch it to the soap, and note the color and corresponding pH.

A low pH (0–6) is considered acidic and a high pH (8–14) is considered alkaline on the pH scale. pH 7 is considered neutral. But even good, mild, completely saponified soap is generally more or less alkaline, with a pH between 8 and 10. There is a temptation to attach too much importance to the pH registered by the test paper. Far more important than the pH of the soap is its alkali concentration, a quantity we'll learn to measure in Chapter 15. For now, our only consideration is that the soap is not *excessively* alkaline. We'll refer to such a soap as tongue neutral whether it was evaluated by actual taste or by using a pH test strip.

Occasionally the top of a bar is found to be more alkaline than the bottom. It may be that the oil and lye separated in the mold, making the soap unfit for use. It may be that one side of the bar was warmer than the other while in the oven and the cool side simply needs more time for complete saponification. It may be that the evaporation of water brought a thin layer of lye to the surface but that the soap underneath is neutral. It is important for us to distinguish between these possibilities if we are to diagnose any defects in the soap.

If the top of the bar is alkaline, we would like to determine how deep the alkali runs. To this end, we can thoroughly wipe half the bar with a damp paper towel, leaving the other half in its original condition. Test the wiped half again for alkalinity, either by taste or by pH test strip. If the soap underneath is tongue neutral, there is no defect in this soap. For a production batch, you would simply wipe the surface of the bars to remove the alkali layer. For our experimental soap, we leave half the bar in its original condition to see what happens when the surface alkali is not removed.

If the top of the soap remains alkaline after wiping, we would like to know whether this condition is temporary or permanent. We'll retest the bar once per week to see whether the top of the bar catches up with the bottom. If so, there is no defect in this soap. For a production batch you would simply wait until the top is tongue neutral before packaging the soap. If the top remains alkaline, however, the soap has separated in the mold and should be discarded, perhaps after further testing to find out what went wrong.

 A soap is considered *tongue neutral* if a test strip indicates a pH of 8–10 or if there is no stinging sensation when the soap is tasted.

4.5 Curing Soap

Once a soap is tongue neutral it may safely be used for washing, but because of the moisture it contains the bar may be softer than we would like. To harden the bar we allow it to cure in an environment where it can get plenty of air circulation to facilitate the evaporation of excess moisture. It is important that both the top and bottom of the bar be allowed to breathe. I use a chrome-plated wire rack and cover the shelves with a layer of paper towel to prevent the soap from coming into direct contact with the metal. You may come up with any system you like to store the soap undisturbed for several weeks.

An active soap lab will have many bars of experimental soap curing at any given time, and it is important to be able to tell them apart. When I pour raw soap into a mold, I label the mold with a self-adhesive label before placing it into the oven. This label contains a **batch code,** which uniquely identifies the soap. I generate batch codes from my initials and the date of pouring. If I make more than one soap on a given day, I add a letter to the end of the batch code, *e.g.* KMD2008.1.7A. When the soap is removed from the mold and placed on the curing rack, I transfer the label to the spot on the rack where the soap will cure. When the soap is hard enough, I use a pencil or ball-point pen to engrave the batch code into the end of the bar. That way, when I remove several bars from the rack for testing, I don't get them mixed up. You may come up with another method for labeling your soap as long as it allows you to know which bar is which.

Three things happen to a bar of soap as it cures; it loses weight as moisture evaporates, it hardens, and any leftover alkali is neutralized by atmospheric carbon dioxide. The first of these is easy to measure, but we'll defer a quantitative discussion of hardness until Chapter 21. In the following example, I have included the hardness values to illustrate how they change as soap cures. For now, you should store your labeled soaps on a curing rack and measure their weight once per week until the weight stops falling. Beyond that point the soap is considered fully cured, though the weight may fluctuate as the humidity in the room changes.

I am going to presume that you have succeeded in producing four fully cured bars of soap and that your linoleic and linolenic soaps have failed to saponify or harden completely. We'll return to these soaps in Section 13.5. For now, simply have some fun using your four cured bars.[10] Wash your hands with each bar and pay attention to the lather they produce and the feeling of your hands when you are done. How are the four bars similar? How are they different? Record the results in your notebook along with the other information as illustrated in the following example.

4.6 Scientific Soapmaking

Though the instructions I have given you may differ in appearance from a typical cookbook, I have, in fact, given you little more than recipes wrapped up in technical-looking formulas. The essence of science is not the mastery of arcane jargon and cryptic symbols. At the heart of science is the following proposition: that by changing one thing at a time and observing the results we can learn something about nature. This is often maddeningly more difficult than it sounds at first blush. Fortunately, for the soaps you have explored so far, there are not that

---

10. In a classroom setting, the instructor may wish to distribute soap samples for student evaluation rather than waiting for the current soaps to cure.

Example 4-2. KMD2008.1.7A

Olive$_{1000}$Lye$_{264}$ (AR 132 used before Table 4-1 was finalized)

This olive oil soap was produced as part of a study of the effect of water concentration on curing times. Soap ingredients were vigorously shaken for 15 seconds and then gently shaken until poured into an Upland experimental mold 8 minutes after the initial shaking. The pour temperature was 37°C (99°F). The soap was processed for 4 hours at 60°C (140°F), removed from the mold the next day, and tested for alkalinity. 1.54 g of soap was removed for a total alkali test. The remaining soap was cured on a chrome-plated wire rack. The cured soap was free of visible defects, did not produce much in the way of lather, but left my hands feeling clean and moist.

Olive Oil	Kroger Pure	93.86 + 6.14 g	100.00 g
Lye, 500 ppt	AAA-Chem		26.37 g
Total Weight			126.37 g
Bar Weight			101.49 g
Yield			80%

Date	Alkalinity		Hardness		Weight
	Top	Bottom	Top	Bottom	(g)
1-9-2008	TN	TN	2.5	3.0	99.95
1-15-2008			3.4	4.3	97.08
1-22-2008			4.4	5.2	96.04
1-28-2008			4.9	5.2	95.29
2-6-2008			5.5	6.1	94.71
2-12-2008			6.4	6.4	94.20
2-17-2008			5.8	6.7	93.99
2-24-2008			7.0	7.0	93.66
3-2-2008			7.8	7.0	93.40

many things that *can* be changed. Only three things went into each soap. For the next two soaps, we'll *break* a soap formula and observe the effects on the resulting soaps. You can save time by cooking these soaps at the same time.

Broken Soaps

- $Palm_{1000}Lye_{240}Aq_{135}$
- $Palm_{1000}Lye_{300}Aq_{135}$

In the first soap, we will use "too little" lye and in the second, "too much" lye. Otherwise, try to make the soaps as close to identical as possible, following the procedure of Section 4.2.2 and taking extra care to label the soaps so as not to mix them up. Take careful notes in your notebook and compare the hardness and alkalinity of the resulting soaps to those of your original palm oil soap.

Every experiment is designed to answer a question. We ask questions all the time: "Will I save time taking the Midlothian Turnpike instead of Hull Street?" "What if I put chicken in the casserole instead of beef?" "Will one more beer put me over the legal limit?" We try things out and learn from our mistakes. That is the scientific method. In this section we have asked, "What are the consequences of using too much or too little lye?" Your instincts might lead you to expect that when it comes to lye, too much of a good thing may be a bad thing. Listen to those instincts, but do not allow them to cloud your objectivity.

Practice Problems

Answers to practice problems appear in Appendix A (page 335).

1. Palm and palm kernel oils have similar names, which can lead to confusion. What would be the consequence of using the recommended AR for palm oil for a soap produced from palm kernel oil?

2. What soap formula would describe a soap made only from palm kernel oil, 500 ppt NaOH, and water?

3. Most soapmaking books advocate using lye with a concentration of 25–30%. What advantage is there to using lye with a concentration of 50% (500 ppt)?

4. One bottle of lye was produced from 142.88 g of NaOH and 142.88 g of water. 225.78 g of this lye was used to make soap, and then 135.33 g of NaOH and 135.33 g of water were added to the same bottle. What was the final concentration of the lye?

5. An employee insists that tasting soap is dangerous. How would you answer this employee's concerns?

6. You discover that you left the lid off of your lye bottle overnight. What would be the consequences of using this lye for making soap?

7. Why was extra water included in the formulas for the palmitic, lauric, and ricinoleic soaps?

8. Many people would prefer not to wear gloves when making lye and soap. Considering the properties of the oils discussed in this chapter, what practice might protect skin from chemical burns without the use of gloves?

9. Many people would prefer not to wear glasses when making lye and soap. What practice might protect the eyes from chemical burns without the use of glasses?

10. Suppose that as you were weighing the lye for your soap, a drop of lye fell on the pan of your balance. What effect would this have on the accuracy or uncertainty of your lye weight?

Chapter 5

Multi-Oil Soaps

*E*ACH of the oils used in Chapter 4 contributed unique qualities to its soap. You may have noticed that olive oil soap was mild with a thin lather. Palm oil produced a hard bar of soap. Coconut soap produced a lot of lather and castor oil soap was similar to coconut oil soap. Because all of these qualities are desirable in soap, oils are often blended to produce soaps that combine these qualities. This chapter will explore soaps made from such blends.

Let's start with four of the soaps from the last chapter:

Single-Oil Soaps
- $Olive_{1000}Lye_{262}$
- $Palm_{1000}Lye_{270}Aq_{135}$
- $Coconut_{1000}Lye_{352}Aq_{176}$
- $Castor_{1000}Lye_{250}Aq_{250}$

5.1 Simple Oil Blends

What do you suppose the formula ought to be for a 50/50 mixture of olive and palm oil? Your instinct might tell you that the lye portion should be about halfway between that of the two oils, and your instinct would be correct. Here are formulas for some simple soap blends:

- $Olive_{500}Palm_{500}Lye_{266}Aq_{68}$
- $Palm_{500}Coconut_{500}Lye_{311}Aq_{156}$
- $Coconut_{500}Olive_{500}Lye_{307}Aq_{88}$

What does your instinct tell you about a soap blended from equal portions of olive, palm, and coconut oils? Does it look something like this? $Olive_{333}Palm_{333}Coconut_{334}Lye_{294}Aq_{104}$. Your instinct tells you that the amount of lye needed for a blend of oils is just an average of that needed for each oil individually. This will always be true as long as there are equal portions of each oil in the blend. In practice this is seldom the case, so we need to understand *why* the average works in these simple cases.

Consider first what each multi-oil soap formula really means. $Olive_{333}Palm_{333}Coconut_{334}Lye_{294}Aq_{104}$ just means that we could make soap from 333 g (or oz or lb) of olive oil, 333 g of palm oil, and 334 g of coconut oil. The grams of sodium hydroxide required follow simply from the AR for each oil. For the olive oil we can ask, "How many grams of sodium hydroxide are needed for 333 g of olive oil?"

$$? \text{ g NaOH} = 333 \text{ g } Olive \left(\frac{131 \text{ g NaOH}}{1000 \text{ g } Olive} \right)$$
$$= 333 \, (0.131) \text{ g NaOH}$$
$$= 43.623 \text{ g NaOH}$$

This is just the oil weight times the AR expressed as a decimal.

The same is true for each of the other oils:

Olive	333 (0.131) g NaOH =	43.623 g NaOH
Palm	333 (0.135) g NaOH =	44.955 g NaOH
Coconut	334 (0.176) g NaOH =	58.784 g NaOH
Total		147.362 g NaOH

Since the lye portion is just double the weight of NaOH, we can write the complete formula:

$Olive_{333}Palm_{333}Coconut_{334}Lye_{294.742}$

There is some flexibility in the amount of extra water used. After all, we added it only to slow the reaction down. This issue will be explored further in Chapter 21. Until then we shall use the rule of thumb that the weight of the extra water should be about half that of the lye: $Olive_{333}Palm_{333}Coconut_{334}Lye_{294.724}Aq_{147.362}$. It may look a little odd to have so many digits in the Lye and Aq subscripts, and we'll return to this topic in Section 5.4.

When designing a soap formula, the weight of water should initially be half that of the lye portion. This may be raised or lowered as needed to control the rate of saponification.

5.2 Complex Oil Blends

The same principles apply when the oils are not present in equal amounts. Take for example a very nice, balanced blend of four oils: 28% coconut oil, 28% palm oil, 39% olive oil, and 5% castor oil. The formula will be:

$$Coconut_{280}Palm_{280}Olive_{390}Castor_{50}Lye_?Aq_?$$

We have:

Coconut	280 (0.176) g NaOH =	49.28 g NaOH
Palm	280 (0.135) g NaOH =	37.80 g NaOH
Olive	390 (0.131) g NaOH =	51.09 g NaOH
Castor	50 (0.125) g NaOH =	6.25 g NaOH
Total		144.42 g NaOH

We can now write the complete formula:

$$Coconut_{280}Palm_{280}Olive_{390}Castor_{50}Lye_{288.84}Aq_{144.42}$$

5.3 General Oil Blends

Sometimes we encounter a recipe that is not expressed in percent or parts per thousand. Consider a recipe that calls for 20 oz of olive oil, 40 oz of palm oil, and 22 oz of coconut oil. The same method works in ounces or pounds as in grams, and it works even if the total oil does not add up to 1000. Whatever units are used for the oil weights will be the units for the weight of NaOH:

Olive	20 (0.131) oz NaOH =	2.620 oz NaOH
Palm	40 (0.135) oz NaOH =	5.400 oz NaOH
Coconut	22 (0.176) oz NaOH =	3.872 oz NaOH
Total		11.892 oz NaOH

11.892 oz of NaOH are called for in this recipe, which translates into 23.784 oz of lye. There is absolutely nothing wrong with the calculation so far, and it will suffice for working out the amount of lye needed for any amount of any number of oils in any units. The only restriction is that the same units should be used for the lye as for the oil. This lesson is so important, as a matter of fact, that you should read no farther in this chapter until you are completely comfortable with the calculation.

General Blend Problems

Answers to practice problems appear in Appendix A (page 335).

1. How many pounds of 500 ppt NaOH should be used for an oil blend consisting of 20 lb of olive oil, 40 lb of palm oil, and 22 lb of coconut oil?

2. How many ounces of 500 ppt NaOH should be used for an oil blend consisting of 20 oz of olive oil, 40 oz of palm oil, and 22 oz of coconut oil?

3. How many grams of 500 ppt NaOH should be used for an oil blend consisting of 100 g of olive oil, 250 g of palm oil, and 150 g of coconut oil?

4. How many grams of 500 ppt NaOH should be used for an oil blend consisting of 1000 g of olive oil, 2500 g of palm oil, and 1500 g of coconut oil?

5. What would be the recommended alkali ratio for an oil blend consisting of 280 g of coconut oil and 280 g of palm oil?

5.4 Introducing the Duck

The method of this chapter works for any number of oils, in any amounts, and in any units. It is difficult, however, to compare soap formulas when they are expressed in different amounts and units. To facilitate such comparison I have invented a new unit, the **duck**.[1] A duck is defined as that quantity of raw soap produced from a total of 1000 g of oil. You can think of a *duck* as a batch of soap resulting in *approximately* ten bars. There are several advantages to using a one-duck formula. First, all

---

1. I had originally intended to call this unit the *decabar*, since 1000 g of oil will produce about ten bars of soap. But in Chapter 6 we'll find that bars come in different shapes and sizes, so 1000 g of oil may produce more or less than ten bars. As I continued to say the term *decabar*, it often came out as duckbar. I have shortened this to duck.

the quantities are given with a relative uncertainty of ±1 ppt of the oil weight. Second, the calculated weight of NaOH acts as an effective AR for the blend. In fact, the Lye subscript for a single-oil one-duck formula *is* just twice the AR for that oil. Third, one-duck formulas are easily compared to one another. And finally, it will prove to be easy to scale a one-duck formula to larger batch sizes in Chapter 6. It is a mistake to make up new jargon for no good reason, but I think the duck has enough going for it to warrant its introduction.

Recall that the blend of 20 oz olive oil, 40 oz palm oil, and 22 oz coconut oil called for 11.892 oz of NaOH. Thus we need 23.784 oz of lye. We might be tempted to write the following formula:

$$\text{Olive}_{20}\text{Palm}_{40}\text{Coconut}_{22}\text{Lye}_{24}\text{Aq}_{12}$$

But with integer subscripts there is a significant round off error when 11.892 is rounded off to 12. One way to remedy this would be to include the decimal places in the formula:

$$\text{Olive}_{20.000}\text{Palm}_{40.000}\text{Coconut}_{22.000}\text{Lye}_{23.784}\text{Aq}_{11.892}$$

There is absolutely nothing wrong with this, and it does solve the accuracy problem, but I think it makes for an ugly formula.

Another way to write the formula, however, is to calculate it for exactly 1000 parts of oil. To begin with, we determine the parts per thousand of each oil in the blend. Since the total amount of oil in this example is 82 oz, we have:

$$\left(\frac{20 \; oz \; Olive}{82 \; oz \; Total}\right) 1000 \; \text{ppt} = 244 \; \text{ppt Olive}$$

$$\left(\frac{40 \; oz \; Palm}{82 \; oz \; Total}\right) 1000 \; \text{ppt} = 488 \; \text{ppt Palm}$$

$$\left(\frac{22 \; oz \; Coconut}{82 \; oz \; Total}\right) 1000 \; \text{ppt} = 268 \; \text{ppt Coconut}$$

The blend is 244 ppt (24.4%) olive oil, 448 ppt (44.8%) palm oil, and 268 ppt (26.8%) coconut oil. Now we can calculate the amount of NaOH required for each oil:

Olive	244 (0.131) ppt NaOH =	31.964 ppt NaOH
Palm	488 (0.135) ppt NaOH =	65.880 ppt NaOH
Coconut	268 (0.176) ppt NaOH =	47.168 ppt NaOH
Total		145.012 ppt NaOH

If you were to make soap from 1000 oz of this oil blend, it would require 290 oz of lye. If you were to make it from 100.00 g of oil, it would require 29.00 g of lye. If you were to make it from 1000 g of oil, it would require 290 g of lye. And if this oil blend were a single oil, its AR would be 145 ppt.[2] We can write the formula as:

$Olive_{244}Palm_{488}Coconut_{268}Lye_{290}Aq_{145}$

But we might as well rearrange it so that the oils are listed in order of amount:

$Palm_{488}Coconut_{268}Olive_{244}Lye_{290}Aq_{145}$

These formulas are equally usable in pounds, ounces, or grams, but we'll reserve the term *duck* for a batch of soap produced from 1000 g of oil.

Monduckular Formula Problems

Answers to practice problems appear in Appendix A (page 335).

1. What is the one-duck formula for a blend of 2 lb olive oil, 3 lb palm oil, and 1 lb coconut oil?

2. What is the one-duck formula for a blend of 140 g of coconut oil, 140 g of palm oil, 195 g of olive oil, and 25 g of castor oil?

3. What is the one-duck formula for a blend of 16 oz of palm kernel oil, 19 oz of palm oil, 6 oz of olive oil, and 10 oz of hempseed oil?

4. The recommended alkali ratio of palm oil is 135. What would be the one-duck formula for a coconut/olive blend with the same recommended alkali ratio?

5. Imagine a coconut/olive blend for which alkali required by the coconut oil is equal to that required by the olive oil. What

---

2. While there is some round off error here, it is the same level of uncertainty as was used for the individual alkali ratios. Thus the same uncertainty applies to the formulas for multi-oil and single-oil soaps. From now on, we'll round the alkali ratio to the nearest integer and then double it to get the Lye subscript for the formula.

would be the one-duck formula for this blend?

Unless otherwise indicated, all formulas for the remainder of the book will be for one ducksworth of soap. Duckworth? Duckful? They will be one-duck formulas. Uni-duck formulas? Single-duck formulas. OK, if we need a special term, let it be the monduckular formula. But from now on, any formula will contain 1000 g of oil unless otherwise stated.

5.5 Duckbar's Delight

$\text{Olive}_{390}\text{Coconut}_{280}\text{Palm}_{280}\text{Castor}_{50}\text{Lye}_{288}\text{Aq}_{144}$ seems like a very nice formula. Let's make a one-deciduck bar.

1. *Gather your materials:*
   - Goggles or glasses
   - An eyewash bottle
   - Gloves
   - A centigram balance
   - A filled 125 mL PP bottle labeled `Lye`
   - Four 125 mL polypropylene bottles labeled `Olive Oil`, `Coconut Oil`, `Palm Oil`, and `Castor Oil`
   - A clean, dry 500 mL PP bottle labeled `Soap`, with lid
   - Two pipets labeled `Lye` and `Oil`
   - A thermometer
   - A soap oven (or microwave oven) and oven mitts
   - A single-bar soap mold
   - Your soapmaking notebook and a pen

2. *Arrange your workspace:* Sodium hydroxide is an essential soapmaking material that can be handled safely, but it deserves your respect. You *must* wear safety goggles or glasses for eye protection and you *ought* to wear gloves. You should make soap in an area with adequate ventilation, preferably near a ventilation fan. Your notebook should be opened to a new page with your pen at the ready. Record the name of the soap, the date, and the time that you begin.

3. *Preheat your oven:* Preheat your oven to 140°F or 60°C.

4. *Heat the oils:* You will have packaged the solid oils into 125 mL bottles, as described in Section 4.2.2. Fill the `Olive Oil` and `Castor Oil` bottles and heat all four bottles to

a temperature of 43°C (109°F). You may heat them in the soap oven while it preheats or you may use a microwave oven. If you use a microwave oven, set it for only 30 seconds at a time to avoid overheating the oils. While the oils are being heated, place the lids on the bottles but *do not tighten them.* Remove the lids and place them aside once the oils are hot.

5. *Weigh the oils:* Synthetically weigh 39.00 g of olive oil from the `Olive Oil` bottle into the `Soap` bottle. Follow this with 28.00 g from the `Coconut Oil` bottle, 28.00 g from the `Palm Oil` bottle, and 5.00 g from the `Castor Oil` bottle. You may weigh the oils using the procedure of either Section 2.4 (page 29) or Section 2.5 (page 31), whichever you prefer. Note that because you are weighing *from* the balance, you are very unlikely to overshoot your target weights. Whatever the actual weights are, *record all of the digits on a right-hand page* of your notebook.

6. *Weigh the water:* Synthetically weigh 14.40 g of water from the `Water` bottle into the `Soap` bottle. Whatever the actual weight is, record *all four digits* on a right-hand page of your notebook.

7. *Weigh the lye:* Synthetically weigh 28.80 g of lye from the `Lye` bottle into the `Soap` bottle. Whatever the actual weight is, record *all four digits* on a right-hand page of your notebook.

8. *Mix the soap thoroughly:* The temperature of the oil/lye mixture should be somewhere in the vicinity of 38°C (100°F). Measure this initial temperature and record it on a right-hand page of your notebook. Screw the lid onto the `Soap` bottle and shake it vigorously. When your soap reaches the consistency of a milkshake, you are ready to pour. Measure the pour temperature and record it on a right-hand page of your notebook.

9. *Pour:* Pour your soap into the mold.

10. *Bake:* The soap should be fully saponified after 4 hours in the oven.

11. *Cleanup:* Alkaline spills may be cleaned up with household vinegar. While your soap is baking, you can clean up your utensils. The spoons and cups can be washed immediately.

Wipe down your balance and put it away. The liquid oil bottles may be refilled immediately for your next soapmaking session. The solid oil and lye bottles may be refilled whenever it is convenient to do so. The raw soap in the `Soap` bottle will be easier to remove after saponification is complete; let it sit for a day before washing it with hot water.

12. *Cure:* Remove the soap from the mold. While the saponification reaction is complete, or nearly so, the soap will continue to harden over the next few weeks as excess water evaporates. Place the soap in an area where it can dry with adequate air circulation and weigh it each day until the weight stops changing. Record the weights on a right-hand page of your notebook.

The four-oil blend used in this section is only one of an infinite number of oil blends. It will be used, however, as a frequent example in the remainder of the book. For this reason, we give it a specific name, Duckbar's **Delight.** We can write the formula $Delight_{1000}Lye_{288}Aq_{144}$ as a shorthand for $Olive_{390}Coconut_{280}Palm_{280}Castor_{50}Lye_{288}Aq_{144}$.

Never heat a sealed container! When heating oils in a microwave or roaster oven, place the lid on the container but do not screw it on tight. A sealed container may explode if the contents overheat.

5.6 Scientific Soapmaking

In Chapter 4 you made soaps from six different oils and rather than telling you what to expect, I asked you to evaluate each for its properties. I expect that you found soaps made from coconut oil or castor oil to be very hard, perhaps too hard, and those made from safflower oil or hempseed oil to be very soft. Palm oil and olive oil soaps were probably closest in consistency to what you have come to expect of soap, with palm oil soap being on the hard side and olive oil soap on the soft side. On the other hand, palm oil and olive oil soaps produced very little in the way of lather, while coconut oil soap produced copious suds. I expect that none of these single-oil soaps was ideal. I gave you the formula for a very nice four-oil soap in the previous section to show you just how well oils may be combined to produce soap with many desirable properties. But if I hadn't given you the formula, how would you have known which oils to blend and in what proportions?

Every experiment is designed to answer a question. If you don't have a question, there is very little point in going to the trouble of doing an experiment. Eventually you will come up with your own questions, but to get you started, here's a good one: "Is it possible to blend only two oils to produce a soap with about the same hardness as palm oil soap, the lathering ability of coconut oil soap, and the mildness of olive oil soap?" We have limited ourselves to two oils because we can easily change the oil proportions while holding everything else constant. Which oils should we choose?

Coconut oil soap was hard and olive oil soap soft. Perhaps a combination of these two might produce a soap that Goldilocks might have judged as "just right." Complete the following formulas and make a bar of each soap for comparison with the single-oil soaps and the four-oil soap, Duckbar's Delight, from the previous section.

Two-Oil Soaps

- $Coconut_{700}Olive_{300}Lye_?Aq_?$
- $Coconut_{500}Olive_{500}Lye_?Aq_?$
- $Olive_{700}Coconut_{300}Lye_?Aq_?$

Every experiment is designed to answer a question. Evaluate the hardness and lather of each of these soaps and compare them to those of your single- and multi-oil soaps. Your notebook entry for this experiment should make clear the question to be answered, the procedure you followed, the data you collected, and the conclusions drawn from the experiment.

Chapter 6

Scaling Up

*W*E have produced experimental bars of soap designed to answer questions. Single bars are efficient for this purpose because they allow us to produce many variations without wasting lots of material. It would be very inefficient, however, to produce commercial quantities of soap one bar at a time. But many of the same techniques used for making experimental bars can be applied to the manufacture of soap in commercial quantities. Two separate procedures must be scaled up: the preparation of the lye and the mixing of the raw soap. Both of these procedures involve using larger balances and larger containers than were used for single experimental soap bars. The constraints are different, however, for lye preparation than for soap production and they will be addressed in separate sections.

Balances are needed for the preparation of both lye and soap. In order to make the discussion more concrete, I have chosen to use the MyWeigh family of balances described in Table 6-1. Though I have had good experience with these balances, there are many fine balances on the market. By choosing a particular set of balances as examples, though, we can get some idea of the capacities, readabilities, and relative prices available in the market. This will allow me to make recommendations on which balance would be most appropriate for a given number of soap bars to be produced.

The iBalance 201 is typical of centigram balances—those with a readability of 0.01 g. The iBalance 2600 is representative of **decigram** balances and the KD 7000 of **gram** balances. The BCS 40 has a readability of 10 g and would be termed a decagram balance.[1] With these four balances, it will be possible to weigh precisely the amounts of sodium hydroxide, water,

---

1.   Deci = 1/10; Deca = 10.

Table 6-1. MyWeigh Balance Specifications

Balance	Specifications	Pan	Price ($)
iBalance 201	200 × 0.01 g	3.9 in circle	98.90
iBalance 2600	2600 × 0.1 g	5.8 in × 5.8 in	128.50
KD 7000	7000 × 1 g	6.8 in × 6.8 in	44.50
BCS 40	40000 × 10 g	9.3 in × 9.3 in	199.90

200 × 0.01 g means a balance with a capacity of 200 g and a readability of 0.01 g.

www.OldWillKnottScales.com [26].

lye, and oil for any size soap batch from 1 bar to 400 bars. The choice of balance will be different, however, when preparing lye from sodium hydroxide and water than when preparing soap from lye and oil. We turn first to the preparation of large batches of lye.

6.1 Great Big Lyes

There is a key difference between my recommended procedure and that advocated in other soapmaking books. Most books have you weigh the sodium hydroxide you need for a particular batch immediately before using it to make soap. You then have to wait for it to cool. In the experimental procedure, I have had you make up the lye in advance, days or even weeks before you will use it to make soap. If you make it up the same way every time, you are less likely to make mistakes. When it comes time to make soap, you need only weigh the amount of lye you need without waiting for it to cool. Of course, the amount of lye needed is exactly two times the quantity of sodium hydroxide called for in your soap formula. For production quantities of soap, you will want to make up larger batches than were produced in Section 4.1. The most critical constraint is the size of the container you will use to mix your lye. The technique used with a 500 mL polypropylene bottle scales up easily to 1000 mL or 2000 mL bottles. Larger bottles are called *carboys,* and they often come fitted with a convenient spigot for draining the lye. In this sec-

Table 6-2. Laboratory Supplies

Description	Part Number	Price ($)
HDPE Jug, 1 gal	150-23793	2.50
PP Wide Mouth Bottle, 2000 mL	150-23851	5.90
PP Carboy, 5 L, w/spigot	150-23677	36.00
PP Carboy, 10 L, w/spigot	150-23679	50.25
PP Carboy, 20 L, w/spigot	150-23681	60.50

www.Cynmar.com [9].

tion we'll calculate the size of each lye batch and choose an appropriate balance for weighing the materials.

How much lye can a given bottle hold? We can estimate the capacity of a bottle by noting that 1 mL of water weighs about 1 g, so a 500 mL bottle can hold about 500 g of water. If the density of lye were about the same as that of water, we might expect the bottle to hold 500 g of lye.[2] This is not a bad rule of thumb. Whatever the volume of the bottle in milliliters, we'll assume that it can hold that many grams of lye. Since our lye is 500 ppt NaOH, the maximum number of grams of NaOH to be used for a given bottle is just half its volume in milliliters. A 1000 mL bottle, for example, can hold 1000 g of lye made from 500 g of NaOH and a 2000 mL bottle can hold 2000 g of lye made from 1000 g of NaOH. The same rule of thumb may be used for the larger carboys.

Which balance should be used to weigh the NaOH and water? It is convenient to use the most precise balance available as long as the weight of NaOH does not exceed the capacity of the balance. Using the MyWeigh balances as examples, the upper limits are 200 g for the centigram balance, 2600 g for the decigram balance, and 7000 g for the gram balance. Table 6-3 summarizes the combinations of bottles and balances to be used for various batch sizes.

---

2. In actual fact, 500 ppt NaOH has a density about 1.5 times that of water, so the bottles will not be full to the brim. This works in our favor, ensuring that there is plenty of room for swirling the lye to mix it.

The procedure for making lye will be nearly identical to that given in Section 4.1. You will use larger weighing bottles, of course, and the target weights will be larger. In fact, the bottle used to ship the NaOH may be used as one weighing bottle and an empty bottle from a previous batch may be used as the other. Place the NaOH bottle onto the balance and note its weight. Then fill the other bottle with distilled water but make sure that the NaOH bottle is the heavier of the two. Place the water bottle onto the balance along with the powder funnel and press the tare button on the balance. Use the funnel to pour the water into the lye container, return the water bottle and funnel to the balance, and record the weight of the water transferred to the lye container. After drying the funnel, place it and the NaOH bottle onto the balance and press the tare button. Use the funnel to pour the NaOH into the lye container, return the funnel and NaOH bottle to the balance, and record the weight of NaOH transferred to the lye container. Subtract the weight of the water from the weight of the NaOH to get the target weight for the rest of the water. Then synthetically weigh the second water portion into the lye container. Make sure that the total weight of the water is as close as possible to the weight of the NaOH. Swirl the solution to mix the lye and set the bottle aside to cool. Remember to open the lid periodically while mixing to release any pressure from the hot lye. Also remember to open the bottle when it is cool to allow air back into the bottle.

For larger batches you can use a polypropylene carboy for mixing the lye. As the carboys get larger, they get heavier and more difficult to mix by swirling the solution. In these cases you can use a length of half-inch PEX pipe as a stirring rod. This kind of pipe is chemically resistant and may be found wherever plumbing supplies are sold. Cut the pipe to a convenient length and insert it into the mouth of the carboy for stirring. Since a carboy is much more expensive than a jug, it makes a great deal of sense to mix the lye in the carboy and then to drain it into 1 gal HDPE jugs for storage.[3] That way, you can build up a stock of 1 gal lye jugs using only a single carboy. In addition, when it comes time to make soap, each jug may be used as if it were a giant weighing bottle.

---

3. Lye may be safely stored in HDPE containers, but it should not be mixed in them because of the high temperatures involved.

Table 6-3. Convenient Lye Batches

Soap Bars	NaOH Weight	Balance	Container Mixing	Storage
13	190 g	Centigram	500 mL	500 mL
26	380 g	Centigram*	1000 mL	1000 mL
32	1 lb	Decigram	1000 mL	1000 mL
35	500 g	Decigram	1000 mL	1000 mL
64	2 lb	Decigram	2000 mL	2000 mL
70	1000 g	Decigram	2000 mL	2000 mL
162	5 lb	Gram	5 L	1 gal
178	2500 g	Gram	5 L	1 gal
324	10 lb	Gram	10 L	1 gal
357	5000 g	Gram	10 L	1 gal
428	6000 g	Gram	20 L	1 gal
486	15 lb	Gram	20 L	1 gal

*NaOH is weighed in three portions. See Section 2.6 (page 34).

Example 6-1. A Middling Lye

I wanted to make lye from a 2 lb bottle of NaOH from AAA Chemicals. I analytically weighed 875.7 g of water and 927.0 g of NaOH, the entire contents of the 2 lb bottle, into a 2000 mL polypropylene bottle. I finished up by synthetically weighing 51.3 g of water into the same bottle. With the lid on the bottle, I gently swirled the lye until the NaOH was completely dissolved. I loosened the lid periodically, but there was never any significant pressure. The lye reached a maximum temperature of 102°C (216°F), well below its boiling point of 145°C (293°F). The concentration of the lye was 500.00±0.05 ppt NaOH.

How much soap can we expect from each bottle of lye? A typical oil blend will use about 14 g of NaOH per bar. For each size bottle we simply divide the weight of NaOH used by 14 to estimate the number of bars of soap that can be produced. Of course, this is just an approximation, since different formulas use different alkali ratios and soap may be cut into bars of different sizes, but it gives you a rough idea of what to expect.

Whatever your scale of operation, I would advise you to make up your lye by the same procedure every time. The regularity of the assembly-line process will ensure that your lye is consistent from batch to batch. You can then weigh out the required quantity of lye for each batch of soap as you have for the experimental bars, and the jug itself can serve as the weighing bottle. By making up batches of lye in advance of your soapmaking sessions you will streamline your operation and promote both safety and efficiency.

 You can make up lye in any convenient amount. Whatever the size of the batch, however, the weight of the NaOH should be at least 1000 times the readability of the balance. The weights of NaOH and water should be as close to identical as possible. When preparing fresh lye, there is no need to wash or empty the lye bottle or carboy as long as it contains only 500 ppt NaOH. This will be the case if you remember to replace the cap after each use. Also remember *not* to return waste lye to the bottle; doing so would risk contaminating the lye stock.

 Never seal a container while its temperature is rising! You should tighten the cap on the lye bottle only briefly while you are mixing it. Loosen the cap frequently to let off any pressure until the temperature of the lye begins to fall, after which you may leave the cap sealed as the lye cools. Once cool, loosen the cap briefly to let air back in, and then seal it tightly for storage.

6.2 The Three-Duck Jug

When you scale up from experimental to production soap batches, it makes a great deal of sense to streamline the operation

Table 6-4. Convenient Oil Batches

Soap Bars	Ducks	Balance	Container
30	3	Decigram	1 gal
40	4	Decigram	5 L
30	3	Gram	1 gal
40	4	Gram	5 L
90	9	Gram	10 L
160	16	Gram	5 gal
200	20	Gram	25 L

by producing standard containers of lye. For multi-oil soaps, it also makes sense to produce standard containers of pre-mixed oil. As with lye, there is no need to tie the size of an oil container to the size of a particular batch of soap. We make up the oil in convenient containers and use as much or as little as we need when it comes time to make soap.

In the us, oils are sold in 1 gal jugs, 5 gal pails, and 55 gal drums. These containers, once empty, may be used to store your pre-mixed oils. If you are moving an experimental bar into small-scale production, three ducks of oil are conveniently stored in 1 gal jugs. If you are moving into larger-scale production, a 5 gal pail will hold fifteen ducks of oil. For even larger-scale production, the oils may be mixed in a larger container and stored in jugs or pails.

To minimize relative uncertainty, it is important to use the right balance for weighing oils. At the bottom end of the scale, the total oil weight should be at least 1000 times the readability of the balance. At the upper end, the largest oil component should not exceed the capacity of the balance. Since the largest oil component is rarely more than half the total, the total oil weight may be up to twice the capacity of the balance. Table 6-4 gives recommended MyWeigh balances for standard oil batches. The recommendations would be similar for decigram and gram balances from other manufacturers. Note that for batches of 3 or 4 ducks, either a decigram or gram balance may be used to hold the relative uncertainty below ±1 ppt. If you have both balances, however, the decigram balance would be preferred.

When mixing oils and making soap, it will be necessary to heat your oils to the desired temperature. Polyethylene (HDPE) or polypropylene (PP) bottles may be conveniently heated in a microwave oven, which may be turned on its side to accommodate larger bottles. Polypropylene bottles may also be heated in a roaster oven set to its lowest temperature, but polyethylene bottles may melt where they contact the sides the oven. Consequently, only polypropylene containers should be placed into a roaster oven. Large polypropylene bottles tend to be expensive (like carboys), but polypropylene pitchers may be found at low cost wherever kitchenware is sold. Check the bottom of the pitcher for the symbol PP.

Polyethylene containers may melt in a roaster oven. Polypropylene containers may be heated safely in a roaster oven set to its lowest temperature.

The ultimate in convenience is to simply place oil bottles in a suitably warm place until they are at the desired temperature. At Hampden-Sydney, we maintain an incubator set to 45°C (113°F). Oils are placed into the incubator the day before they are to be used, and by the time we mix oil or make soap, the oil is ready to go. There is nothing quite as boring as watching oil warm up, so you would be well served by a system that allows you to safely warm your oil in advance of your soapmaking session. Laboratory incubators tend to run in the hundreds of dollars, but they show up used on auction sites, and if you can find one at a reasonable price, you will come to appreciate the convenience of warming your oils without literally watching the pot.[4]

Never heat a sealed container! When heating oils in a microwave or roaster oven, place the lid on the container but do not screw it on tight.

Oil containers larger than 1 gal are best heated with a bucket or drum heater, also known as a band heater. They come in different sizes for 5 gal pails and 55 gal drums. Timers and thermostats are available to allow oil to be heated overnight. They

---

4. www.LabX.com specializes in laboratory equipment.

may be purchased from vendors of equipment for making soap or biodiesel.[5] Band heaters also show up on online auction sites. Now that you know how to weigh and heat your oils, it is time to get to work.

The following procedure will produce three ducks of Delight, the oil blend from Section 5.5.[6] It may be adapted for different oil blends and larger batches.

1. *Gather your materials:*
   - Goggles or glasses
   - An eyewash bottle
   - Gloves
   - A decigram balance
   - Four filled PP bottles or pitchers labeled `Olive Oil`, `Coconut Oil`, `Palm Oil`, and `Castor Oil`
   - One labeled cup for each of the four oils
   - A clean, dry 1 gal PP bottle or pitcher labeled `Delight`,
   - A powder funnel
   - Your soapmaking notebook and a pen

2. *Arrange your workspace:* Since you will not be handling lye, this procedure is far less hazardous than mixing lye or making soap. Nevertheless, you should be prepared to deal with any situations that might arise from heating and measuring warm oils.

3. *Heat the oils:* You will have packaged the solid oils into 500 mL, 1000 mL, 2000 mL bottles, or into 1 gal pitchers, as described in Section 4.2.2 (page 70). We want to make sure that all of the oils are uniform in composition. Liquid oils may be used at room temperature as long as they are transparent. Cloudy or solid oils should be completely melted and stirred to ensure that their composition is uniform. The oils have not completely melted until they are transparent, like olive oil.

4. *Weigh the oils:* Synthetically weigh 1170.0 g of olive oil from the `Olive Oil` bottle into the `Delight` bottle using the procedure of Section 2.5 (page 31). As we scale up this procedure, the oil bottle is used as a weighing bottle and a cup

---

5. www.SoapEquipment.com [43] carries a variety of bucket and drum heaters.

6. $\text{Delight}_{1000} = \text{Olive}_{390}\text{Coconut}_{280}\text{Palm}_{280}\text{Castor}_{50}$

replaces the pipet. Be sure to use a separate labeled cup for each oil to avoid contaminating the oil in the bottles. Place the Olive Oil bottle onto the balance and press the tare button. Pour some oil from the bottle into the Olive Oil cup, replace the Olive Oil bottle onto the balance, and note the weight. If the registered weight is less than 1170.0 g, use the funnel to pour oil from the cup into the Delight bottle. Continue using the cup to transfer oil from one bottle to the other until the balance reads more than 1170.0 g. Then pour oil from the cup back into the Olive Oil bottle until the weight transferred is exactly 1170.0 g. Any oil remaining in the cup should be drained into the Delight bottle.

Remember the rationale for this method of weighing. The balance tells you how much oil has been removed from the Olive Oil bottle. That oil must be either in the cup or in the Delight bottle. Since we drain the cup, nearly all of the oil removed from the Olive Oil bottle must wind up in the Delight bottle.

Using the same procedure, transfer 840.0 g from the Coconut Oil bottle, 840.0 g from the Palm Oil bottle, and 150.0 g from the Castor Oil bottle. Note that because you are weighing *from* the balance, you are very unlikely to overshoot your target weights and the unused oils remain uncontaminated. Whatever the actual weights are, *record all of the digits on a right-hand page* of your notebook.

5. *Mix the oils thoroughly:* Screw the cap onto the Delight bottle and shake it to thoroughly mix the oils.

6. *Cleanup:* Wipe down your balance and put it away.

As your oil cools, it may become cloudy as some of the higher-melting oils crystallize. Before this happens, you may wish to package some oil into labeled 125 mL, 500 mL, or 1000 mL bottles for use in making smaller batches of soap. To ensure that the oil has a uniform composition, each bottle should be warmed before use until the oil is transparent. By packaging some of the oil in smaller bottles, you will spend less time warming large bottles of oil when making small batches of soap.

Example 6-2. Three Ducks of Delight

I mixed three ducks of Delight in a 1 gal jug. Coconut and palm oils were melted overnight in an incubator at 45°C (113°F). Oils were weighed on an iBalance 2600. The actual weights were:

Olive Oil	Pompeian Extra Virgin	1170.0 g
Palm Oil	Columbus FD0825CC	840.0 g
Coconut	LouAna	840.0 g
Castor	Camden-Grey	150.0 g

It took me 28 minutes to weigh and mix these oils.

6.3 More Soap for You

Many of the soapmaking techniques from Chapter 4 are applicable to making larger batches of soap. The only major differences are that you may need to use a decigram or gram balance rather than a centigram balance and you will need larger containers for weighing the ingredients and mixing the raw soap. Once you can reliably make single bars of soap, the most difficult technical challenge is thoroughly mixing the raw soap before it becomes too thick to pour into the molds. Let's start with the easy part—choosing the balance.

For any particular balance there will be a minimum and a maximum batch size that can be conveniently and accurately produced. We'll make some ballpark assumptions. First, we want the total oil weight to be at least 1000 times the readability of the balance so that the AR will be uncertain to within ±1 ppt. Second, we assume that a bar of soap is made from about 100 g of oil. Third, we do not want our pre-mixed lye and oil containers to exceed the capacity of the balance. Finally, it would be convenient to use the same balance for weighing both the lye and the oil. Given these assumptions, we can come up with ballpark limits on the number of bars of soap that should be produced by a balance with a given readability and capacity. Table 6-5 recommends equipment suitable for any batch size between 1 bar and 400 bars of soap.

The size of the soap container depends on the method to be used for mixing. For the smaller containers, we can continue the practice of shaking the bottle to mix the soap, as we have done with single experimental bars. Because we need space for the soap to move around, these smaller containers should be no more than half-filled with soap. In practice, containers larger than 5 liters become unwieldy, which places an upper limit of about 1.5 ducks on soap mixed by shaking. Beyond this, mixing is better accomplished by stirring.

Containers to be stirred may be made of plastic or stainless steel, but they must be sturdy enough to hold the considerable weight of the raw soap. In addition, you must think carefully about how you are going to get the soap out of the mixing container and into the molds. A 5 gal pail holding 10 ducks of soap may weigh as much as 35 pounds. While a muscular soapmaker might be capable of lifting such a pail and pouring the soap into the molds, such strenuous exercise can be avoided with a little planning. One solution is to mount the mixing container in such a fashion that it may be easily tipped to pour the soap.[7] Another solution is to fit the soap container with a spigot or drum tap, which would allow it to be drained into the molds without tipping it.[8]

The procedure for weighing the lye and oil is similar to that in Section 6.2. We use the pre-mixed containers as weighing bottles and labeled cups to transfer material to the soap container. When multiple containers of oil are to be used, only the last one needs to be weighed synthetically. When making 90 bars, for example, oil from the first and second jugs would be weighed analytically. These weights would then be subtracted from the target weight, and the oil from the third jug would be weighed synthetically. The procedure would be the same as in Section 2.6 (page 34) except for the size of the containers and the use of cups in place of pipets.

Now that we know how to weigh our materials into an appropriate container, we must consider how to mix them. While

---

7. www.SoapEquipment.com [43] sells a 20 gal stainless steel "pot tipper" for $1200.00 (2008).
8. www.ConsolidatedPlastics.com [8] sells pails, drums, spigots, and drum taps. For more information, contact Linda Stevens of www.UplandSoapFactory.com [41].

Table 6-5. Convenient Soap Batches

Soap			Container	
Bars	Ducks	Balance	Lye	Oil
1	0.1	Centigram	125 mL	125 mL
2	0.2	Centigram	125 mL	125 mL*
1–18	1.8	Decigram	500 mL	2000 mL
19–36	3.6	Decigram	1000 mL	2000 mL*
37–54	5.4	Decigram	2000 mL	2000 mL*
10–30	3.0	Gram	1000 mL	1 gal
10–40	4.0	Gram	1000 mL	5 L
31–60	6.0	Gram	2000 mL	1 gal*
61–90	9.0	Gram	2000 mL	1 gal*
91–120	12.0	Gram	1 gal	1 gal*
100–160	16.0	Decagram	1 gal	5 gal
100–200	20.0	Decagram	5 L	25 L
161–320	32.0	Decagram	1 gal*	5 gal*
321–480	48.0	Decagram	1 gal*	5 gal*

*Oil or lye is weighed in three or more portions. See Section 2.6 (page 34).

Soap Bars	Ducks	Mixing Method	Soap Container
1	0.1	shake	500 mL
2–5	0.5	shake	2000 mL
6–12	1.2	shake	1 gal
6–15	1.5	shake	5 L
15–50	5.0	stir	10 L
12–100	10.0	stir	5 gal
50–120	12.0	stir	25 L
100–400	40.0	stir	20 gal

it is possible to stir raw soap with a spoon, spatula, or paddle, the "stick blender" is more frequently recommended by modern handcrafted soapmaking books. The stick blender is a hand-held electrical mixer available wherever cookware is sold.[9] Another choice would be a "paint mixer," which mounts into the chuck of an electric hand drill or drill press. It is important to choose a mixer that can withstand the alkalinity of raw soap. Aluminum utensils should be avoided at all cost because they react violently with alkali. Plastic and stainless steel are the preferred materials for mixing equipment.

The recommendations of Table 6-5 should not be seen as strict rules, but rather as flexible guidelines. If, for example, you wanted to make 50 bars using the BCS 40, your oil weight would be 5000 g and the readability of this balance would allow the lye to be controlled to within ±10 per 5000, or ±2 ppt. Since we are using 500 ppt NaOH, the alkali ratio would be controlled to within ±1 ppt. This would not exactly be a disaster. Similarly, if you wanted to make 150 bars using the KD 7000, you would need 15000 g of oil, which could be weighed in 5 portions instead of 4. Since analytical weights take so little time, weighing 5 jugs would not take much more time than weighing 4. Within the limits discussed above, you have a good deal of flexibility in the choice of containers, balances, and mixing equipment. If you have several balances at your disposal, Table 6-5 may help you to choose among them. With weighing and mixing out of the way, we turn to the question of how much soap is needed to fill our molds.

6.4 Filling Molds

So far we have assumed that a bar of soap contains a total of 100 g of oil; in other words, a monduckular formula produces 10 bars of soap. But different molds produce bars of different sizes. If you make too little soap, you will wind up with fewer bars or smaller bars than you wanted to produce. If you make too much soap, you will have leftover soap or bigger bars than you wanted to produce. A slight shift in thinking will allow us to scale any

---

9. www.SoapEquipment.com [43] sells the Model PB08 "power wand" for $99.50 (2008). Larger versions are also available.

soap formula to produce the amount of soap appropriate for a given mold.

Consider the formula: $Delight_{1000}Lye_{288}Aq_{144}$.[10] The shift in thinking is to consider the *duck* as a quantity of raw soap and the *bar* as a quantity of finished soap. Our initial assumption is that there are 10 bars *per* duck How many ducks of raw soap do we need to fill a dozen-bar mold? Unit Factor Analysis tells us:

$$? \text{ ducks} = 1 \text{ } \cancel{mold} \left(\frac{12 \text{ } \cancel{bars}}{1 \text{ } \cancel{mold}} \right) \left(\frac{1 \text{ ducks}}{10 \text{ } \cancel{bars}} \right)$$
$$= 1.2 \text{ ducks}$$

We multiply each subscript in the formula by the number of ducks required, in this case 1.2:

Delight	(1.2) 1000 g =	1200.0 g
Water	(1.2) 144 g =	172.8 g
Lye	(1.2) 288 g =	345.6 g
Total		1718.4 g

For a dozen-bar mold we begin with 1.2 ducks of raw soap. After making this batch we can see whether, in fact, 1.2 ducks produced too much or too little soap. We can then revise the number of ducks from one batch to the next until we have it just right and label the mold with the number of ducks required to fill it. This refinement will work differently for cavity molds than for other molds and we'll consider each in turn.

6.4.1 Filling a Cavity or Tube Mold

A cavity mold contains several shaped spaces into which soap will be poured. A tube mold stands vertically, is filled from the top with soap, and when removed the soap is cut into bars. Usually the soap is cut using a wire cutter with equally spaced wires. This results in bars that are all the same size except for the one at the end, which may be shorter than the others. For cavity and tube molds, each soap comes out with a predetermined size and shape. The only variable is that there may be an extra, smaller bar that resulted from a partially filled

---

10. $Olive_{390}Coconut_{280}Palm_{280}Castor_{50}Lye_{288}Aq_{144}$

Equation 6-1. Ducks Needed to Fill a Cavity Mold

$$? \text{ ducks} = 1 \; \cancel{mold} \left(\frac{X \; \cancel{bars}}{1 \; \cancel{mold}} \right) \left(\frac{Y \text{ ducks}}{Z \; \cancel{bars}} \right)$$

In this equation, X is the number of bars in the mold. Y is the number of ducks of raw soap used to produce Z bars of finished soap in a previous experiment.

---

cavity or from a short bar at the end of the tube. Thus the cavity and tube molds share the same parameters—the size of the bars is predetermined by the mold/cutter combination, but the number of bars depends on the amount of soap poured. In both cases we would like to pour enough raw soap into the mold to produce the desired number of bars while minimizing the size of the extra, "wasted" bar.

Let's start with the ProForm Soap Mold from Gaily Rebecca Soaps,[11] which makes a dozen shaped bars. This mold consists of two pieces of plastic that fit together in a wire rack. When assembled, there are four vertical cavities, three bars each, which are filled through a port in the top. When the soap has hardened, the mold is removed from the rack and taken apart to remove the soaps. I choose this mold as our first example because it holds a specific volume of soap. If you make too little, one of the four cavities will be only partially filled, and if you make too much, you will have to use another mold for the excess soap. We can start by making 1.2 ducks of raw soap.

Suppose that when the soap is mixed and poured, only three of the four cavities are filled, producing 10.5 bars. We now know that 1.2 ducks produced 10.5 bars so there are 1.2 ducks *per* 10.5 bars. We can now revise the number of ducks required to fill the mold:

$$? \text{ ducks} = 1 \; \cancel{mold} \left(\frac{12 \; \cancel{bars}}{1 \; \cancel{mold}} \right) \left(\frac{1.2 \text{ ducks}}{10.5 \; \cancel{bars}} \right)$$
$$= 1.371 \text{ ducks}$$

---

11. www.SoapnSupplies.com [12] sells several varieties of ProForm mold for $49.95 each. Rounded bars, emerald-cut bars, and scalloped bars may be produced in these molds.

Suppose, on the other hand, that when the soap is mixed and poured, we not only fill the mold, but have enough soap left over to fill 1.25 bars of a second ProForm mold. Now there are 1.2 ducks *per* 13.25 bars and the revised number of ducks should be:

$$? \text{ ducks} = 1 \ \cancel{mold} \left(\frac{12 \ \cancel{bars}}{1 \ \cancel{mold}} \right) \left(\frac{1.2 \text{ ducks}}{13.25 \ \cancel{bars}} \right)$$
$$= 1.087 \text{ ducks}$$

From one batch to the next, keep track of the number of ducks mixed and the number of bars actually produced. Label each mold with the number of ducks required to fill it. When it comes time to make soap, multiply each subscript in the formula by the number of ducks needed to fill the mold you are using.

6.4.2 Filling a Log or Slab Mold

Whereas a tube mold stands vertically, a log mold lies horizontally. When the soap is removed from the mold, it will be cut into bars using a wire cutter just as with a tube mold. Unlike the tube, however, the log has a length that is predetermined by the mold, and if the spacing of the wire cutter matches that length, there will be no wasted bar on the end. The size of the bar, and hence its weight, is determined by the depth of the soap poured into the mold. If the goal is to produce a bar with a given finished weight, we need to know how much raw soap should be poured into the mold. A similar problem arises with the slab mold.

A slab mold is like a large pan filled one bar deep. In this respect, it resembles several log molds merged together into one. When the soap is removed from the mold, it is cut into bars. Unlike the tubes and logs, which are sliced like bread or salami, the slab is cut into bars like cake or fudge. A wire cutter with equally spaced wires is often used to produce bars with identical length and width. The thickness of the bar is determined by the depth of the soap poured into the mold. Thus the log and

---

Equation 6-2. Ducks Needed to Fill a Slab Mold

$$? \text{ ducks} = 1 \text{ mold}\left(\frac{X \text{ bars}}{1 \text{ mold}}\right)\left(\frac{W \text{ oz}}{1 \text{ bars}}\right)\left(\frac{Y \text{ ducks}}{Z \text{ oz}}\right)$$

In this equation, X is the number of bars in the mold. Y is the number of ducks of raw soap used to produce Z (oz, lb, g) of finished soap in a previous experiment. W is the desired weight of a finished bar of soap. The same units must be used for W and Z.

---

slab molds share the same parameters—the number of bars is predetermined by the mold/cutter combination, but the weight of the finished bars depends on the depth of the pour. In both cases we would like to pour enough raw soap into the mold to produce bars of a desired weight.

As an example, consider the dozen-bar slab mold from Upland Soap Factory.[12] This mold is designed to be cut into 12 bars, 2.25 in × 3.25 in, and it can be filled to any depth up to a maximum of 1.5 in. The specifications state that it holds a maximum of 4.5 lb of raw soap, or 2043 g. Our initial assumption is that we need 1.2 ducks for this mold.

Suppose that after cutting, trimming, and curing, the combined weight of all 12 finished bars is 54.0 oz; that is, 1.2 ducks produced 54.0 oz of soap. If we want to produce 4.0 oz bars, we need to revise the number of ducks for that mold:

$$? \text{ ducks} = 1 \text{ mold}\left(\frac{12 \text{ bars}}{1 \text{ mold}}\right)\left(\frac{4.0 \text{ oz}}{1 \text{ bars}}\right)\left(\frac{1.2 \text{ ducks}}{54.0 \text{ oz}}\right)$$
$$= 1.067 \text{ ducks}$$

If we want 4.0 oz bars, we should label this mold "1.067 ducks." If, on the other hand, we want 5.0 oz bars we would have:

$$? \text{ ducks} = 1 \text{ mold}\left(\frac{12 \text{ bars}}{1 \text{ mold}}\right)\left(\frac{5.0 \text{ oz}}{1 \text{ bars}}\right)\left(\frac{1.2 \text{ ducks}}{54.0 \text{ oz}}\right)$$
$$= 1.333 \text{ ducks}$$

---

12. www.UplandSoapFactory.com [41] sells the SMS12A dozen-bar slab mold for $47.15 each. The mold has a silicone liner and disassembles for removal of the soap.

Be sure to use the *desired* weight per bar in this equation. Use the *actual,* total finished weight for all of the bars produced by the *actual* number of ducks mixed. Note that even if you used grams to weigh the ingredients, you can use any unit you wish for the desired bar weight. Just be sure to use the same units for the actual weight of the soap as for the desired weight of a bar.

 Label each of your log or slab molds with the number of ducks of raw soap and the total weight of the finished bars from a recent batch. You can then use Equation 6-2 to calculate the number of ducks required for any desired bar weight. When it comes time to make soap, multiply each subscript in the formula by that number of ducks.

6.4.3 Filling a Block Mold

A block mold is like a large log or slab mold. It may have a depth similar to a log mold, in which case it will probably be cut into multiple logs, which will then be cut into bars. It may be two or three times the depth of a slab mold, in which case it will probably be cut into logs, which are then cut in halves or thirds, depending on the depth. The result in either case is division into logs and then into bars. As in the case of a log or slab mold, the number of bars is determined by the mold/cutter combination, but the weight of the bars depends on the depth of the pour. We might, in fact, treat the block mold exactly as a very large log mold and calculate the amount of raw soap required as in Equation 6-2.

But suppose that we desire to produce a certain weight of soap rather than a certain number of bars? The problem is almost identical to that for filling a slab mold. Instead of using a desired bar weight and number of bars, we have the desired weight of finished soap. In fact, you could just look at the block as a single bar of soap with a specified weight. In order to make the calculation, we need to know the weight of soap produced by a number of ducks in a previous batch of soap. Equation 6-3 shows how to calculate the number of ducks required.

Equation 6-3. Ducks Needed to Make a Specific Soap Weight

$$? \text{ ducks} = X \; \cancel{oz\text{-}soap}\left(\frac{Y \text{ ducks}}{Z \; \cancel{oz\text{-}soap}}\right)$$

In this equation, X is the weight of finished soap to be produced. Y is the number of ducks of raw soap used to produce Z (oz, lb, g) of finished soap in a previous experiment. The same units must be used for X and Z.

Imagine that in a previous batch, 1.375 ducks of raw soap produced 51.3 oz of finished soap, and we would like to make 48.0 oz of soap. In that case we need to make up:

$$? \text{ ducks} = 48.0 \; \cancel{oz\text{-}soap}\left(\frac{1.375 \text{ ducks}}{51.3 \; \cancel{oz\text{-}soap}}\right)$$
$$= 1.287 \text{ ducks}$$

Unlike our previous calculations, this one has very little to do with the properties of the mold. The yield of soap depends on the soap formula, on the number of ducks used, on losses suffered in mixing, pouring, and cutting, and on the loss of moisture during curing, but not on the size or shape of the mold. Thus the data used in the calculation may be easily transferred from one mold to another. Keep a chart listing your soap formulas and the yield to be expected from them. When it comes time to make soap, this data may be used to determine the number of ducks required for the desired soap weight.

Label your block molds with the maximum number of ducks that they can hold. When you make soap, you will easily be able to choose which mold or set of molds are sufficient for the batch.

Equation 6-4. Ducks Needed to Use a Specific Oil Weight

$$? \text{ ducks} = X \, g \, \cancel{oil}\left(\frac{1 \text{ ducks}}{Y \, g \, \cancel{oil}}\right)$$

In this equation, X is the number of (g, oz, lb) of oil available and Y is the subscript of that oil in the soap formula. The same units must be used for X and Y.

6.4.4 Scaling to a Specific Oil Weight

In the previous sections our goal was to produce a certain number of bars or a certain weight of soap. But suppose that we have a container of oil we would like to use up. Perhaps it is the last of a particular oil that we are phasing out. Perhaps it is the entire stock of an oil that we have not yet replaced. For this example, consider that we have a fixed amount of palm oil from which we wish to make some Delight:

$\text{Olive}_{390}\text{Coconut}_{280}\text{Palm}_{280}\text{Castor}_{50}\text{Lye}_{288}\text{Aq}_{144}$

We would begin by analytically weighing the melted palm oil into the soap bottle. In this example let's imagine that we have 427.5 g of palm oil to work with. We need to know how much soap it is possible to make and how much of the other ingredients are needed to go with the palm oil. We first ask the question, "How many ducks of soap can be made from 427.5 g of palm oil?"

Once phrased this way, the Unit Factor Analysis is quite simple:

$$? \text{ ducks} = 427.5 \, g \, \cancel{palm \, oil}\left(\frac{1 \text{ ducks}}{280 \, g \, \cancel{palm \, oil}}\right)$$
$$= 1.5268 \text{ ducks}$$

Where did the "280 g palm oil" come from? The formula tells us that 1 duck contains 280 g of palm oil. Therefore (1 duck/280 g palm oil) is a hotdog. We choose to place the duck on top because that is the unit of our answer. If we had rounded the answer to 1.526 ducks, we would have required only 427.3 g of palm oil. If we had rounded to 1.527, we would have required 427.6 g of

---

Equation 6-5. Converting from Grams

$$? \text{ oz} = 1 \; g\left(\frac{1 \; \cancel{lb}}{454 \; \cancel{g}}\right)\left(\frac{16 \; \text{oz}}{1 \; \cancel{lb}}\right)$$

$$= 0.035242 \text{ oz}$$

$$? \text{ lb} = 1 \; g\left(\frac{1 \; \text{lb}}{454 \; \cancel{g}}\right)$$

$$= 0.002203 \text{ lb}$$

$$? \text{ kg} = 1 \; g\left(\frac{1 \; \text{kg}}{1000 \; \cancel{g}}\right)$$

$$= 0.001000 \text{ kg}$$

---

palm oil. Instead, we round to however many digits are needed to get the palm oil *just right* to within the readability of our balance. Now that we know that our target is 1.5268 ducks, scaling the formula occurs as in the previous cases:

Palm	(1.5268) 280 g =	427.5 g
Olive	(1.5268) 390 g =	595.5 g
Coconut	(1.5268) 280 g =	427.5 g
Castor	(1.5268) 50 g =	76.3 g
Water	(1.5268) 144 g =	219.9 g
Lye	(1.5268) 288 g =	439.7 g
Total		2186.4 g

You might very well wish to use this oil, water, and lye to make soap immediately, which would make sense if you were using up a supply of oil that you do not plan to replace. This would then be the final run for this particular formula, and you could use the calculations from the preceding sections to choose a set of molds to contain the soap. On the other hand, you might simply be using up one bottle of oil before opening the next. In the example above, you would wind up with 1.5 ducks of Delight (without the water and lye) that could be saved for another day.

6.5 Working in Other Units

All of the equations of this chapter have the flexibility of working in grams, ounces, or pounds, as long as we use the same units throughout. These equations tell us how many ducks we need for the task at hand. But when it comes time to actually make soap, we need to convert these ducks back into units that can be read from the balance. Because we defined the duck as the amount of soap made from 1000 g of oil, we must also convert if we wish to use any other units. Using the methods developed in Section 2.1, we can calculate the conversion factors of Equation 6-5. We ask, "How many (oz, lb, kg) are there in 1 g?" These conversion factors are then simply multiplied by the number of desired ducks to get us into the desired units.

To make 1.287 ducks, for example, of $Delight_{1000}Lye_{288}Aq_{144}$ we have:

Delight	(1.287) 1000 g =	1287.0 g
Water	(1.287) 144 g =	185.3 g
Lye	(1.287) 288 g =	370.6 g
Total		1842.9 g

To get into ounces, we include the conversion factor:

Delight	(1.287)(0.035242) 1000 oz =	45.356 oz
Water	(1.287)(0.035242) 144 oz =	6.531 oz
Lye	(1.287)(0.035242) 288 oz =	13.063 oz
Total		64.950 oz

Take a moment to repeat this calculation in pounds and kilograms. You should get total weights of 4.0593 lb and 1.8429 kg.

6.6 Lye Calculators

You now know everything you need to know in order to calculate the amount of lye needed for any combination of oils in any amounts. The calculations are not complicated, but they are tedious, and it is easy to make a mistake that could ruin a batch of soap. For a single experimental bar, this could mean that the bar is not what you think it is and that the results of the experiment are not what you think they are. For a production batch, it could mean the waste of the entire batch. While it is important to understand the calculations of the last two chapters, most soapmakers use a dedicated lye calculator to determine the relative amounts of oils, water, and NaOH. There are a great many of these available on the Internet for free or at low cost. A few of them are listed in *References* (page 398).

Each of these lye calculators has advantages but as a companion to this book I wrote one of my own, the *Lye-on*. I don't claim that it is better or worse than any of the other calculators. As a supplement to this book, however, it has the advantage of working in ducks for comparison with the calculations of the last two chapters. In addition, it stores information on the costs of your materials and calculates the material costs per batch and per bar. The Lye-on may be downloaded from reference [46].

6.7 A Dozen Delights

In every soap book I have seen, soap is mixed in a stainless steel pot and stirred with a whisk or a stick blender. There is nothing wrong with this, but for a dozen-bar batch it is easy to scale up the procedure used for single bars. The advantage is that mixing in a bottle is more uniform than mixing in a pot. In addition, the possibility of splattering raw soap is minimized, and it is easier to pour soap from a bottle than from a pot. If the soap hardens in the bottle, however, you will have to cut it open to get the soap out. If you are comfortable with making soap in a pot, by all means go with what you know. But if you are happy with the single-bar method and would like to try it on a larger scale, give this method a shot. In this example we'll make 1.2 ducks of $Delight_{1000}Lye_{288}Aq_{144}$.

Delight	(1.2) 1000 g =	1200.0 g
Water	(1.2) 144 g =	172.8 g
Lye	(1.2) 288 g =	345.6 g
Total		1718.4 g

1. *Gather your materials:*
   - Goggles or glasses
   - An eyewash bottle

- Gloves
- A decigram or gram balance
- A 1000 mL PP bottle labeled `Lye`
- A 2000 mL PP bottle labeled `Delight`
- A clean, dry 1 gal HDPE bottle labeled `Soap,` with lid
- A powder funnel
- Three cups labeled `Lye,` `Water,` and `Delight`
- A thermometer
- A dozen-bar soap mold
- Your soapmaking notebook and a pen

2. *Arrange your workspace:* Sodium hydroxide is an essential soapmaking material that can be handled safely, but it deserves your respect. You *must* wear safety goggles or glasses for eye protection and you *ought* to wear gloves. You should make soap in an area with adequate ventilation, preferably near a ventilation fan. Your notebook should be opened to a new page with your pen at the ready. Record the name of the soap, the date, and the time that you begin. Multiply each subscript in the formula by the number of ducks required, in this case 1.2. Of course, these calculations belong on a left-hand page to avoid confusing the target weights with the actual ones.

3. *Heat the oil:* Delight may be a clear liquid, a cloudy liquid, or it may have solid oil at the bottom, depending on the temperature of your soap lab. Our goal is to heat it until it is completely transparent and thoroughly mixed. The temperature of your oil should be in the neighborhood of 43°C (109°F).

4. *Weigh the oils:* If the gallon of Delight you produced in Section 6.2 exceeds the capacity of your balance, you will need to use a smaller bottle to weigh the oil. You may use a 1000 mL bottle to weigh in two portions or a 2000 mL bottle to weigh in one.

   If you are weighing in two portions, remember that the first portion is weighed analytically and the second synthetically. As when you mixed your Delight, a plastic cup replaces the pipet you used for synthetically weighing on the centigram balance. Use this cup to transfer oil to the `Soap` bottle until you have transferred exactly 1200.0 g. Note that because you are weighing *from* the balance, you are very unlikely to overshoot your target weight. Whatever the actual weight is, *record all of the digits on a right-hand page* of your notebook.

5. *Weigh the water:* Synthetically weigh 172.8 g of water from the Water bottle into the Soap bottle. As with the oil, use a cup to transfer water from bottle to bottle. Whatever the actual weight is, record *all four digits* on a right-hand page of your notebook.

6. *Weigh the lye:* Synthetically weigh 345.6 g of lye from the Lye bottle into the Soap bottle. You should easily be able to hit the target to within 0.1 g. Whatever the actual weight is, record *all four digits* on a right-hand page of your notebook.

7. *Mix the soap thoroughly:* The temperature of the oil/lye mixture should be somewhere in the vicinity of 38°C (100°F). Measure this initial temperature and record it on a right-hand page of your notebook. Screw the lid onto the Soap bottle and shake it vigorously. When your soap reaches the consistency of a milkshake, you are ready to pour. Measure the pour temperature and record it on a right-hand page of your notebook.

8. *Pour:* Pour your soap into the mold.

9. *Insulate:* Unlike single-bar batches, larger batches will generate and retain enough heat to raise the temperature without external heating. Different molds have different insulation requirements and you should follow the directions that came with your mold. The soap should remain in the mold at least overnight, perhaps longer with some molds. During the first six hours you may wish to periodically check the temperature of the soap and note it in your notebook. An infrared thermometer is particularly convenient in this regard.

10. *Cleanup:* Alkaline spills may be cleaned up with household vinegar. Wipe down your balance and put it away. Leave the Soap bottle for a day or two before washing it.

11. *Cut and cure:* Remove the soap from the mold. With a cavity mold, you simply pop the soap out. With a block, log, or slab mold you will cut it into bars. You are likely to be able to

buy a special soap cutter to go with your mold.[13] The soap will still be fairly soft and easy to cut when it comes from the mold, but will get harder as it cures. Place the soap in an area where it can dry with adequate air circulation. Since you tracked the weight for the single bar, you will have a pretty good idea of how long this soap takes to cure completely. Record the initial and final combined weight for the batch on a right-hand page of your notebook.

12. *Revise your number of ducks:* For a cavity mold use the number of bars actually produced to revise the number of ducks needed to fill the mold. For a block, log, or slab mold use the final, cured batch weight and the desired bar weight to revise the number of ducks needed to fill the mold. Record the number of ducks in your notebook and label the mold itself with the number of ducks required to fill it.

Dozen-bar batches are a convenient size for scaling up an experimental bar into commercial development. It may even be a convenient size for the small-scale soapmaker to manufacture product. But the time you spend on a batch of soap is likely to be about an hour, whether it is for a few experimental bars, a dozen bars, or a hundred. If you are in the business of making soap, you will quickly find yourself moving to larger batch sizes to improve efficiency. The mathematics of scaling the dozen-bar batch will be exactly the same for larger batches.

---

13. www.ForCraftsSake.com [11] sells the UP-GRID-CUT cutter for the dozen-bar Upland slab mold. The price is $179.95.

Example 6-3. KMD2008.3.19A

1.2 ducks of $Delight_{1000}Lye_{288}ROE_1$ were poured into a 12-bar ProForm contour mold. Because hard bars are easier to unmold than soft ones, no extra water was used in the formula. Rosemary Oleoresin Extract (ROE) was dissolved in the oil as a preservative. The ingredients were weighed into a 1 gal jug, shaken vigorously for 30 seconds, swirled for 30 seconds, and poured into the mold at a temperature of 39°C (102°F). The mold was insulated by placing it in a cardboard box. It took me 23 minutes to weigh, mix, and pour this soap.

Delight	mixed 3-15-2008	1200.0 g	
ROE	Camden-Grey	1.2 g	
Lye	AAA-Chemicals	345.6 g	

The temperature of the soap was checked periodically and the highest recorded temperature was 59°C (138°F). The soap was unmolded two days after it was poured and was found to be tongue neutral.

Ingredients	oil, ROE, lye	1546.8 g	
Soap Bars	12 pieces	1384.0 g	89.5%
Sprues	4 pieces	61.5 g	4.0%
Flash	flakes	41.5 g	2.7%
Remainder	mixing bottle, etc.	59.8 g	3.8%

The flash consisted of soap that oozed through the seams of the mold, an unavoidable consequence of the mold design. The remainder was soap that was presumably left in the bottle or otherwise lost. The soap left in the sprues (filling spouts), however, might have been avoided if I had poured less soap. Since the average bar weight was 115.3 g, the soap in the sprues amounted to about half a bar. Consequently, it should take only 1.152 ducks of soap to fill this mold. To ensure that the mold is completely filled, however, I labeled the mold `1.16 Ducks`.

6.8 Scientific Soapmaking

People are natural scientists. They get an idea, try it out, and if it doesn't work, they try something else. The essence of science is really no more complicated than this. Most of what looks complicated in science comes from trying to decide in advance which ideas are worth trying and which would be a waste of time.

Every experiment is designed to answer a question. We have spent a good deal of time in these first chapters learning to work carefully enough that the answers can be trusted. The essence of these early experiments has been to change only one thing at a time and to observe the consequences. In Section 4.6 we asked the question, "What are the consequences of using too much or too little lye?" By tasting your experimental soaps, you most likely found that using too much lye produced a soap that was alkaline. In Section 5.6 we asked, "Is it possible to blend only two oils to produce a soap with about the same hardness as palm oil soap, the lathering ability of coconut oil soap, and the mildness of olive oil soap?" I imagine that you found one of your two-oil soaps to be superior to the others and to any of the single-oil soaps. In this chapter you grappled with the question, "Can I fill a large mold with soap that is identical to one of my experimental bars?" If your dozen bars are much different from the experimental bar, you will be disappointed. If you continue to produce too much soap or too little soap for the mold you are using, you will be disappointed. And if you are disappointed enough, your answer to the question will be "no." But if your answer to the question is "yes," you will probably do what soapmakers call "the happy soaper dance" and experience that wonderful, confidence-building emotion that scientists call "understanding."

Practice Problems

Answers to practice problems appear in Appendix A (page 335).

1. One duck of raw Delight produces 9.25 bars from a cavity mold. How many kilograms of oil, lye, and water should be used to produce 144 bars from a set of these molds?

2. Soap from a slab mold is to be cut into 12 bars. When 1.2 ducks of raw Delight was used, the total weight of finished bars was 41.93 oz. If you would like the bars to weigh 4 oz, how much raw soap should you use next time?

3. You find that you have 927 g of olive oil, which you are phasing out in favor of high-oleic canola oil. You would like to use up all of this olive oil to make one last batch of Delight. How much coconut, palm, and castor oil should you use to make this batch?

4. 17.3 ducks of raw soap produced 44 lb of finished soap. How many ducks would be needed to produce 40 lb of soap using the same mold?

5. Delight has a recommended alkali ratio of 144. Suppose that you used a decagram balance like the BCS 40 to weigh the ingredients for 9 ducks of Delight. What would be the uncertainty in the actual alkali ratio?

6. Delight has a recommended alkali ratio of 144. Suppose that you used a decagram balance like the BCS 40 to weigh the ingredients for 1 duck of Delight. What would be the uncertainty in the actual alkali ratio?

7. What would be the recommended alkali ratio for an oil blend consisting of 390 g of olive oil and 50 g of castor oil?

8. Suppose that you have a 3-duck jug of Delight and you wish to make one experimental bar of soap. The oil in the jug is cloudy but pourable, and you hate to go to the trouble of heating the whole jug. Instead, you pour 100 g of oil into a smaller bottle and heat it to the recommended temperature. Why should this action be considered a mistake?

9. What is the smallest batch of lye that should be weighed and mixed using a decagram balance like the BCS 40?

10. What is the smallest batch of oil that should be weighed and mixed using a decagram balance like the BCS 40?

Part II

Basic Chemistry

Every experiment is designed to answer a question. In Part I you learned to use small, experimental batches to answer questions about soap. But there are so many questions that could be asked. Some of them have no answers, and others have answers that nobody has yet found. Many of these potential questions have never even been asked. The vast majority of these potential questions may not even be worth asking. Using an experiment to answer a question is not the hardest part of being a scientist. The hardest part is discovering which questions worth asking can be answered by an experiment.

Discovering such questions is the job of theory. A scientific theory is more than a hunch or a guess; it consists of all those mental constructs that allow us to pose questions and to distinguish interesting questions from boring ones, important questions from trivial ones, and answerable questions from those that have no answer. A successful theory poses meaningful questions and suggests experiments designed to answer them.

Part II will focus on the properties of acids, bases, salts, alcohols, and the chemistry of the fatty acids. It will provide a theory of soap that will serve as a foundation for asking good questions to be answered in the later chapters of the book.

Mastering this material will enable you to:
- understand the interactions between oil and water
- understand the interactions between acids and bases
- standardize a dilute KOH solution using citric acid
- understand the forces that dominate the interactions between water, oil, and soap molecules
- understand the structure of fatty acids, alcohols, and esters
- understand the fundamental chemical reaction that turns oils into soaps
- understand how soaps and detergents do what they do

Chapter 7

Oil and Water

O IL and water don't mix. Were it not for this fundamental truth, there would be no need for soap in the first place. Thus, a thorough understanding of oil and water is the beginning of wisdom for the soapmaker. The interaction between oil and water is dominated by the mutual attraction of opposite electrical charges and the repulsion of like charges. Indeed, all chemical interactions arise from the elaborate dance of negative electrons around positive atomic nuclei. When electrons flit from one nucleus to another they bind the nuclei together, since each nucleus is attracted to the shared electrons. Were it not for these electrons, the positive nuclei would repel one another and there would be no tendency for atoms to assemble into molecules. But to understand oil and water, we need not grapple with the details of sub-atomic structure. It will be enough to look at the distribution of electrical charge in molecules and to understand the way that these charges interact.

Molecules of oil and water are made up of just three kinds of atoms: carbon, oxygen, and hydrogen. Carbon is the defining constituent of organic molecules, of which oils, fats, soaps, and proteins are examples. We need to understand just two things about carbon. First, a carbon atom may bond to as many as four other atoms. Second, carbon and hydrogen atoms share equally the electrical charge of the electrons that bind the molecule together. Whenever carbon is bonded to hydrogen, the electrical charge is uniformly distributed across the CH bond. We say that the bonding is *covalent,* meaning that the electrons are shared between the carbon and hydrogen atoms. We further describe the CH bond as *non-polar*—that is, the bonding electrons are shared more or less equally, and neither atom is more negative or positive than the other.

If carbon and hydrogen are relatively generous with their electrons, oxygen is greedy. As with carbon, we need to understand two things about oxygen. First, it can bond with as many as two other atoms. Second, though it shares electrons with carbon and hydrogen, it does so unequally. The electrons that make up the bond spend more time near the oxygen nucleus and less time near the carbon or hydrogen nuclei. Since the electrons are negative and the nuclei positive, the oxygen atom holds a partial negative electrical charge, and the carbon or hydrogen atoms are left with a partial positive charge. We describe this covalent bond as *polar,* the oxygen end of the bond being negative and the other end positive. The most important such bond, from the standpoint of soap chemistry, is the OH bond.

As with carbon and oxygen, we need to know two things about the hydrogen atom. It may bond to only one other atom. When it bonds to oxygen, it carries a partial positive charge; when it bonds to carbon, it shares the electrons equally in a non-polar bond. While the polar OH bond will dominate the chemistry of water, the non-polar CH bond will largely determine the chemistry of oil.

7.1 Petroleum

It may seem strange to include petroleum in a book on soap, but the contrast between the structures of water and petroleum molecules will help us to understand why soap works the way it does. Petroleum is a natural mixture of many different compounds, most of them containing only carbon and hydrogen. Among these *hydrocarbons,* we'll focus on the class of compounds known as the *alkanes.* Alkane molecules consist of carbon atom chains of various lengths. The simplest alkane, methane, contains a single carbon atom. Since carbon can bond with as many as four other atoms, the methane molecule has the formula, CH_4. Methane is the principle component of natural gas.

The next alkane in the series, ethane, contains two carbon atoms bonded to one another. Since each carbon can bond with as many as four other atoms, and since the two carbons are already bonded to one another, that leaves each carbon three

Figure 7-1. Ethane

available bonding positions. Consequently, ethane has the formula, CH_3CH_3.[1] Seeing such a formula, a chemist imagines one CH_3 group, or *methyl* group, bonded back-to-back with another one.

Figure 7-1 shows a **molecular model** for ethane. Unlike a simple formula like CH_3CH_3, a molecular model shows the three-dimensional structure of a molecule. Atoms are shown as spheres and molecules as collections of overlapping spheres. The diameters of the spheres are proportional to the sizes of the atoms they represent. In this book, atoms are shown in various shades of gray. Black atoms carry a negative charge, white atoms carry a positive charge, and gray atoms carry little or no charge—they are neutral. Since opposite charges attract, we may expect black atoms to be attracted to white ones and *vice versa*. Black and white atoms attract one another and are largely indifferent to gray atoms. Furthermore, neutral gray atoms do not interact strongly with other atoms, be they black, white, or gray.

The molecular model for ethane shows it to be uniformly gray. Consequently it interacts only very weakly with other molecules. The interaction between ethane molecules is so weak that they prefer to roam as independent, isolated gas molecules. Though the interaction is weak, it is not zero. When compressed or chilled, the molecules find themselves close enough to one another that very weak attractive forces can hold them together—the gas condenses into a liquid. The weak intermolecular

---

1. CH_3CH_3 is often shortened to C_2H_6.

forces seen in ethane are characteristic of the entire alkane family.

Table 7-1 lists names and formulas for several alkanes. Though all of the alkanes share with ethane relatively weak intermolecular forces, these forces get slightly stronger as the carbon chain grows. As the chains get longer and longer, the melting points and boiling points increase. Propane is familiar as the stuff used for gas grills; butane and pentane fill "butane" lighters. Though they are gases at room temperature, propane, butane, and pentane are more easily compressed to liquids than are methane and ethane. Hexane, heptane, and octane are liquids at room temperature and are the principle components of gasoline. The heavier alkanes are components of mineral oil, fuel oil, kerosene, jet fuel, and diesel oil. The heaviest alkanes are waxy solids at room temperature and appear as components of petroleum jelly and paraffin wax. In fact, an older name for *alkane* is *paraffin*.

Formulas like H_2O and CH_3CH_3 are great for showing the number of atoms in a molecule. Molecular models like Figure 7-1, on the other hand, provide a detailed depiction of the relative distances and orientations of atoms in molecules. Molecular models, however, are difficult to draw free-hand and they often provide more information than we really need to convey. To fill the gap between formulas and molecular models, chemists have developed **structural formulas** to convey some of the information on molecular structure in an easy-to-draw formula. Figure 7-2, for example, shows a molecular model and structural formula for the sixteen-carbon hexadecane, $CH_3(CH_2)_{14}CH_3$.[2] Each carbon-carbon bond is shown as a line, and a string of such bonds is kinked to separate one bond from the next. There are carbon atoms at the end of each chain and at the vertex of each kink in the chain. For simplicity, the non-polar CH bonds are not included in the structural formula, but every chemist knows they are there. Since each carbon atom makes four bonds, there must be three "invisible" hydrogen atoms at each end. At each interior vertex, there must be two hydrogen atoms. By drawing these simplified formulas, chemists can more easily communicate with one another about complex molecular structures.

---

2. $CH_3(CH_2)_{14}CH_3$ is often shortened to $C_{16}H_{34}$.

Table 7-1. The Alkanes

ethane	C_2H_6	
propane	C_3H_8	
butane	C_4H_{10}	
pentane	C_5H_{12}	
hexane	C_6H_{14}	
heptane	C_7H_{16}	
octane	C_8H_{18}	
nonane	C_9H_{20}	
decane	$C_{10}H_{22}$	
undecane	$C_{11}H_{24}$	
dodecane	$C_{12}H_{26}$	
tridecane	$C_{13}H_{28}$	
tetradecane	$C_{14}H_{30}$	
pentadecane	$C_{15}H_{32}$	
hexadecane	$C_{16}H_{34}$	
heptadecane	$C_{17}H_{36}$	
octadecane	$C_{18}H_{38}$	
nonadecane	$C_{19}H_{40}$	
eicosane	$C_{20}H_{42}$	

Figure 7-2. Hexadecane

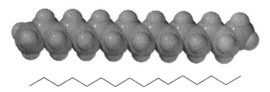

If you use your imagination, Figure 7-2 looks something like an earthworm. Like earthworms, alkane molecules are not strongly attracted to one another. If you could magnify a liquid alkane sufficiently, you would see something that looked like a bucket of earthworms, with the worms gliding silently and smoothly past one another. It makes little difference to a given worm whether its neighbor is a long worm or a short one. And so it is with alkane molecules. The weak attraction between two octane molecules is similar to that between an octane and a hexane molecule. Consequently, octane is soluble in hexane and *vice versa*. In fact, all of the alkanes are more or less soluble in one another. We say that *like dissolves like*.

 An alkane molecule is held together by non-polar covalent bonds. Non-polar molecules interact weakly with one another. The alkanes are mutually soluble in one another.

7.2 Water

The chemistry of water is dominated by the interactions between electrical charges. As discussed previously, the OH bond in water is polar, with the oxygen atom holding a partial negative charge and the two hydrogen atoms holding partial positive charges. What happens when two water molecules are near one another? The negative end of one water molecule is attracted to the positive end of its neighbor. This interaction, dubbed **hydrogen bonding,** is among the strongest forces that attract one molecule to another, and it accounts for the propensity of water molecules to associate with one another to the exclusion of those molecules that lack OH bonds. Figure 7-3 shows a molecular model of two water molecules interacting with one another. Note that the black, negative oxygen atom of one molecule is aligned with the white, positive hydrogen atoms of its neighbor. We say that *opposites attract;* here I have chosen opposite colors to represent opposite charges.

It is important to note that while the individual atoms are charged, the water molecule as a whole is electrically neutral; it has a total charge of zero. This might seem odd, since there are two positive hydrogen atoms and only one negative oxygen

Figure 7-3. The Dance of the Water Molecules

atom, but the magnitude of the charge on each hydrogen atom is only half that of the oxygen atom. The two hydrogen atoms taken together have a charge that is equal and opposite to that of the oxygen atom. Thus a polar molecule like water has a positive end and a negative end, but a net charge of zero.

Beginning chemistry students find it difficult to visualize the interactions of invisible atoms and molecules. I might be tempted to tell you that water molecules attract one another like magnets, the north and south poles of the magnet behaving like positive and negative charges. Rather than sliding past one another like earthworms in the night, water molecules stick together like magnets. Imagine what would happen if you placed two separate magnets into a bucket of earthworms. At first, the magnets would be too far apart to strongly attract each other. But as the earthworms crawled randomly past one another, the magnets would move closer and closer, little by little, until they were at last close enough to snap together. Once together, they would not separate again unless they were wrenched apart by some outside agency.

Now repeat the experiment with 100 magnets in a bucket of worms. Though the magnets were initially distributed throughout the bucket, the time would come that all of the magnets were clumped together to the exclusion of the worms. To someone observing the scene, it might appear that the worms are afraid of the magnets—that they crawl away from the magnets and congregate in the magnet-free parts of the bucket. Such an observer might describe the worms as *magnetophobic*. We can see, however, that the worms don't fear the magnets and the magnets don't fear the worms. In fact, the worms are largely indifferent to their neighbors, be they magnets or other worms.

The separation of worms and magnets occurs simply because the magnets are more attracted to one another than they are to the worms. Similarly, though chemists describe the alkanes as *hydrophobic,* they understand this as a poetic way of saying that water molecules are more attracted to one another than they are to alkane molecules. Consequently, the alkanes are not soluble in water; in other words, *oil and water don't mix.*

I hope that the worm/magnet imagery helps you to visualize the interactions between polar and non-polar molecules, but like all analogies, this one has its limitations. First, alkane molecules are not alive like worms. They don't "crawl" past one another; they simply move around in response to the forces imposed on them by other molecules in motion. Second, water molecules attract one another by electrical forces, not magnetic ones. While magnetic and electrical forces are similar (opposites attract), there are some important differences to be discussed in the next section. Use the worm/magnet analogy only as a poetic description of these interactions, and be prepared to revise your imagery as our discussion deepens.

The water molecule is held together by polar covalent bonds. The partially negative oxygen atom attracts the partially positive hydrogen atoms on neighboring water molecules. This intermolecular attraction is called a hydrogen bond.

Non-polar molecules lack the -OH group needed to participate in hydrogen bonding, and these hydrophobic molecules tend to be insoluble in water. The alkanes are one such class of molecules, whose structural formulas consist of long, kinky lines. Whenever chemists see such a kinky line in a structural formula, they think to themselves, "Hmm, that part looks pretty greasy."

7.3 Ions

Water molecules are attracted to one another by electrical forces, not magnetic ones. While the behavior of magnets is easily visualized in everyday life, a magnet always has both a north pole and a south pole. When a magnet is broken, each of the resulting pieces becomes a complete magnet, with both north and south poles. This is where the magnetic analogy ceases to

Figure 7-4. Hydronium Hydroxide

be appropriate for the interaction of water molecules. When a water molecule is broken, one piece holds a positive charge and the other a negative charge. We say that it has *ionized* into a positive **cation** and a negative **anion**.[3]

Review Figure 7-3 and imagine that the water molecule on the right is about to fall apart. As the saga begins, the hydrogen atom nearest you is bonded to its oxygen atom via a polar covalent bond. The oxygen atom retains the lion's share of the bonding electrons, leaving the hydrogen atom with a partial positive charge. Just behind it is another oxygen atom sporting a partial negative charge. Who could blame this hydrogen atom for wondering whether the grass is greener on the other molecule? But if the hydrogen atom leaves its original home, it leaves its bonding electrons behind, carrying a positive charge to its new home.

Figure 7-4 shows that when a hydrogen atom jumps ship, it leaves its electrons behind and carries a full, +1, positive charge with it. This kind of hydrogen atom, this happy wanderer, this wild rover, this runaway bride deserves a new name to distinguish it from the kind of hydrogen atom that stays at home. We call it a *proton*. The proton does not remain single for long; it soon attaches to the neighboring water molecule whose oxygen atom tempted it from home in the first place. The resulting (proton + water) ion is called a *hydronium* ion, H_3O^+. The water molecule that lost a proton is left with a full, -1, negative charge, and also deserves a new name: the *hydroxide* ion, OH^-. We might very well use the name *hydronium hydroxide* as a synonym for two ionized water molecules.

---

3. The *t* in *cation* may remind you of a plus sign; the *n* in *anion* may remind you that it is negative.

The colors of Figure 7-4 have been chosen to help you visualize the new charge distribution. Note that while the three hydrogen atoms on the hydronium model are white, the oxygen atom is lighter in color than that of the original water molecule. These light colors reflect the fact that if you add the charges of the three hydrogen atoms to the charge on the oxygen atom, the total, net charge on the hydronium ion is +1. Similarly, while the oxygen atom on the hydroxide model is black, the hydrogen atom is darker in color than those of the original water molecule. These dark colors reflect the fact that the total, net charge on the hydroxide ion is -1. This color convention will be held through the rest of the book.

It is not necessary to know the exact atomic, ionic, and molecular charges, but curious readers may benefit from seeing how they add up. Table 7-2 compares the charges for the atoms, ions, and molecules we have been discussing.[4] The leftmost column of numbers gives the charges on the individual atoms. Multiplying by the number of atoms in the molecule or ion, we get the total charge for each kind of atom. Finally, the sum of these charges is the net charge—0 for a neutral molecule, +1 for a cation, and -1 for an anion. Take a moment to reconcile the colors in Figure 7-1, Figure 7-3, and Figure 7-4 with the charges in Table 7-2. From now on, this color scheme will allow us to understand molecular interactions without worrying about the numerical values of the charges.

The molecular models of non-polar molecules will be colored uniformly gray. Those of polar molecules will be colored black and white.

The molecular models of cations will be colored white or white and gray. Those of anions will be colored black or black and gray.

The molecular models convey a wealth of information about the structure of water, hydronium, and hydroxide. You should study them until you are completely comfortable with the changes in shape and charge that accompany the ionization of water. But chemists like to express things concisely, using a few

---

4.   On this scale, the charge of an electron is exactly -1. Details of the calculations appear in the notes to references [95]–[98].

Table 7-2. Atomic, Ionic, and Molecular Charges

Atom				Ion or Molecule	
Name	Charge			Charge	Name
C	-0.258	× 2 =	-0.516	0.000	Ethane
H	+0.086	× 6 =	+0.516		
O	-0.476	× 1 =	-0.476	0.000	Water
H	+0.238	× 2 =	+0.476		
O	-0.155	× 1 =	-0.155	+1.000	Hydronium
H	+0.385	× 3 =	+1.155		
O	-1.024	× 1 =	-1.024	-1.000	Hydroxide
H	+0.024	× 1 =	+0.024		

well-placed typographical symbols to represent the epic drama of ionization. We use an equation:

$$2\ H_2O = H_3O^+ + OH^-$$

This simple equation is shorthand for the ionization process described in this section. Every chemist knows that when a proton is passed from one water molecule to another, it carries with it a positive charge. Every chemist knows that the water molecule that loses the proton is left with a negative charge. In fact, since every chemist knows that the itinerant proton is attached to a water molecule, we write an even more concise equation:

$$H_2O = H^+ + OH^-$$

And the sooner you recognize these equations as shorthand for the entire contents of this section, the sooner you will be able to talk like a real chemist.

The ionization of water is an important, but rare occurrence. In pure water, of course, the number of hydronium ions must be exactly equal to the number of hydroxide ions, but the number of each of these ions is vanishingly small. While our lye has a concentration of 500 parts per thousand, the hydronium concentration in pure water at room temperature is only 1.9 parts per trillion. An Olympic swimming pool of pure water would contain only 4.7 g of hydronium ion and 4.2 g of hydroxide ion. As small as these numbers are, you must thoroughly understand the ionization of water before proceeding to the acid/base chemistry of subsequent chapters.

7.4 Solutions and Emulsions

Oil and water don't mix. What do we mean by this statement? Clearly it is possible to add oil to water and shake them up. In this exercise you will do just that, paying more than the usual attention to the resulting mixture.

You are already familiar with *solutions* from Section 4.1 (page 57); you dissolved sodium hydroxide in water to produce lye. What exactly do we mean when we say that something dissolves? When you dissolve sugar in water it appears that the sugar disappears; the resulting solution looks just like water. The same is true when you dissolve salt or sodium hydroxide in water. Apple juice, wine, honey, and tea are all examples of solutions. Though they may or may not be colored, they are all transparent, and this is the hallmark of a solution.

Chemists refer to the substance being dissolved as the *solute* and the substance into which it is being dissolved as the *solvent*. In our lye, for example, sodium hydroxide is the solute and water is the solvent. When a solute dissolves, it breaks up into particles (usually individual molecules or ions) that are much smaller than the wavelength of visible light. This allows light to go right past these particles rather than bouncing off of them, making the solution transparent.

Many familiar liquids are not solutions. Milk, orange juice, salad dressing, and house paint are colloidal suspensions, or *colloids*. Most frequently we'll be dealing with colloidal suspensions of one liquid in another; these are called *emulsions*. Emulsions may be translucent, but they are not transparent; light may pass through them, but you cannot see through them; they may appear milky, cloudy, or opaque. When one liquid is emulsified in another, it breaks up into droplets that are microscopic, but larger than the wavelength of visible light. Light bounces off of these droplets, and since light entering from one direction exits in another, you cannot see through an emulsion. Moreover, a beam of light entering from one direction can be seen from the side, like a flashlight beam on a foggy night. In this demonstration, we use a laser pointer to visualize the differences between an oil/water emulsion and a glycerine/water solution.

 Though laser pointers have become common items, they should be handled with respect. Never point a laser into someone's eyes.

1. *Gather your materials:*
   - Distilled water
   - Mineral oil
   - Glycerine
   - Two 30 mL glass vials labeled `Oil/Water` and `Water/Glycerine`, with caps
   - Three pipets, labeled `Oil`, `Water`, and `Glycerine`
   - A laser pointer (optional)
   - Your soapmaking notebook and a pen

2. *Fill the vials:* Synthetically weigh 10.00 g of water into the `Oil/Water` vial. *Carefully* weigh 10.00 g of mineral oil into the `Oil/Water` vial; try not to mix the oil and water. Synthetically weigh 10.00 g of glycerine into the `Water/Glycerine` vial. *Carefully* weigh 10.00 g of water into the `Water/Glycerine` vial; try not to mix the water and glycerine. Screw the caps onto both vials.

3. *Compare the vials:* Though glycerine and mineral oil are similar to one another in appearance and viscosity, glycerine is more dense than water and oil is less dense than water. That is why we placed glycerine on the bottom and oil on the top of their respective vials. Look carefully at the oil/water and water/glycerine interfaces. How do they differ in shape and appearance?

    Look at your finger through the top and bottom layers of each vial. Compare the appearance of your finger through each liquid.

    In a darkened room, shine the laser pointer up through the bottom of each vial. In which (if any) of the vials is the beam visible from the side? You can try pointing the laser at the vials from different directions.

4. *Mix:* Thoroughly shake the two vials for 60 seconds to mix the contents. Repeat the observation of the previous step. What has changed?

5. *Wait:* Have a snack; take a walk; smell the roses; enjoy some quality time with friends or family. Repeat your observations for each vial.

This simple demonstration shows the most striking difference between a solution and an emulsion. Eventually, this emulsion returns to its original, un-mixed condition. Emulsions may be stabilized, however, as we'll see in Chapter 13.

Practice Problems

Answers to practice problems appear in Appendix A (page 335).

1. What are the chemical and structural formulas of pentane, octane, and hexadecane?
2. Describe the electrical charge distribution for the water molecule. What are the charges on the oxygen atom, the hydrogen atoms, and the molecule as a whole?
3. Describe the electrical charge distribution for the ethane molecule. What are the charges on the carbon atoms, the hydrogen atoms, and the molecule as a whole?
4. What are the differences between a proton and a hydrogen atom?
5. What are the differences between a proton and a hydronium ion?
6. Why are alkanes described as hydrophobic?
7. What is the difference between an OH bond and a hydrogen bond?
8. When water ionizes, which ion is the cation and which is the anion?
9. What is the difference between a colloidal suspension and an emulsion?
10. What is the difference between a chemical formula and a chemical equation?

Chapter 8

Acids and Bases

SOAPMAKING chemistry is dominated by the interaction of *acids* and *bases.* Defining exactly what constitutes an acid is complicated enough that there are several definitions within chemistry, but the only one that will concern us is the Bronsted-Lowry definition:

> An acid is a substance that can donate a hydrogen ion, or *proton*. A base is a substance that can accept a proton.

Under these definitions, acids and bases react by passing protons from one to the other. To make these reactions concrete, let's first meet five major players in the chemistry to come: two acids and three bases. Once we are familiar with them, we can examine their mutual interactions.

8.1 Acetic Acid

This is very likely the first acid to have been produced (first accidentally and then intentionally) by human beings. Acetic acid is produced when alcoholic beverages "go sour," and in the absence of fancy chemical gizmos, acids can still be recognized by their sour taste. Acetic acid is, in fact, responsible for the characteristic smell and taste of vinegar, which contains approximately 5% acetic acid in water.

Figure 8-1 shows a model of an acetic acid molecule interacting with a water molecule. The structure of acetic acid gives us a clue as to its chemistry. Here we see that acetic acid has structural similarities to both water (page 131) and ethane (page 127). Like water, acetic acid has a positively charged hydrogen atom, or proton, bonded to a negatively charged oxygen atom.[1]

---

1. Recall from the previous models that positive atoms are shown as white spheres, negative atoms as dark spheres, and neutral atoms as gray spheres.

Figure 8-1. Acetic Acid and Water

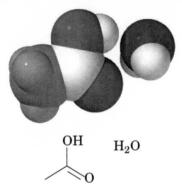

OH   H₂O

It can engage in hydrogen bonding with a neighboring water molecule by orienting its negative oxygen atoms to the water's positive hydrogen atoms and its positive hydrogen atom to the water's negative oxygen atom. But in addition to these features, which render it soluble in water, acetic acid also bears a resemblance to ethane. Like ethane, acetic acid contains a roughly neutral carbon atom covalently bonded to three roughly neutral hydrogen atoms. A second, partially positive carbon atom links the two halves of the molecule. Thus the left end of the model looks like ethane and the right end of the model looks like water. The astute reader might expect acetic acid to be soluble in both oil and water. And it is.

The interaction of acetic acid with water is especially interesting because it is in the nature of acids, by definition, to donate protons to bases. Figure 8-2 shows what happens when acetic acid donates a proton to water. The proton carries with it its positive charge. What's left of the acetic acid molecule is left with a negative charge. We call the remnants of the acetic acid molecule an *acetate ion.* Any time an organic acid donates a proton, the remnant left behind is a negative ion whose name ends in *-ate.* The water molecule, having accepted the positive proton, now has a net positive charge. We call this water-plus-proton conglomerate a *hydronium ion,* which we first encountered in Chapter 7. Any time a base accepts a proton, the conglomeration formed is a positive ion whose name ends in *-ium.* The interaction displayed in Figure 8-2 is the fundamental acid/base reaction.

Figure 8-2. Acetate and Hydronium Ions

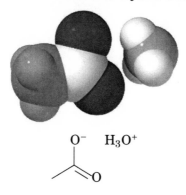

$$O^- \quad H_3O^+$$

While a model shows us this reaction in detail, it is convenient to use a chemical equation to give the same information more concisely.

$$HC_2H_3O_2 + H_2O = C_2H_3O_2^- + H_3O^+$$

The first object in the equation is the formula for acetic acid. The "H" at the beginning of the formula is the proton, the one that may be passed from acid to base. The rest of the formula shows that the molecule contains two carbon atoms, three non-proton hydrogen atoms that may *not* be passed around, and two oxygen atoms. The second item in the equation is the familiar formula for water. The *equal* sign in the middle is what makes this an *equa*tion. The products to the right of the equal sign represent the acetate and hydronium ions. Note that the charges on these ions are shown as superscripts. This equation shows every atom in every molecule for both the reactants on the left and the products to the right.

One more level of simplification, however, will make our subsequent discussions of acid/base chemistry a little easier to follow.

$$HAce + H_2O = Ace^- + H_3O^+$$

This equation represents the same fundamental chemistry as the first one, but it hides the trees to make the forest more obvious. The glob of atoms, $C_2H_3O_2^-$, is replaced with the shorthand, Ace^-, short for the acetate ion. When a positive proton sticks to a negative acetate, the charges cancel, and we get the un-charged acetic acid molecule, represented by HAce. The fundamental chemistry is a little easier to follow here; HAce gives up an H^+ to water.

If you liked that shorthand, we can take it one step further. Chemists assume that, with rare exception, acid/base chemistry takes place in water. Since the presence of water is assumed, there is no real need to include it in the reaction. We can, therefore, rewrite the equation as:

$$HAce = Ace^- + H^+$$

In words, HAce can break apart into H^+ and Ace^-. Conversely, Ace^- can accept a proton and turn into HAce. But accepting a proton is a job for a *base,* not an acid. Thus the acid, acetic acid, has a fundamental relationship to the base, acetate. We say that acetate is the **conjugate base** of acetic acid and that acetic acid is the **conjugate acid** of acetate. Acetic acid and acetate are really the same thing, the one with a proton attached and the other without. You can think of acetic acid as *hydrogen acetate.*

In aqueous solution, some of the acetic acid remains intact and some of it falls apart, dissociates, or *ionizes* into proton and acetate. Because this ionization is incomplete, acetic acid is known as a **weak** acid. This designation has nothing to do with its usefulness or its safety.

Every chemist knows that in an aqueous solution like vinegar, some of the acetic acid has remained intact and some of it has ionized into acetate and proton. Every chemist knows that *proton* is just shorthand for the hydronium ion. Every chemist knows that the equations of this section are simply shorthand for the proton hand-off depicted in Figure 8-1 and Figure 8-2. And now that you know a few more things that every chemist knows, you are one step further to becoming a chemist yourself.

8.2 Citric Acid

Citric acid is a weak acid familiar to soapmakers for its use in making bath bombs, which bubble and fizz when dropped into water. Chemically, it is very similar to acetic acid except for four things. First, unlike acetic acid, citric acid is a solid at room temperature. Shipping citric acid is less expensive than shipping

Figure 8-3. Citric Acid

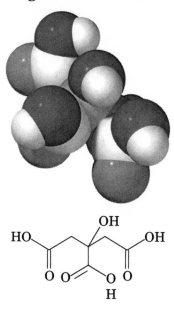

acetic acid because solids are less likely than liquids to leak in transit. Second, unlike acetic acid with its strong, characteristic smell, citric acid is odorless. This alone will make you appreciate our use of citric acid rather than acetic acid for chemical analysis. Third, citric acid is a *tri-protic* acid; each molecule is capable of delivering up to three protons in acid/base reactions. Finally, because a molecule of citric acid contains more atoms than one of acetic acid, the molecular weight of citric acid is higher than that of acetic acid, an issue that will be explored in Chapter 9.

Figure 8-3 shows a molecular model of citric acid. The three acidic protons are shown as white spheres. Curiously, there is a fourth OH group (in the middle) that is polar, but not acidic. We'll encounter this kind of OH group when we discuss the alcohols in Chapter 11. While it does not ionize as the acids do, it does interact strongly with water molecules, and it is responsible, in part, for the extraordinary solubility of citric acid and citrate salts.

8.2.1 Preparation of 500 ppt H₃Cit (Red)

In later chapters we'll learn to analyze soap and soapmaking ingredients. In doing so, we'll need a solution whose concentration is known to the best possible uncertainty. I have chosen citric acid as the ***primary standard*** for several reasons. First, it is a chemical that is widely available to soapmakers from the same vendors who provide oils and alkalis for soapmaking. Second, the material commonly available as "anhydrous" citric acid has high purity at low cost. Third, though it is strong enough for our purposes, it is not as hazardous as the strong mineral acids like hydrochloric or sulfuric acids. Finally, as an odorless solid, it is more pleasant to use than the smelly acetic acid. Since the preparation of the citric acid standard is quite similar to that of lye, your previous experience should serve you well here.

Because citric acid can absorb moisture from the air, the citric acid sold for making "bath bombs" may or may not contain hidden moisture. Wherever you order your acid, be sure to specify ***anhydrous*** citric acid. The better the quality of your citric acid, the more consistent your results will be from one supply of acid to the next.

This procedure is quite straightforward. We simply weigh 50 g each of citric acid and water into a *dispensing* bottle.[2] To distinguish it from the more dilute acid solutions that follow, this standard will be color coded red using a colored marker or self-adhesive label.

1. *Gather your materials:*
    - Goggles or glasses
    - An eyewash bottle
    - Gloves
    - A centigram balance
    - Anhydrous citric acid
    - Distilled water
    - Two plastic cups labeled `Acid` and `Water`
    - A clean, dry 125 mL *dispensing* bottle labeled `500 ppt H₃Cit (Red)`
    - A plastic spoon
    - A pipet labeled `Water`
    - A powder funnel

---

2. This kind of bottle is discussed in Section 8.2.2.

- Your soapmaking notebook and a pen

2. *Arrange your workspace:* Though not as hazardous as sodium hydroxide, citric acid deserves your respect. Review the MSDS for citric acid before proceeding. You *must* wear safety goggles or glasses for eye protection and you *ought* to wear gloves. Your notebook should be opened to a new page with your pen at the ready.

3. *Weigh the citric acid:* Using the procedure of Section 2.3 (page 25), *analytically* weigh 50.*XX* g of citric acid from the `Acid` cup into the `500 ppt H₃Cit` (Red) bottle. Remember that in an analytical weight it is not important to hit the target exactly as long as you record all digits of the actual weight. Also remember that the powder funnel is part of the tare weight. You can use the plastic spoon to load the `Acid` cup with citric acid. Place the powder funnel in the cup and press the tare button. Use the powder funnel to deliver citric acid into the `500 ppt H₃Cit` (Red) bottle, returning both the weighing cup *and funnel* to the balance. Record the actual weight of citric acid in your notebook.

4. *Weigh the water:* Using the procedure of Section 2.5 (page 31), *synthetically* weigh 50.*XX* g of water from the `Water` cup into the `500 ppt H₃Cit` (Red) bottle, where the *XX* is the same as it was for your citric acid. It is important to hit the target weight to within 1 drop. You should now have weighed a total of 50.*XX* g of citric acid and 50.*XX* g of water.

5. *Mix the standard acid solution:* Screw the cap onto the `500 ppt H₃Cit` (Red) bottle and gently swirl it until all of the citric acid has dissolved. Note that the solution will get cool. Nifty, huh? Since it may take a while for the last few crystals of citric acid to dissolve, it is a good idea to let it sit for an hour or even overnight before using your new standard. Give the bottle one more good shake before using it for the first time.

6. *Cleanup:* Acid spills may be cleaned up with household ammonia. The spoons and cups can be washed immediately. Wipe down your balance and bring your notebook up to date. To avoid confusing the various concentrations, color-code the bottle and cap with a red marker or self-adhesive sticker.

Example 8-1. Preparation of 500 ppt H₃Cit (Red)

I made up some of the primary standard by weighing 50.29 g of citric acid (analytically) and 50.29 g of distilled water (synthetically), giving me a concentration of 500 ppt. If I had fallen 1 drop short of the target weight for water, the concentration would have been 500.25 ppt; if I had gone 1 drop past the target, the concentration would have been 499.75 ppt. I am confident, then, that whenever I make up primary standard using this procedure, the concentration will be 500.0±0.3 ppt.

This procedure took 15 minutes.

In the following sections we'll dilute this standard acid for analytical use. When it's time to mix up another batch of standard acid, you can add it directly into the previous batch without emptying or washing the bottle. After all, when you add 500 ppt acid to 500 ppt acid, its concentration remains 500 ppt.

8.2.2 Analytically Weighing a Liquid

So far we have always weighed solids analytically. The advantage of an analytical weight is that every digit is correct to within the readability of the balance. Since the powder funnel is included in the tare weight, there is no place for the solid to "hide." It must be either in the weighing cup or in the destination container. So when the balance registers the weight missing from the weighing cup, this must be equal and opposite to the weight transferred to the destination container, which gives us full confidence in every digit of an analytical weight.

So far we have always weighed liquids synthetically because we have had specific target weights in mind. We use a pipet to transfer the liquid, but because we need to be able to see how much has been transferred so far, the pipet cannot be part of the tare weight. As in an analytical weight, we have assumed that the liquid is either in the weighing cup or in the destination container. However, since the pipet may not be completely empty at the end of the procedure, the weight registered by the balance may be larger than the actual weight transferred. As long as the target weight is much larger than the amount of liquid remaining in the pipet, the relative error will be small. But if the target weight is small, the relative error will be correspondingly large. For this reason, we have always managed things so that synthetic target weights are much larger than the few drops of liquid that may remain in the pipet.

The time is coming, however, when we'll want to weigh small quantities of liquids. Fortunately, we'll not care about hitting the target in these cases; we'll simply want to be confident of each digit in the weight. In other words, we'll weigh small quantities of liquids analytically. If we are to have this confidence, we must eliminate the possibility of liquid remaining in the pipet, and the easiest way to accomplish this is to eliminate the pipet entirely. Since we would like to retain the ability to deliver single drops, we use a special kind of bottle whose cap includes a nozzle capable of delivering single drops. Such a bottle is known variously as a *dropping bottle* or a *dispensing bottle*. There are many varieties to choose from, but the most important feature for our purposes is that it should be possible to deliver a single drop of liquid without dribbling. Different vendors will stock different styles of bottles, but I have tested the bottles listed in Table 1-1 (page 8) and found them to be suitable.

The following procedure will allow you to determine whether a bottle will be suitable for our work.

1. *Gather your materials:*
    - Goggles or glasses
    - A centigram balance
    - A 125 mL dispensing bottle labeled `Water`
    - An empty cup labeled `Destination`

2. *Arrange your workspace:* As usual, you should wear safety goggles or glasses for eye protection.

3. *Weigh the water:* Place the `Water` bottle onto the balance and press the tare button. Squeeze a drop of water into the `Destination` cup and return the `Water` bottle to the balance. The weight registered on the balance is equal and opposite to the weight transferred to the cup.

That's all there is to it. Practice weighing 1 drop, 2 drops, 10 drops, and 20 drops of water. You can even shoot for approximate target weights, as we have done when analytically weighing solids. Try weighing 1.XX g, 2.XX g, and 10.XX g of water. Remember to tare the bottle before starting each new weight. You may have to put the bottle back onto the balance several times to see how close you are to the target weight. If you have a good bottle, it may take 90 seconds to transfer 10.XX g, but you will be confident of all four digits of that weight.

 When weighing a liquid analytically, remember to tare the dispensing bottle before delivering liquid to the destination. If you are shooting for a target, you can return the bottle to the balance to see how much has been transferred so far. As you near the target, you can sneak up on it a few drops at a time. It makes no difference if you exceed the target by a few drops as long as you write down every digit of the weight.

8.2.3 Preparation of 50 ppt H₃Cit (Orange)

Our 500 ppt citric acid standard is too concentrated for most experiments. In this procedure we'll dilute it with distilled water to make a standard with a concentration of 50 ppt. To make the 50 ppt citric acid standard we simply weigh 10 g of 500 ppt citric acid standard and 90 g of water into a plastic bottle. This procedure should take no more than a few minutes. This standard will be color coded orange.

1. *Gather your materials:*
    - Goggles or glasses
    - An eyewash bottle
    - Gloves
    - A centigram balance
    - A filled 125 mL dispensing bottle labeled `500 ppt H₃Cit (Red)`
    - A filled 125 mL PP bottle labeled `Water`
    - A pipet labeled `Water`
    - A clean, dry 125 mL dispensing bottle labeled `50 ppt H₃Cit (Orange)`
    - A calculator
    - Your soapmaking notebook and a pen

2. *Arrange your workspace:* As usual, you should wear safety goggles or glasses for eye protection. Your notebook should be opened to a new page with your pen at the ready. *If you*

have just made up the 500 ppt standard, make sure that the citric acid has completely dissolved.

3. *Weigh the acid:* Using the procedure of Section 8.2.2 (page 146), *analytically* weigh 10.XX g of acid from the `500 ppt H₃Cit (Red)` bottle into the `50 ppt H₃Cit (Orange)` bottle. It is not necessary to hit the target exactly, but whatever the actual weight turns out to be, you must record *all four digits.*

4. *Weigh the water:* The target weight is exactly nine times the weight of the acid from the last step.[3] Calculate this target weight and use the procedure of Section 2.5 (page 31) to *synthetically* weigh 9(10.XX) g of water from the `Water` cup into the `50 ppt H₃Cit (Orange)` bottle. You should get to within 1 drop of the target weight. Screw the cap onto the `50 ppt H₃Cit (Orange)` bottle and give it a gentle shake to mix the contents.

5. *Cleanup:* Acid spills may be cleaned up with household ammonia. Wipe down your balance and bring your notebook up to date.

We'll use this standard primarily for making up the next, more dilute standard. The orange standard will make up about 10 of these more dilute standards. When it is time to make up more orange standard, there is no need to empty or rinse the bottle. Just add the new standard to the old one.

8.2.4 Preparation of 5 ppt H₃Cit (Yellow)

The working standard for most of our experiments will be a 5 ppt citric acid standard made by weighing 10 g of 50 ppt H₃Cit and 90 g of water into a plastic bottle. This procedure should take no more than a few minutes. This standard will be color coded yellow.

1. *Gather your materials:*
   - Goggles or glasses
   - An eyewash bottle
   - Gloves

---

3. If, for example, you weighed 10.08 g of acid, you would need 90.72 g of water. Of course, if you weighed exactly 10.00 g of acid, you would need exactly 90.00 g of water.

- A centigram balance
- A filled 125 mL dispensing bottle labeled 50 ppt H₃Cit (Orange)
- A 125 mL PP bottle labeled Water
- A pipet labeled Water
- A clean, dry 125 mL dispensing bottle labeled 5 ppt H₃Cit (Yellow)
- A calculator
- Your soapmaking notebook and a pen

2. *Arrange your workspace:* As usual, you should wear safety goggles or glasses for eye protection. Your notebook should be opened to a new page with your pen at the ready.

3. *Weigh the acid:* Using the procedure of Section 8.2.2 (page 146), *analytically* weigh 10.XX g of acid from the 50 ppt H₃Cit (Orange) bottle into the 5 ppt H₃Cit (Yellow) bottle. It is not necessary to hit the target exactly, but whatever the actual weight turns out to be, you must record *all four digits.*

4. *Weigh the water:* The target weight is exactly nine times the weight of the acid from the last step.[4] Calculate this target weight and use the procedure of Section 2.5 (page 31) to *synthetically* weigh 9(10.XX) g of water from the Water cup into the 5 ppt H₃Cit (Yellow) bottle. You should get to within 1 drop of the target weight. Screw the cap onto the bottle and give it a gentle shake.

5. *Cleanup:* Acid spills may be cleaned up with household ammonia. Wipe down your balance and bring your notebook up to date.

We'll use this solution primarily for measuring the alkali remaining in soap after saponification. Each analysis will require only a couple of grams, so a bottle should last for 30–100 analyses. When it is time to make more standard, there is no need to empty or rinse the bottle. Just add the new standard to the old bottle.

---

4. If, for example, you weighed 10.23 g of acid, you would need 92.07 g of water. Of course, if you weighed exactly 10.00 g of acid, you would need exactly 90.00 g of water.

Example 8-2. Preparation of 5 ppt H₃Cit (Yellow)

To allow sufficient time for the citric acid to dissolve, I waited an hour after making up my 500 ppt standard before starting this procedure. I shook the 500 ppt standard repeatedly and examined it to make sure there were no un-dissolved particles of citric acid.

I began making up the 50 ppt standard by analytically weighing 10.74 g of 500 ppt standard into the 50 ppt bottle. I calculated a target weight of 96.66 g for the water, which I weighed in two portions. The larger portion, 89.84 g, was weighed analytically and the smaller portion, 6.82 g, was weighed synthetically. The weight of acid was 10.74 g and the total weight was 107.40 g, giving a concentration exactly one-tenth the original concentration, or 50.0 ppt.

I made up the 5 ppt standard by analytically weighing 10.31 g of 50 ppt standard, 79.73 g of water, and 13.06 g of water into the 5 ppt bottle. The weight of acid was 10.31 g and the total weight was 103.10 g, giving a concentration exactly one-tenth the original concentration, or 5.00 ppt.

The worst-case scenarios would have entailed either falling 1 drop shy or going 1 drop past the water target weights for all three standards. At the high end the concentrations would have been 500.25 ppt, 50.05 ppt, and 5.01 ppt. At the low end they would have been 499.75 ppt, 49.95 ppt, and 4.99 ppt. Thus I am confident that whenever I make up these standards they will have concentrations of 500.0±0.3 ppt, 50.00±0.05 ppt, and 5.00±0.01 ppt.

It took 16 minutes to make up both standards.

If pure, anhydrous citric acid is used to make up the acid standards, they may confidently be labeled 500 ppt, 50.0 ppt, and 5.00 ppt.

8.3 Sodium Hydroxide

Sodium hydroxide is, perhaps, the most important chemical in soapmaking. In chemistry, it is known as a ***strong*** base, where the word *strong* contrasts with *weak* as discussed in the previous sections. When dissolved in water, a strong base completely falls apart, separating its first name from its last name. Sodium hydroxide, for example, falls apart into a positive sodium ion and a negative hydroxide ion.

$$NaOH = Na^+ + OH^-$$

In chemistry, a strong base is one for which this ionization, or dissociation into ions, is complete. Sodium hydroxide is considered a strong base not because it is dangerous or caustic, but because *all* of the sodium hydroxide molecules dissociate into sodium and hydroxide ions.

Figure 8-4 shows a sodium hydroxide molecule interacting with a single water molecule. The hydrogen and oxygen atoms of the water molecule appear as overlapping light and dark spheres. The spheres overlap because the bonding is covalent; that is, the electrons that bind the molecule together are shared between the atoms. The difference in color, however, shows that they are not shared equally—the oxygen holds a partial negative charge and the hydrogen atoms hold partial positive charges. The bonding in sodium hydroxide is more extreme than that in water. The sodium and hydroxide ions do not share electrons with one another, and the model represents this with non-overlapping spheres. Rather than carrying a partial charge, the sodium ion carries a full +1 charge while the hydroxide ion carries a full -1 charge. This extreme kind of bonding is called ***ionic*** bonding. A chemist thinks of sodium hydroxide as two separate, mutually attractive ions rather than as a single molecule.

Figure 8-4. Water and Sodium Hydroxide

One water molecule is not enough to tempt the positive sodium ion away from the negative hydroxide ion. But in an aqueous solution, the water molecules so outnumber the ions that the ions separate, as shown in Figure 8-5. The positive sodium ion attracts a harem of water molecules, each one orienting its partially negative oxygen atom toward the positive sodium ion. Once in solution, the sodium ion really plays very little part in subsequent chemistry. Chemists refer to such an ion as a *spectator ion*. We imagine a very contented sodium ion surrounded by so many attractive water molecules that it has little interest in pursuing other opportunities.

The story is different for the hydroxide ion. Initially, it too attracts a harem of water molecules, each one orienting its partially positive hydrogen atoms toward the negative hydroxide ion. Under these circumstances, the hydroxide ion may very easily bump into a water molecule, grab one of its protons, and thereby become a water molecule itself. It leaves behind a distraught, proton-less water molecule that can only be described as a hydroxide ion. In equation form:

$$OH^- + H_2O = H_2O + OH^-$$

This seeming non-reaction goes on all the time, with the effect that it is impossible to tell whether a hydroxide ion in solution originated as sodium hydroxide or water. Can you find the hydroxide ion in Figure 8-5?[5]

There is one more twist to this melodramatic tale. What if a hydroxide ion happens to encounter a hydronium ion? The

---

5. The hydroxide ion in this snapshot appears to the immediate left of the central, white sodium ion. In an instant, however, any unwary water molecule could fall prey to this proton stealer.

Figure 8-5. Ionization of Sodium Hydroxide

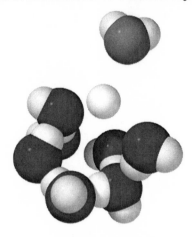

hydronium passes a proton to the hydroxide, becoming a water molecule; the hydroxide accepts the proton, also becoming a water molecule. You may consider *hydronium hydroxide* as a synonym for two water molecules. The fundamental reaction is that of hydroxide ion with a proton to make water:

$$H^+ + OH^- = H_2O$$

Note that this fundamental reaction leaves out the source of the proton, which must have come from an acid, and leaves out the source of the hydroxide, which must have come from a base. The proton might come from any acid and the hydroxide from any base, but let's take for example the reaction of sodium hydroxide with acetic acid. This reaction may be represented by either of these equations:

$$NaOH + HC_2H_3O_2 = NaC_2H_3O_2 + H_2O$$
$$NaOH + HAce = NaAce + H_2O$$

In reading these equations, a chemist understands that every sodium hydroxide molecule has ionized into a sodium ion and a hydroxide ion, that some acetic acid molecules have ionized into protons and acetate ions, and that these protons are actually present as hydronium ions. So when sodium hydroxide reacts with acetic acid, the proton is passed from the acid, via a water molecule, to the hydroxide ion, which then becomes a water molecule.

Figure 8-6. Water and Potassium Hydroxide

What of the sodium and acetate ions? They remain in solution as separate ions for the time being. But if we boiled the water away or allowed it to evaporate, we would be left with a white powder—a salt known as sodium acetate. When an acid reacts with a base, you get water and a salt whose first name comes from the base and whose second name comes from the acid. Sodium hydroxide reacts with acetic acid (hydrogen acetate) to yield sodium acetate and water.

 A hydronium ion is just a water molecule in temporary possession of an extra proton; a hydroxide ion is just a water molecule looking for its missing proton.

8.4 Potassium Hydroxide

Chemically, there is very little difference between sodium and potassium hydroxide. They are both strong bases and react with acids in the same way. Only two differences are of interest to the soapmaker. First, potassium salts tend to be more soluble in water than sodium salts. For this reason, we use potassium hydroxide rather than sodium hydroxide to produce liquid soaps. Second, a molecule of potassium hydroxide weighs more than one of sodium hydroxide, an issue that will be explored in Chapter 9.

8.4.1 Preparation of 5 ppt KOH (Green)

In Section 8.2 we made up three acidic standards to be used in the analysis of alkaline materials. In this procedure, we make up an alkaline standard for the analysis of acidic materials. We might use sodium or ammonium hydroxide as a standard, but because of its high solubility, potassium hydroxide has become the alkali of choice for analytical work. You might think that we could make up a KOH standard as we did with the acidic standards, by carefully making a concentrated solution and then diluting it by a factor of 10 or 100. As with our citric acid standard, this would require material with sufficiently high purity that we could rely on it as a primary standard.

It is nearly impossible, however, to find *pure* KOH. I realize that your vendor probably tells you that your KOH is pure. I realize that the msds supplied by the manufacturer says 99–100%. But there is an impurity that is nearly impossible to remove completely, and since everyone knows this, the manufacturer doesn't even include it on the label. This impurity is water.

As it comes out of the can or bottle, your KOH certainly appears dry enough. But put it in a beaker, weigh it, and leave it out in the open for an hour or so and you will find that it gains weight just by sitting out in the air. Such a material is described as *hygroscopic*. KOH (and NaOH) are super-hygroscopic. If you leave your beaker out for a few hours, you may find that the top layer of KOH begins to look wet or clumpy. In fact, if you leave the beaker out overnight, the KOH may absorb so much moisture that it dissolves in the very water it pulled from the air, leaving you with a beaker half-full of solution. Such a super-hygroscopic material is described as *deliquescent*. The manufacturer ships KOH that is as dry as can be managed, but it is in the nature of deliquescent materials to absorb any available moisture, whether found in shipping or in storage. For this reason, you should keep your supplies of KOH, NaOH, and lye tightly sealed except when you are actually using them. We take it as given that the KOH available to you contains a variable and unknown amount of water.

It will prove convenient to have a 5 ppt KOH standard for the analysis of acidic substances. Since we can't rely on the purity of our KOH, it makes little sense to make the solution as carefully as we made our acid standards. Instead, we make a solution of about the right concentration and will determine its exact concentration in Section 9.4. The good news is that this is perhaps the easiest procedure in the book and should take no more than a few minutes. This solution will be color coded green.

1. *Gather your materials:*
   - Goggles or glasses
   - An eyewash bottle
   - Gloves
   - A centigram balance
   - Distilled water
   - KOH
   - A clean, dry 500 mL PP bottle labeled 5 ppt KOH (Green) with lid
   - A clean, dry 125 mL *dispensing* bottle labeled 5 ppt KOH (Green)
   - A plastic cup labeled KOH
   - A powder funnel
   - Your soapmaking notebook and a pen

2. *Arrange your workspace:* As usual, you should wear safety goggles or glasses for eye protection. Your notebook should be opened to a new page with your pen at the ready.

3. *Fill the bottle:* Fill the 500 mL 5 ppt KOH (Green) bottle up to the shoulder with distilled water. The exact amount of water does not matter, but you should not fill the bottle to the brim.

4. *Weigh the KOH:* Using the procedure of Section 2.3 (page 25), *analytically* weigh 2.5X g of KOH from the KOH cup into the 500 mL 5 ppt KOH (Green) bottle.

5. *Mix the solution:* Screw the cap onto the 5 ppt KOH (Green) bottle and invert it repeatedly until the KOH has dissolved.

6. *Fill the dispensing bottle:* Pour your fresh standard into the labeled dispensing bottle. This dispensing bottle will be used in the analytical work to come. Refill it from the larger bottle as needed.

7. *Cleanup:* Alkaline spills may be cleaned up with household vinegar. Wipe down your balance and bring your notebook up to date.

We'll use this solution primarily for measuring the acid concentration of oils. Each analysis will require only a couple of grams, so a bottle should last for a very long time. For the moment, we know only that its concentration is approximately 5 ppt, but this value is relatively uncertain because we doubt

---

Example 8-3. Preparation of 5 ppt KOH (Green)

I made up the 5 ppt KOH standard by dissolving 2.62 g of KOH in about 500 mL of distilled water. The elapsed time for this procedure was 2 minutes.

---

the purity of our KOH and we did not bother to weigh the water. The exact concentration will be determined in Section 9.4.

8.5 Ammonium Hydroxide

Our discussion of bases would not be complete without a brief introduction to ammonia. Ammonia (NH_3) is a gas with a pungent aroma familiar to anyone who has ever cleaned a window. Like all bases, ammonia can accept a proton from an acid. When it does so, the ammonia-plus-proton ion is called the *ammonium* ion, NH_4^+. We may say that ammonia is the conjugate base of ammonium ion or that ammonium ion is the conjugate acid of ammonia. Most frequently, ammonium ion results from the reaction of ammonia with an acid, but it can even result from the reaction of ammonia with water:

$$NH_3 + H_2O = NH_4OH$$
$$NH_4OH = NH_4^+ + OH^-$$

In fact, the "ammonia" you buy at the grocery store is actually a solution of the gas, ammonia, in water. Chemists will refer to this solution either as *aqueous ammonia* or, more often than not, as *ammonium hydroxide*. Unlike strong bases such as sodium or potassium hydroxide, ammonium hydroxide is a weak base, meaning that it ionizes incompletely in water. Whereas sodium hydroxide ionizes completely into Na^+ and OH^- ions, ammonium hydroxide ionizes partially into NH_4^+ and OH^- ions, leaving quite a lot of un-ionized NH_3 and NH_4OH molecules in solution. If ammonium hydroxide were a strong base, there would be no NH_3 molecules left in solution and, consequently, none to escape as a gas and confront our nostrils. In other words, you can *smell* the equilibrium between ammonia and ammonium, a phenomenon that we'll exploit in Chapter 10.

8.6 Salts

All acids act as proton donors.[6] A weak acid like citric acid, for example, will pass some (but not all) of its three protons to neighboring water molecules. When it reacts with a strong base, however, it may yield up one, two, or three of its protons, depending on how much base is available. For the time being, let's consider the reaction of three molecules of potassium hydroxide with one of citric acid:

$$3\ KOH\ +\ H_3C_6H_5O_7\ =\ K_3C_6H_5O_7\ +\ 3\ H_2O$$
$$3\ KOH\ +\ H_3Cit\ =\ K_3Cit\ +\ 3\ H_2O$$

Potassium hydroxide reacts with citric acid to produce the salt *potassium citrate* and water. In the first version of the equation, we have used the formulas for citric acid, $H_3C_6H_5O_7$, and citrate ion, $C_6H_5O_7^{3-}$. We can say that citric acid is the conjugate acid of citrate ion and that citrate ion is the conjugate base of citric acid. In the second version of the equation, we have removed the trees to make the forest more obvious; citrate has been abbreviated as Cit^{3-}. Because each proton has a charge of +1 and citrate has a charge of -3, it takes three protons to balance the charge of a citrate ion; the formula for citric acid is H_3Cit. Potassium ion, like proton, has a charge of +1, so the formula of potassium citrate is K_3Cit. Of course, a chemist understands these equations as shorthand for an elaborate dance, with citric acid donating protons to water molecules, which shuttle them to waiting hydroxide ions, which, in turn, become water molecules themselves. Potassium and citrate ions remain floating around in solution and come together only if the water is boiled away or evaporated, leaving the salt potassium citrate. As a chemist,

---

6. Many rules have exceptions, and the rule that all acids act as proton donors is no exception to the rule. There is a class of acids known as Lewis acids, which are acidic even though they contain no protons. The Lewis theory of acidity is more general than the Bronsted-Lowry theory used in this book, and the interested reader will find more information in most first-year college chemistry textbooks.

this dance should be playing itself out in your imagination as you finish up this paragraph.

We have now seen a variety of acids, bases, and salts that dissociate, or ionize, when dissolved in water. Acetic and citric acids do so. Sodium, potassium, and ammonium hydroxides do so. In fact, any compound with first name *sodium, potassium,* or *ammonium,* and any compound with last name *acetate* or *citrate* will ionize when dissolved in water. It would be handy to have a name for such materials. And we do. We call them **electrolytes.** Electrolytes are simply materials that dissociate into ions when dissolved in water. We may think, for example, of sodium chloride as a salty white powder, but every chemist knows that on contact with water the positive sodium and negative chloride ions go their separate ways. The motion of these charged ions constitutes an electrical current. Consequently, electrolyte solutions conduct electricity. That's what puts the *electro* in *electrolyte.*

We have introduced a lot of new concepts in this chapter: acids/bases, strong/weak, hydronium, acetate, citrate, invisible ions, and conjugate acid/base pairs. It may seem a little overwhelming at the moment, but all of our future discussions of soap chemistry will depend on your thorough understanding of these terms.

All compounds with first names *sodium, potassium,* or *ammonium* or with last names *acetate* or *citrate* dissociate into ions when dissolved in water. Such compounds, whether acids, bases, or salts, are called *electrolytes.*

8.7 pH

As noted in Section 7.3, the hydronium ion concentration in pure water is 1.9 parts per trillion. Chemists, however, do not generally discuss hydronium concentration in these terms. Instead, they use the *pH* (little p, big H) scale. Acidic solutions have a pH less than 7, alkaline solutions more than 7, and pure water exactly 7. Each step down the pH scale represents a tenfold increase in the hydronium ion concentration and a ten-fold decrease in the hydroxide ion concentration. A solution at pH

6, for example, has a hydronium concentration of 19 parts per trillion; one at pH 5 has a concentration of 190 parts per trillion.

A similar scale, *pOH,* is used for the hydroxide ion concentration. Pure water (at pH 7) has a hydroxide ion concentration of 1.7 parts per trillion; a solution at pH 8 has a concentration of 17 parts per trillion; a solution at pH 9 has a concentration of 170 parts per trillion. Because water ionizes into both hydronium and hydroxide, the two scales are fundamentally linked:

$$pH + pOH = 14$$

The number *14* is a fundamental constant for water. In pure water, there are an equal number of hydronium and hydroxide ions, pH equals pOH, and both must be equal to 7. The pH of a solution depends on the nature of the solute (acid or base), its strength (strong or weak), and on its concentration. The details of this dependency, however, must be deferred to the next chapter.

Practice Problems

Answers to practice problems appear in Appendix A (page 335).

1. What are the conjugate bases of citric acid and acetic acid? What are the conjugate acids of hydroxide ion and ammonia? What are the conjugate acids of water and ammonium ion?

2. Write balanced chemical equations for the following reactions. Acetic acid reacts with sodium hydroxide. Citric acid reacts with ammonia. Ammonium acetate reacts with potassium hydroxide.

3. Describe the sequence of events that occur when sodium acetate dissolves in water.

4. Describe the sequence of events that occur when acetic acid dissolves in water.

5. Describe the sequence of events that occur when acetic acid reacts with sodium hydroxide.

6. Nitric acid is a strong acid with formula HNO_3. Write a balanced equation for the reaction of nitric acid with sodium hydroxide.

7. Sulfuric acid is a strong acid with formula H_2SO_4. Write a balanced equation for the reaction of sulfuric acid with sodium hydroxide.

8. Calcium hydroxide (slaked lime) is used in canning and pickling. It has the formula $Ca(OH)_2$ and from this one may infer that it gives up two hydroxide ions upon dissociation. Write the balanced equation for the reaction of calcium hydroxide with acetic acid.

9. A 1 ppt solution of NaOH in water has a pH of 12.4. What is the pH of a 0.1 ppt solution of NaOH in water?

10. Hydrochloric acid, HCl, is a strong acid. A 1 ppt solution of HCl in water has a pH of 1.56. What is the pH of a 0.01 ppt solution of HCl in water?

Chapter 9

Stoichiometry

*T*HE fundamental question of soapmaking is "How many grams of alkali are required to react with a given quantity of oil?" This is an example of a more general question: "How many grams of A are required to react with a given quantity of B?" Such a question is known in chemistry as a *stoichiometric* question and the method used to answer such questions is known as **stoichiometry.** We'll apply stoichiometry to the reaction of alkali and oil in Chapter 12, but in this chapter we apply it to a simpler reaction: the reaction of an alkali and an acid.

9.1 The Mole

Consider the reaction of sodium hydroxide with acetic acid:

$$NaOH + HC_2H_3O_2 = NaC_2H_3O_2 + H_2O$$
$$NaOH + HAce = NaAce + H_2O$$

In words, one molecule of sodium hydroxide reacts with one molecule of acetic acid to produce one molecule of sodium acetate and one molecule of water. Consider now the question, "How many dozens of sodium hydroxide molecules react with a dozen molecules of acetic acid?" "How many gross (144) of sodium hydroxide molecules react with one gross molecules of acetic acid?" "How many millions of sodium hydroxide molecules react with one million molecules of acetic acid?" The answer to each of these question is simply "one." One dozen, one gross, one million.

Now let me introduce a new number. It is a number like a dozen, a gross, or a million, but it is almost unimaginably larger than these. The number is called a **mole,** and it is so

Table 9-1. Atomic Weights

Element	Symbol	Atomic Weight (g/mol)
Hydrogen	H	1.01
Carbon	C	12.01
Oxygen	O	16.00
Sodium	Na	22.99
Potassium	K	39.10

large that I'm not even going to tell you what the number is. You can answer a great many questions without knowing the exact number of things in a mole as long as you remember it's just a very large number.

I'm about to ask you the most important question in the chapter. If you can answer it, you will understand almost everything you need to know to answer stoichiometric questions. Are you ready? "How many moles of sodium hydroxide react with one mole of acetic acid?"

If you don't get the answer immediately, think about it some more. If you are really stumped after five minutes of stamping and huffing, you can read the footnote.[1] Now, I said the answer to this question is almost everything you need to know to answer stoichiometric questions. The rest of what you need to know is that one mole of carbon atoms weighs 12.01 g. Of course, this gives us a hotdog:

$$\left(\frac{12.01 \text{ g C}}{1 \text{ mol C}} \right)$$

This particular hotdog is called an ***atomic weight***. Scientists over the past two hundred years have determined ever more precise values of the atomic weights for every atom known to humankind. These are listed in the Periodic Table of Elements, but as it turns out, soapmakers deal almost exclusively with only a handful of elements, whose atomic weights are given in Table 9-1.

---

1.   ǝuO

Table 9-2. Molecular Weights

Compound	Formula	Shorthand	Molecular Weight (g/mol)
Water	H_2O	H_2O	18.02
Sodium Hydroxide	NaOH	NaOH	40.00
Potassium Hydroxide	KOH	KOH	56.11
Acetic Acid	$HC_2H_3O_2$	HAce	60.06
Citric Acid	$H_3C_6H_5O_7$	H_3Cit	192.12

Knowing these atomic weights, you can calculate the ***molecular weight*** for any formula that contains these atoms. Water, for example, has the formula H_2O. One mole of water contains 2 moles of hydrogen (weighing 2.02 g) and one mole of oxygen (weighing 16.00 g), so a mole of water weighs 18.02 g. By the same arithmetic, one mole of sodium hydroxide weighs 22.99 + 16.00 + 1.01, for a total of 40.00 g. One mole of acetic acid weighs 1.01 + 2(12.01) + 3(1.01) + 2(16.00), for a total of 60.06 g.

9.2 Stoichiometric Questions

You now know *everything* you need to know to answer the following stoichiometric question: "How many grams of sodium hydroxide react with 1000 g of acetic acid?" We have at our disposal the three important hotdogs. From Table 9-2 we have the molecular weights of sodium hydroxide (40.00 g NaOH/1 mol NaOH) and acetic acid (60.06 g HAce/1 mol HAce). From the balanced equation we know that 1 mole of NaOH reacts with 1 mole of acetic acid (1 mol NaOH/1 mol HAce). Knowing these, the math is quite simple:

$$? \text{ g NaOH} = 1000 \text{ g HAce} \left(\frac{1 \text{ mol HAce}}{60.06 \text{ g HAce}} \right)$$
$$\left(\frac{1 \text{ mol NaOH}}{1 \text{ mol HAce}} \right) \left(\frac{40.00 \text{ g NaOH}}{1 \text{ mol NaOH}} \right)$$
$$= 666 \text{ g NaOH}$$

It takes 666 g of sodium hydroxide to react with 1000 g of acetic acid. What do you suppose would happen if you mixed 667 g of sodium hydroxide with 1000 g of acetic acid? 666 g would react with all of the acetic acid and there would be 1 gram of sodium hydroxide left over. What if you reacted 666 g of sodium hydroxide with 1001 g of acetic acid? There would be enough acetic acid to react will all of the sodium hydroxide and there would be 1 gram of acetic acid left over. When two reactants are not in perfect balance, the mole police don't arrest them. One of the reactants is simply left over when the reaction is complete. This will have important consequences when we turn our attention to soap in Chapter 12. For now, let's consider another example.

Consider the reaction of potassium hydroxide with citric acid. As in the previous example, the base reacts with the acid to produce a salt and water. The major difference is that citric acid is a tri-protic acid, and as such, it may react with one, two, or three molecules of base. Let's take as our example the reaction with three molecules of KOH:

$$3 \text{ KOH} + \text{H}_3\text{C}_6\text{H}_5\text{O}_7 = \text{K}_3\text{C}_6\text{H}_5\text{O}_7 + 3 \text{ H}_2\text{O}$$
$$3 \text{ KOH} + \text{H}_3\text{Cit} = \text{K}_3\text{Cit} + 3 \text{ H}_2\text{O}$$

The stoichiometry is similar to the acetic acid example except that the molecular weight of KOH is higher than that of NaOH, the molecular weight of citric acid is higher than that of acetic acid, and (from the balanced equation) there are 3 moles of KOH per mole of citric acid. We ask the stoichiometric question, "How many grams of potassium hydroxide are needed to react completely with 1000 grams of citric acid?"

$$? \text{ g KOH} = 1000 \text{ } g\text{ } H_3Cit\left(\frac{1 \text{ } mol \text{ } H_3Cit}{192.12 \text{ } g \text{ } H_3Cit}\right)$$
$$\left(\frac{3 \text{ } mol \text{ } KOH}{1 \text{ } mol \text{ } H_3Cit}\right)\left(\frac{56.11 \text{ g KOH}}{1 \text{ } mol \text{ } KOH}\right)$$
$$= 876 \text{ g KOH}$$

876 g of KOH will react with 1000 g of citric acid. If you add 877 g of KOH to 1000 g of citric acid, all of the citric acid will react and there will be 1 gram of KOH left over. What will happen if you add 876 g of KOH to 1001 g of citric acid? You might

expect to have 1 gram of citric acid left over, but the situation is more complicated than that. Indeed, all of the KOH will react, but you will wind up with a mixture of K_3Cit, K_2HCit, and KH_2Cit. These salts result from the reaction of three, two, and one moles of KOH with citric acid, respectively. The details need not concern us at this point.

We can also answer stoichiometric questions about solutions. Consider the question, "How many grams of 10 ppt potassium hydroxide are needed to react completely with 1000 grams of 5 ppt citric acid?"

$$? \text{ g base} = 1000 \text{ g acid} \left(\frac{5 \text{ g } H_3Cit}{1000 \text{ g acid}} \right) \left(\frac{1 \text{ mol } H_3Cit}{192.12 \text{ g } H_3Cit} \right)$$
$$\left(\frac{3 \text{ mol } KOH}{1 \text{ mol } H_3Cit} \right) \left(\frac{56.11 \text{ g } KOH}{1 \text{ mol } KOH} \right) \left(\frac{1000 \text{ g base}}{10 \text{ g } KOH} \right)$$
$$= 438 \text{ g base}$$

Here we have used the generic term *base* for the alkaline solution and the generic term *acid* for the acidic one. Compared to the previous stoichiometric question, the solution to this one involves two more hotdogs: (5 g H_3Cit/1000 g acid) represents the concentration of the acid solution and (1000 g base/10 g KOH) represents the concentration of the base.

We are now prepared to answer any stoichiometric question. In the next section, we apply this skill to questions involving pH.

 Rather than go around saying, "the numbers in front of each participant in a balanced chemical equation," chemists have adopted the much shorter term ***stoichiometric coefficient***. Trot out this term at a cocktail party and every chemist present will recognize you as the genuine article. In the reaction of potassium hydroxide with citric acid, the stoichiometric coefficient of KOH is 3.

9.3 pH

We introduced the pH scale in Section 8.7 (page 160). Pure water has a pH of 7; acidic solutions have a pH below 7 and alkaline solutions a pH above 7. The mathematics of pH is relatively straightforward for dilute solutions of strong acids and bases. As soapmakers, we are most familiar with the strong bases NaOH and KOH.

Let us begin with a 1 ppt solution of NaOH in water. We ask the simple stoichiometric question, "How many moles of OH^- are in 1 liter of such a solution?" We use the fact that 1 liter of a dilute aqueous solution weighs approximately 1000 g. Since the concentration is 1 ppt, 1000 g of this solution contains 1 g of NaOH. From Table 9-2 (page 165) we know that 1 mole of NaOH weighs 40.00 g. From Section 8.3 (page 152) we know that 1 mole of NaOH produces 1 mole of OH^-. Putting these all together, we have:

$$? \text{ mol OH}^- = 1 \, L \left(\frac{1000 \, g \, soln}{1 \, L} \right) \left(\frac{1 \, g \, NaOH}{1000 \, g \, soln} \right) \left(\frac{1 \, mol \, NaOH}{40.00 \, g \, NaOH} \right)$$
$$\left(\frac{1 \text{ mol OH}^-}{1 \, mol \, NaOH} \right)$$
$$= 0.025 \text{ mol OH}^-$$

While we have used parts per thousand as a unit of concentration, chemists more frequently use moles per liter. This is referred to as the ***molarity.*** We would say that a 1 ppt solution of NaOH has a molarity of 0.025. We could also refer to it as 0.025 molar NaOH, or 0.025 M NaOH. A chemist might also write *[NaOH] = 0.025 M,* the square brackets denoting the molarity of the substance within.

The pH and pOH scales are logarithmic—they count powers of ten of the hydronium and hydroxide molarities, respectively. We calculate pOH as the negative logarithm of the hydroxide molarity:

$$\text{pOH} = -log([OH^-]) = -log(0.025) = 1.60$$

And finally, the pH is simply 14 minus the pOH:
$$\text{pH} = -log([H^+]) = 14.00 - 1.60 = 12.40$$

For more dilute solutions, we recognize that for each dilution by a factor of 10, we move one step down the pH scale. The pH and pOH of dilute NaOH solutions are shown in Table 9-3.

Hydrochloric acid, HCl, is an example of a strong acid with a molecular weight of 36.46 g/mol. A 1 ppt solution of HCl has a molarity of 0.0274 M. Since HCl is a strong acid, each mole

Table 9-3. Dilute NaOH and HCl

ppt NaOH	[OH$^-$]	pOH	pH
1.	0.0250	1.60	12.40
0.1	0.00250	2.60	11.40
0.01	0.000250	3.60	10.40
0.001	0.0000250	4.60	9.40
0.0001	0.00000250	5.60	8.40
0.00001	0.000000250	6.60	7.40

ppt HCl	[H$^+$]	pOH	pH
0.00001	0.000000274	7.44	6.56
0.0001	0.00000274	8.44	5.56
0.001	0.0000274	9.44	4.56
0.01	0.000274	10.44	3.56
0.1	0.00274	11.44	2.56
1.	0.0274	12.44	1.56

of HCl ionizes into one mole of H$^+$ and one mole of Cl$^-$. The pH and pOH for dilute HCl solutions are shown in the bottom half of Table 9-3.

For solutions more dilute than those in Table 9-3, more ions come from the ionization of water itself than from the dissolved acids or bases. Recall from Section 7.3 (page 132) that in pure water, the number of H$^+$ ions equals the number of OH$^-$ ions. Consequently, pH equals pOH. Since the sum of pH and pOH is 14, it follows that the pH (and pOH) of pure water must be exactly 7. Thus, the pH of pure water falls between those of the most dilute solutions of Table 9-3.

9.4 The 5 ppt KOH (Green) Standard

In Section 8.4.1 (page 155) we made up a KOH solution with a concentration of approximately 5 ppt. While we do not yet know the exact concentration of this solution, we are quite certain of the concentration of the 5 ppt citric acid standard described in Section 8.2.4 (page 149). In this procedure we'll *standardize* the

KOH solution with our primary citric acid standard by *titrating* it with the standard. In an acid/base **titration,** an acid is added to a known quantity of base (or *vice versa*) until the moles of proton donated by the acid equals the moles of hydroxide donated by the base. In practice, an **indicator** such as phenolphthalein is used to detect the **endpoint**—the point at which the indicator changes color. To set up this experiment, we can ask the stoichiometric question, "How many grams of 5 ppt citric acid are equivalent to 10.00 g of 5 ppt potassium hydroxide?"

$$? \text{ g acid} = 10.00 \, g \, base \left(\frac{5 \, g \, KOH}{1000 \, g \, base} \right) \left(\frac{1 \, mol \, KOH}{56.11 \, g \, KOH} \right)$$
$$\left(\frac{1 \, mol \, H_3Cit}{3 \, mol \, KOH} \right) \left(\frac{192.12 \, g \, H_3Cit}{1 \, mol \, H_3Cit} \right) \left(\frac{1000 \text{ g acid}}{5 \, g \, H_3Cit} \right)$$
$$= 11.41 \text{ g acid}$$

If we used pure potassium hydroxide and pure citric acid to make up 5 ppt solutions, we would expect a titration of 10.00 g of 5 ppt KOH to reach the endpoint after 11.41 g of 5 ppt citric acid had been added. In practice, we expect the number to be somewhat smaller than this because of the water contained in the KOH used to make the solution. The actual concentration may be determined using the following procedure.

1. *Gather your materials:*
    - Goggles or glasses
    - An eyewash bottle
    - Gloves
    - A centigram balance
    - Distilled water
    - A filled 125 mL dispensing bottle labeled `5 ppt KOH` `(Green)`
    - A filled 125 mL dispensing bottle labeled `5 ppt H₃Cit` `(Yellow)`
    - 1% phenolphthalein solution
    - Three 125 mL Erlenmeyer flasks labeled `A`, `B`, and `C`
    - Your soapmaking notebook and a pen

2. *Arrange your workspace:* Put on your safety glasses and gloves.

3. *Add water to the flasks:* Add approximately 50 mL of distilled water to each of the three flasks. The exact amount of

water used is not important. You may use the graduations on the sides of the flasks to measure this water.

4. *Add the phenolphthalein solution:* Add 5 or 6 drops of 1% phenolphthalein solution to each of the flasks. The exact amount of indicator is not important as long as there is enough to give a definite color change.

5. *Weigh the base: Analytically* weigh 10.XX g of base from the `5 ppt KOH (Green)` bottle to flask A using the procedure of Section 8.2.2 (page 146). It is not important to hit the target weight exactly, but you must record *all four digits* of the weight in your notebook.

    Repeat the step with flasks B and C. Make clear in your notebook which weight belongs to each flask. Swirl the flasks to mix their contents.[2] Their color should be bright pink.

6. *Titrate flask A:* Place the `5 ppt H₃Cit (Yellow)` bottle onto the balance and press the tare button. Transfer about 8 g of acid to flask A and give it a gentle swirl to mix the acid with the base. The solution should remain pink. Transfer another gram of acid to the flask and give it another swirl. Continue adding acid to the flask, swirling the flask after each addition, until the solution suddenly changes from pink to colorless. In this first titration, we have gone past the endpoint—but at least we have an idea of how far is too far. In the next two titrations we'll be more careful.

7. *Titrate flasks B and C:* Place the `5 ppt H₃Cit (Yellow)` bottle onto the balance and press the tare button. Titrate flask B as before, but this time, when you get to within about 1 g of the endpoint, add acid to the flask one drop at a time. Drop, swirl, drop, swirl. The pink color will fade as you approach the endpoint. When the last trace of color is gone, return the `Acid` bottle to the balance and record the weight, YY.YY g, in your notebook. Then proceed to titrate flask C in the same way.

8. *Cleanup:* Acid spills may be cleaned up with household ammonia. Alkaline spills may be cleaned up with household

---

2. The Erlenmeyer flask is designed to be swirled rather than stirred or shaken. Hold the flask by its neck and gently rotate your wrist to swirl the solution in the flask.

Equation 9-1. Calculating KOH Concentration

$$? \text{ g KOH} = 1000 \, \cancel{g \ base}\left(\frac{\text{YY.YY} \, \cancel{g \ acid}}{10.\text{XX} \, \cancel{g \ base}}\right)\left(\frac{5 \, \cancel{g \ H_3Cit}}{1000 \, \cancel{g \ acid}}\right)$$

$$\left(\frac{1 \, \cancel{mol \ H_3Cit}}{192.12 \, \cancel{g \ H_3Cit}}\right)\left(\frac{3 \, \cancel{mol \ KOH}}{1 \, \cancel{mol \ H_3Cit}}\right)\left(\frac{56.11 \text{ g KOH}}{1 \, \cancel{mol \ KOH}}\right)$$

$$C_{\text{KOH}} = 4.381 \left(\frac{\text{YY.YY}}{10.\text{XX}}\right) \text{ppt KOH}$$

In these equations, 10.XX is from step 5 and YY.YY from step 7.

---

vinegar. Wipe down your balance and bring your notebook up to date.

9. *Calculate the lye concentration:* Two numbers are needed to calculate the lye concentration: the weight of the base, 10.XX g, and the weight of the acid needed to titrate that base, YY.YY. Equation 9-1 details the calculation for turning these two numbers into the lye concentration in ppt. Calculate the concentration twice—once for flask B and again for flask C. Replace "5 ppt" on the label of the 5 ppt KOH (Green) bottle with the average of these two values.

The titration of flask A was intended simply to give us a heads-up for flasks B and C. Knowing the approximate amount of acid required allows us to add a few large squirts to get in the vicinity of the endpoint, and then to sneak up on the endpoint one drop at a time. We do two careful titrations so that we have some idea of how precise the results are. If they are within about 0.05 ppt of one another, your technique is pretty good. If they differ by more than that, you could use some more practice.

 You must relabel your "5 ppt" KOH solution with its actual concentration if you are to get accurate results later on. When it comes time to make up more KOH standard, you need not rinse the bottle, but you must standardize it again to get the new concentration.

Practice Problems

Answers to practice problems appear in Appendix A (page 335).

1. How many grams of citric acid are needed to react completely with 10 grams of sodium hydroxide?

2. When 10 grams of sodium hydroxide react with excess citric acid, how many grams of sodium citrate are produced?

3. How many grams of sodium citrate can be produced from 10 grams of sodium hydroxide and excess citric acid?

4. How many grams of sodium hydroxide are needed to react completely with 10 grams of citric acid? How many grams of water would be produced?

5. How many grams of 50 ppt ammonium hydroxide are needed to react completely with 10 grams of citric acid?

6. How many grams of 500 ppt sodium hydroxide are needed to react completely with 100 grams of 50 ppt acetic acid?

7. How many grams of 5 ppt potassium hydroxide are needed to react completely with 1000 grams of 1 ppt citric acid?

8. What is the pH of a 5 ppt solution of potassium hydroxide in water?

9. Nitric acid is a strong acid with a molecular weight of 63.01 g/mol. What is the molarity of a 1 ppt solution of HNO_3 in water? What is its pH?

10. When 10 grams of 50 ppt sodium hydroxide reacts with 10 grams of 50 ppt acetic acid, is the resulting solution acidic or alkaline?

Example 9-1. Using Equation 9-1 to Calculate KOH Concentration

I wanted to determine the actual concentration of my 5 ppt KOH solution from Section 8.4.1. I added 50 mL of distilled water and 5 or 6 drops of 1% phenolphthalein indicator to each of three Erlenmeyer flasks labeled A, B, and C. I then analytically weighed about 10 g of 5 ppt KOH (base) into each flask. I quickly titrated flask A to get a rough idea of where the endpoint would fall. I then carefully titrated flask B, but accidentally overshot the endpoint for flask C. I rinsed out flask A and performed another careful titration, hitting the endpoint to within 1 drop. I collected the following data for this experiment and used Equation 9-1 to calculate the concentrations for the two successful titrations.

Flask	Base (g)	Acid (g)	Endpoint	Concentration (ppt)
A	10.15	10.90	over	
B	10.39	9.93	yes	4.187
C	10.43	10.23	over	
A	10.23	9.76	yes	4.180

I averaged the two concentrations:

½(4.187 + 4.180) = 4.184 ppt.

Half of the difference between the two values gave me the uncertainty in the measurement:

½(4.187 - 4.180) = ±0.004 ppt.

It would appear that I can trust the first three digits of my concentration and that there is some uncertainty in the fourth. But the concentration of this standard can be no more precise than the acid standard used to standardize it. Since the acid concentration was 5.00±0.01 ppt, I relabeled my "5 ppt KOH" solution as 4.18 ppt KOH.

The entire procedure, including the fourth titration, took 47 minutes.

Chapter 10

Fatty Acids

*T*HERE is nothing more important to the science of soapmaking than a thorough understanding of the *fatty acids.* Their molecular structures hold the key to understanding why they are fatty, why they are acidic, and why their sodium and potassium salts are soapy. The simplest of them, acetic acid, we have seen in Chapter 8. Though more acidic than fatty, a brief demonstration with acetic acid will shed a great deal of light on the fundamental chemistry of soap.

10.1 Salts and Solubility

Acetic acid is the principle acidic ingredient in vinegar, which is about 5% acetic acid in water. Because acetic acid has only two carbon atoms, its molecular weight is less than that of any of the fatty acids. The low molecular weight makes acetic acid more *volatile,* than the heavier acids.[1] Because acetic acid is volatile, the vapor above vinegar will have a significant concentration of acetic acid molecules, and if you sniff this vapor, your nose will collect a lot of them. There they will dissolve in the fluids that bathe your nasal cavities, the fluids will become acidic, and you will experience the pungent, sour aroma that we all associate with vinegar. In short, acetic acid is smelly because it is a small, volatile, acidic molecule.

We can see this in action with a very brief demonstration. You will need a vial containing about 10 g of vinegar, some 500 ppt NaOH, and a pipet. Smell the vinegar and re-familiarize yourself with its aroma. Add a drop of lye, screw the cap onto the vial, and give it a couple of shakes. Remove the cap,

---

1. Chemists endow the word *volatile* with a very specific meaning: A volatile substance is simply one that evaporates easily—nothing more, nothing less.

and sniff again. Continue this process, adding drop after drop
of lye, and observe two things about the vial. First, note that
the vinegar gets warm as the acid and base react. Second, note
that the characteristic smell of vinegar becomes fainter with
each drop of lye. Why is this so?

The reaction taking place is one we have seen in Chapter 9:

$$NaOH + HC_2H_3O_2 = NaC_2H_3O_2 + H_2O$$
$$NaOH + HAce = NaAce + H_2O$$

The product, sodium acetate, is more soluble in water than its
conjugate acid, acetic acid. Because it is more soluble, more of it
remains in the water and less of it hovers in the vapor above the
solution. Because there is less of it in the vapor, fewer molecules
get up your nose. If you could smell them, they would smell
alkaline, like ammonia, rather than acidic, like acetic acid. But
the fact of the matter is that the solution you are holding does
not smell like ammonia—it is odorless. It is odorless precisely
because so few molecules make it into the vapor, and this is so
because sodium acetate is extremely soluble in water.

The previous reaction is entirely reversible. To continue the
demonstration you will need some 500 ppt citric acid solution.[2]
Remove the cap from the vial formerly containing vinegar and
add a drop of citric acid solution. Replace the cap, give it a couple of shakes, remove the cap, and give the solution a sniff. Repeat this process, drop by drop, until the characteristic smell of
vinegar has been restored. The reaction taking place is:

$$H_3C_6H_5O_7 + 3\ NaC_2H_3O_2 = 3\ HC_2H_3O_2 + Na_3C_6H_5O_7$$
$$H_3Cit + 3\ NaAce = 3\ HAce + Na_3Cit$$

You must take away three important lessons from this demonstration if you are to understand the rest of the chapter. First,
a base reacts with an acid to produce a salt. Sodium hydroxide

---

2. Note that this solution is also odorless. If you were to snort this
solution, it would be every bit as jarring to your olfactory senses as
vinegar is. But citric acid is a heavier and, consequently, less volatile
molecule than acetic acid. It is also more soluble in water than acetic
acid. Hence most of the citric acid molecules remain in the solution and
few of them venture into the vapor above. When you sniff this vapor,
you smell nothing because none of the acid has escaped the solution.

reacts with acetic acid to produce the salt sodium acetate. Second, the sodium salt of a weak acid is more soluble in water than the acid itself. Sodium acetate is more soluble than acetic acid. Your nose tells you this because the sodium acetate solution is odorless. Finally, a stronger acid reacts with the sodium salt of a weaker one to liberate the weaker acid. Citric acid reacts with sodium acetate to reproduce the original acetic acid.

A base reacts with an acid to produce a salt.

The sodium salt of a weak acid is more soluble in water than the acid itself.

A stronger acid reacts with the sodium salt of a weaker one to liberate the weaker acid.

In the previous demonstration, we smelled the conversion of acetic acid to sodium acetate and back again. We now turn our noses to the volatile base ammonia.[3] For this demonstration, you will need a vial containing about 10 g of clear household ammonia,[4] some 500 ppt citric acid, and a pipet. Smell the ammonia and re-familiarize yourself with its aroma. Add a drop of citric acid, screw the cap onto the vial, and give it a couple of shakes. Remove the cap, and sniff again. Continue this process, adding drop after drop of citric acid, and observe two things about the vial. First, note that the ammonia gets warm as the acid and base react. Second, note that the characteristic smell of ammonia becomes fainter with each drop of citric acid. The reaction taking place is:

$$H_3C_6H_5O_7 + 3\,NH_3 = (NH_4)_3C_6H_5O_7$$
$$H_3Cit + 3\,NH_3 = (NH_4)_3Cit$$

The product, ammonium citrate, is more soluble in water than its conjugate base ammonia. Because it is more soluble, more of it remains in the water and less of it hovers in the vapor above the solution. Because there is less of it in the vapor, fewer molecules get up your nose. If you could smell them, they would

---

3.   Ammonia is so volatile that it is a gas at room temperature. While ammonia gas becomes liquid at low temperature or high pressure, the "ammonia" you buy at the grocery store is actually a solution of ammonia gas in water.

4.   Some kinds of household ammonia contain soap. *Clear* household ammonia contains only ammonia and water.

smell acidic, like vinegar, rather than alkaline, like ammonia. But the fact of the matter is that the solution you are holding does not smell like either—it is odorless. It is odorless precisely because so few molecules make it into the vapor, and this is so because ammonium citrate is extremely soluble in water.

As in the case of sodium acetate, odorless ammonium citrate may be converted back into ammonia. To continue the demonstration you will need some 500 ppt NaOH, which is also odorless. Remove the cap from the vial formerly containing ammonia and add a drop of lye. Replace the cap, give it a couple of shakes, remove the cap, and give the solution a sniff. Repeat this process, drop by drop, until the characteristic smell of ammonia has been restored. The reaction taking place is:

$$(NH_4)_3C_6H_5O_7 + 3\,NaOH = Na_3C_2H_3O_2 + 3\,NH_3 + 3\,H_2O$$

$$(NH_4)_3Cit + 3\,NaOH = Na_3Cit + 3\,NH_3 + 3\,H_2O$$

Two more lessons come from this demonstration. First, the citrate salt of a weak base is more soluble in water than the base itself. Ammonium citrate is more soluble than ammonia. Your nose tells you this because the ammonium citrate solution is odorless. Second, a stronger base reacts with the salt of a weaker one to liberate the weaker base. Sodium hydroxide reacts with ammonium citrate to reproduce the original ammonia.

The citrate salt of a weak base is more soluble in water than the base itself.

A stronger base reacts with the salt of a weaker one to liberate the weaker base.

We now have a volatile acid, acetic acid, and a volatile base, ammonia. Instead of using an indicator like phenolphthalein, we can follow reactions involving these compounds by smelling the solutions. An acidic solution containing acetic acid will smell like vinegar. An alkaline solution containing ammonia will smell like ammonia. We can thus use our sense of smell to isolate fatty acids from soaps.

10.2 Preparation of Oleic Acid

In this section, we'll perform an experiment to produce oleic acid. Every experiment is designed to answer a question, and the question in this case is simply, "What is a fatty acid like?" It isn't a very sophisticated question (and you won't be using the product for anything later on), but it will help you to understand the difference between a fat and a fatty acid and will provide a concrete example upon which to hang all of the technical equations and formulas to come later in this chapter.

To prepare a fatty acid, we apply the lessons of the previous section. In this procedure, we'll add a stronger acid, acetic acid, to the sodium salt of a weaker one, sodium oleate. The oleic acid liberated will float to the surface as an oily substance. It might, in fact, pass itself off as an oil, but its chemistry is very different from that of the olive oil from whence it came. Unlike olive oil, oleic acid reacts immediately with any base, strong or weak, concentrated or dilute.

A chemist would normally determine the endpoint of an acid/base reaction by using an indicator that changes color in a specific pH range. For example, in Section 9.4 (page 169) we used phenolphthalein as an indicator to perform a titration to standardize our KOH solution. However, this experiment will require a different indicator because we will encounter a different pH range. As we have seen, acetic acid and ammonia have pungent odors while their salts have none at all, so we will use the smell of the reagents as an indicator.

 Two kinds of household ammonia are commonly available in grocery stores. One contains soap and the other doesn't. For this demonstration you want the kind that doesn't. This is generally called *clear* ammonia, and you will know that it is the right stuff if *no suds form* when the bottle is shaken.

1. *Gather your materials:*
   - Goggles or glasses
   - An eyewash bottle
   - Gloves
   - A gram balance
   - A plastic weighing cup

- Vinegar
- *Clear* household ammonia
- Olive oil soap
- Olive oil
- Distilled water
- Four pipets labeled `Vinegar`, `Ammonia`, `Oleic Acid`, and `Olive Oil`
- A clean, dry 500 mL PP bottle labeled `Soap`, with lid
- Three clean, dry 30 mL glass vials with caps
- A soap oven and oven mitts
- Your soapmaking notebook and a pen

2. *Arrange your workspace:* As usual, you should wear safety goggles or glasses for eye protection. Your notebook should be opened to a new page with your pen at the ready.

3. *Preheat your oven:* Preheat your oven to 200°F or 95°C.

4. *Weigh the soap:* Shave about 10 g of olive oil soap into a plastic weighing cup and pour this into the `Soap` bottle.

5. *Dissolve the soap:* Add distilled water to the `Soap` bottle until it is about half full. Place the bottle into the soap oven, place the lid on the bottle, but do not screw it down tight. Leave it in the oven for one hour. Go fly a kite, read a book, smell a flower. "A watched soap never dissolves." After an hour, the soap should be completely dissolved. If it is not, gently swirl it around and place it back into the oven until the soap completely dissolves. Remove the soap from the oven and allow it to cool to room temperature.

6. *Add vinegar:* The soap solution should not have a strong smell at this point, and this is worth noting in your notebook. Use the `Vinegar` pipet to transfer a pipet-full of vinegar into the bottle. Gently swirl the soap solution to mix in the vinegar. Sniff the contents of the bottle and note the smell (or lack thereof) in your notebook.

7. *Add more vinegar:* Continue adding vinegar until the solution in the bottle smells strongly of vinegar. The solution will have become cloudy as the stronger acid (acetic acid) liberates the weaker acid (oleic acid) from its salt (sodium oleate, soap). The reaction is complete when there is an excess of acetic acid; you will know this from the smell.

8. *Refrigerate:* Screw the lid onto the Soap bottle and place it into a refrigerator for an hour. The oleic acid will solidify into a waxy solid.

9. *Remove the oleic acid:* Remove the lid from the Soap bottle and use a spoon to collect the solid oleic acid. Place it on a paper towel and allow any excess moisture to drain. Place the oleic acid into a labeled vial and allow it to melt back into a liquid.

10. *Compare oleic acid to olive oil:* Add 10 g of household ammonia to each of two vials labeled Oleic Acid and Olive Oil. Using separate labeled pipets, transfer a drop of oleic acid to the Oleic Acid vial and a drop of olive oil to the Olive Oil vial. Screw the caps onto the vials and give them a quick shake. Note in your notebook whether either of them or both of them dissolve in the ammonia. Continue adding oleic acid and olive oil, drop by drop, until the aroma of ammonia disappears from one of the vials. Which vial do you expect to become odorless? Why? You should also notice a remarkable difference between the two vials as they are shaken. Your discussion is worth at least a paragraph in your notebook.

11. *Cleanup:* Acid spills may be cleaned up with household ammonia. Alkaline spills may be cleaned up with household vinegar. Wipe down your balance and bring your notebook up to date.

Never heat a sealed container! When heating soap in the oven, place the lid on the container but do not screw it on tight. A sealed container may explode if the contents overheat.

By the end of this experiment, you will have direct experience with *two* new substances: oleic acid and ammonium oleate. Oleic acid is an oily liquid that is insoluble in water. While olive oil and oleic acid may appear to be similar, olive oil reacts slowly with strong alkalis at elevated temperatures, while oleic acid reacts immediately with weak alkalis at room temperature. The reaction of either olive oil or oleic acid with sodium hydroxide would produce the soap sodium oleate. The reaction with potassium hydroxide would produce potassium oleate. But in this experiment the soap produced was ammonium oleate—one that few makers of handcrafted soap will ever see. Ammonium oleate finds use as a rabbit and deer repellent applied to crops. While this particular soap is unlikely to find a niche among makers of handcrafted soap, it illustrates that a variety of different soaps may be produced by reacting a fatty acid with a variety of alkalis.

Of all the alkalis that might be used to make soap, only three classes of alkalis will produce soaps that are soluble in water. Sodium soaps may be produced by reacting a fatty acid with either sodium hydroxide or sodium carbonate. Potassium soaps may be produced by reacting a fatty acid with potassium hydroxide or potassium carbonate, and ammonium soaps may be produced by doing the same with ammonia. Of these soaps, the sodium soaps are least soluble, the potassium soaps more soluble, and ammonium soaps the most soluble. Reaction of soluble soaps with any other soluble metal compounds will produce insoluble soaps. Calcium salts in hard water, for example, react with soluble soaps to produce insoluble calcium soaps, which we recognize as soap scum. While insoluble soaps are useless as detergents, they find many applications as lubricants. Nevertheless, sodium and potassium soaps are the only ones of interest to the handcrafted soap community.

Fatty acids are fatty because, like fats and oils, they are insoluble in water. Fatty acids are acidic because, like acetic and citric acids, they react with bases to produce salts. The salts of fatty acids are called *soaps,* and the only soaps soluble in water are the sodium, potassium, and ammonium salts of fatty acids.

10.3 The Structure of Fatty Acids

Now that you have some familiarity with the properties of fatty acids and their salts, it is time to understand how the structures of these molecules result in their observed properties. Figure 10-1 shows the structure of stearic acid, which takes its name from the Greek word for beef fat or tallow. The two ends of the molecule are polar opposites, literally. As you can see, the right end of the molecule is non-polar, hydrophobic, or to use a more familiar term, *greasy*. It is comparable to the structure of hexadecane from Figure 7-2 (page 129). The left end of

Figure 10-1. Stearic Acid

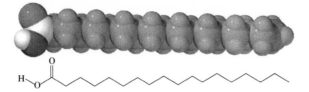

the molecule is polar, hydrophilic, or to use the more familiar term, *watery*. It is comparable to the structure of acetic acid from Figure 8-1 (page 140). It is as if an acetic acid molecule had been glued onto one end of a hexadecane molecule. The structural formula beneath the model shows the long, greasy hydrocarbon tail to the right and the characteristic carboxylic acid group (-COOH) to the left.[5] If you count the kinks in the chain, you should be able to determine that stearic acid contains 18 carbon atoms, two oxygen atoms, and a proton (that is, a polar hydrogen atom bonded directly to an oxygen atom).

Figure 10-2 shows the structural formulas for the **saturated** fatty acids of interest to soapmakers. Lauric and myristic acids come primarily from coconut and palm kernel oils, palmitic and stearic acids from palm oil and tallow. Their systematic names, dodecanoic acid, tetradecanoic acid, hexadecanoic acid, and octadecanoic acid, simply count the 12, 14, 16, and 18 carbon atoms in these molecules. Each carbon atom shares four bonds. For the sake of simplicity, bonds that are not shown are assumed to be filled by hydrogen atoms. The interior kinks in the chain are shown with two explicit bonds to neighboring carbon atoms, so they each must have implicit bonds to two hydrogen atoms. The terminal carbon atom at the acid end (the alpha carbon) has four bonds explicitly shown: two to one oxygen, one to the other oxygen, and one to the beta carbon next door. The terminal carbon at the greasy end (the omega carbon) has only one bond shown explicitly and must consequently share bonds with three hydrogen atoms. The oxygen atoms always share two bonds. One is double-bonded to the alpha carbon and the other has one bond to the alpha carbon and

---

5. Now that you know what to look for, can you spot the carboxylic acid groups in Figure 8-1 (page 140) and Figure 8-3 (page 143)? The formula for acetic acid is sometimes written CH_3COOH.

Figure 10-2. Four Saturated Fatty Acids

lauric acid

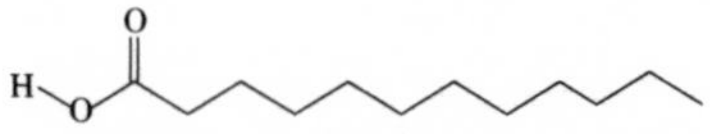

200.32 g/mol   dodecanoic acid, $C_{11}H_{23}COOH$

myristic acid

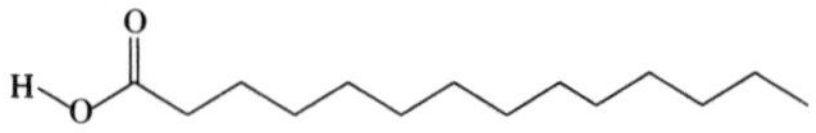

228.42 g/mol   tetradecanoic acid, $C_{13}H_{27}COOH$

palmitic acid

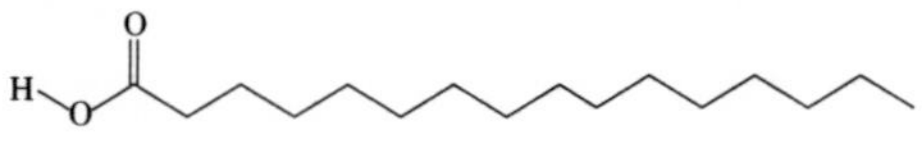

256.42 g/mol   hexadecanoic acid, $C_{15}H_{31}COOH$

stearic acid

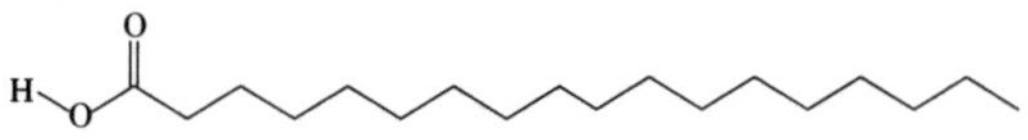

284.48 g/mol   octadecanoic acid, $C_{17}H_{35}COOH$

the other to the acidic proton. Take a moment now to examine the structural formulas—count the carbon, oxygen, and particularly the hydrogen atoms for comparison with the formulas beneath each one.

The water solubility of the acids depends on the number of carbon atoms in the chain. If we were to look to the progenitor of the fatty acids, acetic acid, we would find that it is very soluble in water and not very greasy. Butanoic acid, the four-carbon acid, would be less soluble but still not very greasy. Hexanoic, octanoic, and decanoic acids would become progressively less soluble and more greasy. In lauric, myristic, palmitic, and stearic acids we find that the hydrocarbon tails are so long that the greasiness of the carbon chain outweighs the wateriness of the acid group. These acids are quite fatty and nearly insoluble in water.

All soap relies on a chemical trick to get these fatty acids into solution. As we saw with acetic and oleic acids, the reaction of a fatty acid with a sodium, potassium, or ammonium alkali produces a salt: a soap that is more or less soluble in water. While the alkali soaps are far more soluble in water than their conjugate fatty acids, the solubility does decrease as the

Figure 10-3. Oleic Acid

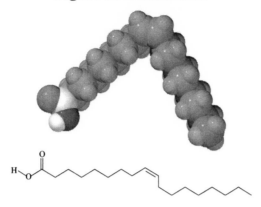

length of the chain increases. Thus we find sodium laurate to be more soluble than sodium myristate, sodium palmitate, or sodium stearate. This is why the lauric soaps derived from coconut and palm kernel oils produce a quick lather while those derived from palm oil or tallow might take a little while to build a lather.

We also find that ammonium laurate is more soluble than potassium laurate or sodium laurate. The most soluble of these soaps would be ammonium laurate and the least would be sodium stearate. Ammonium laurate might, in fact, be useful as a shampoo were it not for the expense of using NaOH to produce the sodium soap, citric acid to liberate the fatty acid, and ammonia to convert the fatty acid back into a soap. The relatively low solubility of stearic acid results in hard soaps that last longer than their more soluble siblings.

Figure 10-3 shows the structure of oleic acid. It is identical to stearic acid except for two missing hydrogen atoms in the middle of the molecule. These missing atoms lead us to classify oleic acid as an ***unsaturated*** fatty acid, since it has fewer than the maximum possible number of hydrogen atoms. Since each carbon atom shares four bonds, and since two of the carbon atoms in the middle are missing hydrogen atoms, these two carbons share a ***double bond.*** The geometry of the double bond is more rigid than that of the single bond, which produces a bend in the carbon chain. This bend and the chemistry of the double

Figure 10-4. Four Unsaturated Fatty Acids

oleic acid

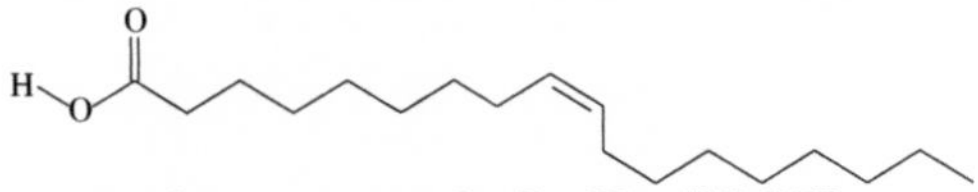

282.46 g/mol   9-octadecenoic acid, $C_{17}H_{33}COOH$

ricinoleic acid

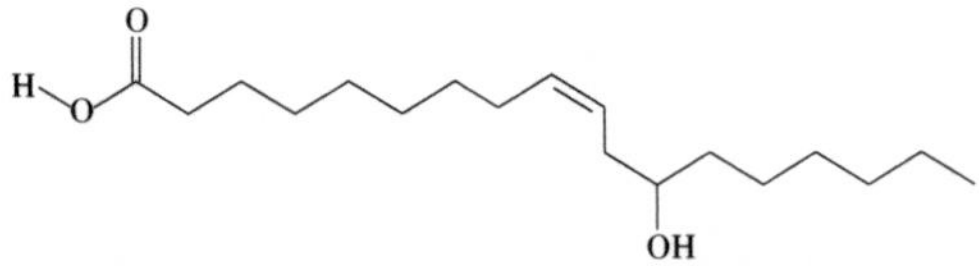

298.45 g/mol   12-hydroxy-9-octadecenoic acid, $C_{17}H_{33}OHCOOH$

linoleic acid

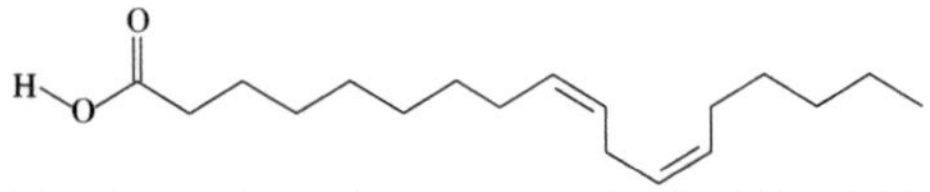

280.46   9,12-octadecadienoic acid, $C_{17}H_{31}COOH$

linolenic acid

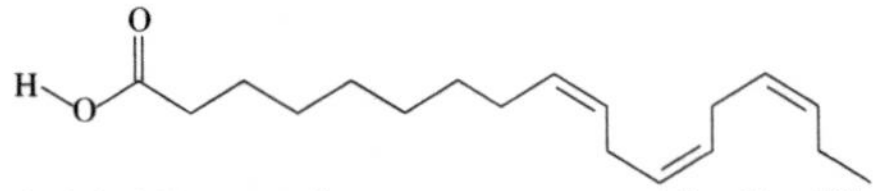

278.44 g/mol   9,12,15-octadecatrienoic acid, $C_{17}H_{29}COOH$

bond is responsible for all of the differences between the saturated and unsaturated fatty acids.

Figure 10-4 shows structural formulas for the unsaturated
fatty acids of primary interest to the soapmaker. All of them
contain 18 carbon atoms and may be viewed as variations on the
stearic acid structure. Soaps derived from these acids tend to be
softer than sodium stearate because the bend in the chain does
not allow them to crystallize compactly. While these soaps are
prized by soapmakers, they are susceptible to discoloration due
to oxidation of the double bonds. This discoloration is known
(not affectionately) among soapmakers as the *dreaded orange
spots,* a topic that will receive much attention in Chapter 19.

Because their carbon chains are 18 carbons long, the unsaturated acids and their soaps are less soluble in water than lauric
acid, myristic acid, palmitic acid, and their soaps. These unsaturated soaps can therefore be expected to lather relatively slowly
compared to the lauric, myristic, and palmitic soaps. An important exception is ricinoleic acid, the principle fatty acid derived

Table 10-1. Abbreviations for Fatty Acids and Soaps

	Fatty Acids		Sodium Soaps	
C12:0	Lauric	HLau	Sodium Laurate	NaLau
C14:0	Myristic	HMyr	Sodium Myristate	NaMyr
C16:0	Palmitic	HPlm	Sodium Palmitate	NaPlm
C18:0	Stearic	HStr	Sodium Stearate	NaStr
C18:1	Oleic	HOle	Sodium Oleate	NaOle
C18:2	Linoleic	HLin	Sodium Linoleate	NaLin
C18:3	Linolenic	HLnn	Sodium Linolenate	NaLnn
C18:1-OH	Ricinoleic	HRcn	Sodium Ricinoleate	NaRcn

from castor oil. Ricinoleic acid has a polar, hydrophilic, *watery* OH group halfway down the carbon chain that enhances the solubility of the fatty acid and its soap, sodium ricinoleate. A multi-oil blend containing castor oil produces a soap that lathers more quickly than the same blend without it. Because of its expense relative to the other oils, castor oil is usually used as a minor component of an oil blend, but a little bit goes a long way.

In future chapters we'll be doing quite a lot with the fatty acids, and it will be helpful to refer to them with abbreviations rather than their full formulas. Table 10-1 gives abbreviations for the fatty acids and their sodium soaps. The first column gives an abbreviation commonly used among soap chemists; it simply counts the number of carbon atoms and the number of double bonds. From this abbreviation, any chemist can draw the structure of the fatty acid. The third and fifth columns give abbreviations that we may use in balancing equations, much as we have used HAce for acetic acid and H_3Cit for citric acid. This will allow us to balance equations in the future without being distracted by the complexity of the chemical formulas.

Consider, for example, the following stoichiometric question: How many grams of 500 ppt NaOH are required to react completely with 1000 g of myristic acid? The balanced equation is simply:

$$\text{HMyr} + \text{NaOH} = \text{NaMyr} + \text{H}_2\text{O}$$

Myristic acid is C14:0 so we know it has 14 carbon atoms. The first of these carbons, the acidic alpha carbon, is attached to 2 oxygen atoms. The last carbon, the omega carbon, is attached to 3 hydrogen atoms. Since there are no double bonds, the rest of the carbon atoms are attached to 2 hydrogen atoms each. There is one more hydrogen atom, the acidic proton, attached to one of the oxygen atoms. Thus myristic acid contains 14 carbons, 2 oxygens, and 24 + 3 + 1 hydrogens. Using the atomic weights from Table 9-1 (page 164), we find the molecular weight of myristic acid to be 228.42 g HMyr/mol.[6] The rest of the problem is just hotdog manipulation. We know that 1 mol HMyr equals 228.42 g HMyr. From the balanced equation we know that 1 mol NaOH equals 1 mol HMyr. From Table 9-2 (page 165) we know that 1 mol NaOH equals 40.00 g NaOH. We know that for 500 ppt NaOH, 1000 g Lye equals 500 g NaOH. The original question, "How many grams of 500 ppt NaOH are required to react completely with 1000 g of myristic acid?" translates into "g Lye = 1000 g HMry." Putting all of these together we find:

$$? \text{ g Lye} = 1000 \text{ g HMyr}\left(\frac{1 \text{ mol HMyr}}{228.42 \text{ g HMyr}}\right)\left(\frac{1 \text{ mol NaOH}}{1 \text{ mol HMyr}}\right)$$
$$\left(\frac{40.00 \text{ g NaOH}}{1 \text{ mol NaOH}}\right)\left(\frac{1000 \text{ g Lye}}{500 \text{ g NaOH}}\right)$$
$$= 350.2 \text{ g Lye}$$

You now know quite a bit about soaps and fatty acids, but not so much about the fats and oils from which they are produced. Before we can consider the fats and oils, we have two more classes of compounds to discuss—the alcohols and esters.

---

6.   14(12.01) + 2(16.00) + 28(1.01) = 228.42 g HMyr/mol

Practice Problems

Answers to practice problems appear in Appendix A (page 335).

1. Write balanced chemical equations for the following reactions. Stearic acid reacts with sodium hydroxide. Ricinoleic acid reacts with ammonia. Sodium palmitate reacts with acetic acid. Potassium linoleate reacts with citric acid. Oleic acid reacts with acetic acid.

2. Use the balanced equations of the previous problem to answer the following stoichiometric questions: How many grams of sodium hydroxide are required to react completely with 1000 g of stearic acid? How many grams of 500 ppt citric acid are required to react completely with 1000 g of potassium linoleate?

3. Without consulting any of the figures in this chapter, draw structural formulas for the following fatty acids: C14:0, C18:1, C18:2, C18:0-OH.

4. What is the molecular weight of the fatty acid C20:0?

5. What is the molecular weight of the fatty acid C22:1?

6. Draw the structural formula of C22:6. This omega-3 fatty acid has its double bonds at carbon atoms 4, 7, 10, 13, 16, and 19, counting from the alpha carbon. Why do you suppose it is called an omega-3 fatty acid?

7. How many grams of sodium hydroxide are needed to react completely with 1000 grams of palmitic acid?

8. How many grams of 50 ppt acetic acid are needed to convert 1000 grams of sodium stearate into stearic acid?

9. When 10 grams of 10 ppt KPlm are added to 10 grams of 50 ppt HAce, is the resulting solution acidic or alkaline?

10. Suppose that you start with 10 grams of NaOle. You wish to add enough acid to convert half of the NaOle to HOle. How many grams of 50 ppt H_3Cit should you add?

Chapter 11

Alcohols and Esters

*A*LL cold-process soap contains glycerol as a byproduct of its manufacture. Glycerol is an example of a broad class of compounds known as the alcohols, and a full understanding of the saponification process requires an understanding of their chemistry. To begin our exploration, let us turn to the oldest, tastiest, and most popular of the alcohols: ethanol (also known as ethyl alcohol or grain alcohol).

11.1 Ethanol

The structure of ethanol determines all of its physical and chemical properties. As shown in Figure 11-1, ethanol has a polar, hydrophilic hydroxyl group that interacts strongly with water. Ethanol also has a non-polar, hydrophobic hydrocarbon tail, admittedly only two carbons long. Thus we would expect one end of the molecule to be soluble in water and the other to be soluble in oils and fats. And indeed, ethanol is *miscible* with water, meaning that ethanol dissolves in water and water dissolves in ethanol in any proportions. To a lesser degree, ethanol dissolves fats and oils and is often used as a solvent for drugs, varnishes, and other materials that are not soluble in water. In fact, the alchemists reverenced ethanol as a universal solvent. Modern soapmakers also cherish it as a solvent for making transparent soap.

Comparing Figure 11-1 to Figure 8-1 (page 140), we might expect ethanol to have much in common with acetic acid. They are both volatile liquids with strong, characteristic aromas. They are both soluble in water and in oils. Their tastes, however, could not be more different. Ethanol has the warming flavor prized in wine and whiskey, while acetic acid has the characteristically sour bite shared by all the acids. The reason for this is

Figure 11-1. Ethanol and Water

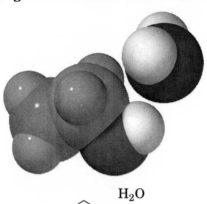

H₂O

OH

that while the hydroxyl group in ethanol is polar, it is not very acidic. If acetic acid is a weak acid, ethanol would have to be classified as a wimpy, puny, 98-pound weakling of an acid. It will, admittedly, react to some small degree with solid NaOH and KOH, but not with even the most concentrated aqueous solutions of these strong bases. Thus we may consider ethanol and most of the other alcohols[1] to be non-acidic under conditions met with in either the soap pot or the mouth.

Several of the procedures given later in the book require ethanol as a solvent, and there are a bewildering variety of grades available commercially. The best grade of alcohol for soap analysis is 190 proof grain alcohol, known in the us by the brand names Everclear, Diesel, Cold Springs, and Graves. These grades contain 95% ethanol and 5% water, the highest concentration of alcohol possible by distillation of fermented materials. Two issues complicate matters for soapmakers. First, this grade is not legally traded in some states without a permit from the relevant regulatory agency. If you live in such a state, you may be able to buy your alcohol by mail, or you may have to travel to another state. Second, beverage-grade alcohol is heavily taxed, increasing the cost to the soapmaker for alco-

---

1. One class of alcohols, the phenols, are weak acids that will react with NaOH or KOH in the soap pot. One phenol in particular, eugenol, is an important component of some essential oils, and we'll meet it in Chapter 13.

hol that will not actually be used as a beverage. A large soap-making operation may find it worthwhile to file the necessary paperwork to be exempt from this tax. Contact your state's alcohol regulatory agency for details. 190 proof grain alcohol is the only grade suitable for making transparent soap. It is the best grade for soap analysis as well, but there are two other grades that are also suitable.

The us government recognizes that there are non-beverage uses for ethanol that should not be subject to the high excise tax on alcoholic beverages. *Denatured* alcohol is ethanol that contains substances intended to discourage its use as a beverage. Many substances are used in a variety of concentrations. The American Oil Chemists' Society (aocs) approves two grades of alcohol for oil and soap analysis: sda 30 and 3A. These grades of *Specially Denatured Alcohol* are not subject to the alcohol excise tax. These grades are sold by vendors of laboratory chemicals and industrial solvents, and if you can convince such a company to do business with you, they will be able to tell you which forms need to be filled out to purchase them legally. These grades contain only methanol as a denaturant, and both are available in strengths of 190 proof, which is appropriate for soap analysis.

There are many other grades of denatured alcohol available at hardware stores, usually alongside the paint thinners. Some of these may contain denaturants that interfere with soap analysis. After making careful measurements of your soap properties, it would be a shame to discover that your results were invalid because of the alcohol you used. Even worse, you might *not* discover that your results are invalid, and then base important decisions on these erroneous results. If you can at all manage it, you should use one of the aforementioned grades of alcohol. But if you are unable to get your hands on anything but hardware-store alcohol, you may test it for suitability using this procedure:

1. *Gather your materials:*
   - Goggles or glasses
   - An eyewash bottle
   - Gloves
   - Denatured alcohol
   - Two 125 mL Erlenmeyer flasks
   - A soap oven and oven mitts

- 5 ppt KOH solution
- 1% phenolphthalein solution

2. *Preheat your oven:* Preheat your oven to 160°F or 70°C.

3. *Neutralize the alcohol:* Add about 100 mL of denatured alcohol to one of the Erlenmeyer flasks. The exact amount is not critical. You may use the graduations on the side of the flask to measure the alcohol. Add three drops of 1% phenolphthalein solution and swirl[2] the flask to mix it with the alcohol. If the alcohol turns pink, it is not suitable for soap analysis.

    The alcohol may contain as small amount of acid that must be neutralized before the soap is added. To neutralize the alcohol, you will add the 5 ppt KOH solution described in Section 8.4.1 (page 155). Add the KOH solution one drop at a time, swirling to mix after each drop, until a faint pink color is just barely detectable. You may hold the flask up against a white piece of paper to view the color. The color should be as faint as you can make it, but there should be no doubt in your mind that it is pink. The alcohol is now said to be neutral to phenolphthalein—the addition of even the slightest amount of base will cause the alcohol to become vividly pink; the addition of even the slightest amount of acid will remove the pink color.

    Pour half of the neutral alcohol into the other Erlenmeyer flask.

4. *Cook the alcohol:* Heat *one* of the Erlenmeyer flasks in a roaster oven[3] for one hour. The alcohol will not boil at the specified temperature, and there is not enough to constitute much of a fire hazard, but you should be aware that alcohol vapor is flammable and have a fire extinguisher handy—just in case.

5. *Check the color:* Compare the color of the cooked alcohol to that of the uncooked alcohol. If both samples remain faintly pink after one hour, the alcohol may be suitable for use in soap analysis. If the color disappears or intensifies, it is not

---

2. The Erlenmeyer flask is designed to be swirled rather than stirred or shaken. Hold the flask by its neck and gently rotate your wrist to swirl the solution in the flask.
3. See Section 1.2 (page 5).

suitable. Be aware that you have only tested that particular bottle of alcohol. If you are going to buy hardware-store denatured alcohol, you should buy it in the largest size available and test each container before using it for the first time.

11.2 Ethyl Acetate

We have come to expect bases to react with acids, but alcohols do as well. Like NaOH and KOH, the alcohols all have polar hydroxyl groups. Like NaOH and KOH, they react with acids to produce water and another product. There, however, the resemblance ends. The product of the reaction of an acid with an alcohol is not a salt, but an ***ester***.

An exemplar of the esters is ethyl acetate, shown in Figure 11-2. At the left end of the molecule, one can make out the remnants of an acetic acid molecule: a carbon atom with three non-polar hydrogen atoms, a second carbon atom, and two oxygen atoms. At the right end, one can make out the remnants of an ethanol molecule: a carbon atom with three non-polar hydrogen atoms, a second carbon atom with two non-polar hydrogen atoms, and an oxygen atom. It is as if a proton had been snipped off of acetic acid, a hydroxyl group had been snipped off of ethanol, and the two remaining chemical lumps had been glued together. What became of the proton and the hydroxyl group? They joined together to make a water molecule. If we abbreviate acetic acid as HAce and ethanol as EthOH, the reaction seems less complicated than it would appear from the full equation:

$$C_2H_5OH + HC_2H_3O_2 = C_2H_5C_2H_3O_2 + H_2O$$
$$EthOH + HAce = EthAce + H_2O$$

Consider for a moment the language that we use to describe this equation. Ethanol reacts with acetic acid to produce ethyl acetate and water. Would you say that ethyl acetate *contains* ethanol? Would you say that it *contains* acetic acid? No, not exactly. Certainly there are recognizable pieces that once belonged to both of these reactants. Older chemistry books would use the term *radical* to describe these molecular chunks, but

Figure 11-2. Ethyl Acetate

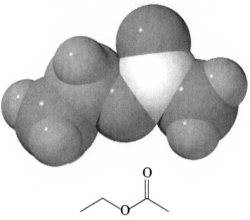

the term has come to have a more specific meaning in modern chemistry that no longer applies to these chunks. Modern chemistry books will refer to them as *moieties* (for example, the ethanol moiety or the acetate moiety). The notion of recognizable moieties within larger molecules will prove very useful when we discuss the structure of fats and oils in the next chapter.

While the ethanol and acetate moieties are recognizable within the ethyl acetate molecule, the proton and hydroxyl groups are missing. Since these functional groups were responsible for the chemical and physical properties of their molecules, we might expect that their absence in the product might be important. And it is. Recall that the proton was responsible for the solubility of acetic acid and the hydroxyl group for the solubility of ethanol in water. Study Figure 11-2 and predict whether ethyl acetate should or should not be soluble in water. Do not proceed to the next paragraph until you have made this prediction.

If you predicted that ethyl acetate is insoluble in water, you have demonstrated a pretty good understanding of the chemistry of acids, alcohols and esters. With no acidic protons or polar hydroxyl groups to interact with water, hydrogen bonding cannot take place. If you add ethyl acetate to water, it will float to the top like oil on water. Shake it up and it will separate again within a few seconds. That said, ethyl acetate is not completely insoluble in water because, while hydrogen bonding is not possible, the carbon-oxygen bond is polar and interacts to some degree with water. Consequently, water can dissolve about 8% of its weight of ethyl acetate, after which the remaining ethyl acetate floats to the surface as a separate, hydrophobic layer. The big picture, however, is that acetic acid and ethanol are *very* soluble in water, and when they react to form an ester, the product is *nearly* insoluble in water.

The reaction in which an acid combines with an alcohol is called a condensation. The reverse of this reaction, breaking an ester apart, is called a hydrolysis reaction. For ethyl acetate it looks like this:

$$C_2H_5C_2H_3O_2 + NaOH = C_2H_5OH + NaC_2H_3O_2$$
$$EthAce + NaOH = EthOH + NaAce$$

Both of the products, ethanol and sodium acetate, are soluble in water. Thus a condensation reaction produces an insoluble product from two soluble reactants, and a hydrolysis reaction produces two soluble products from an insoluble reactant.

11.3 Other Alcohols and Esters

Ethanol is just the most famous member of a large alcoholic family. Other alcohols, though less prominent, have gained some notoriety as well. Figure 11-3 shows a selection of important alcohols. Methanol (methyl alcohol, wood alcohol) is used as an additive for removing water from gasoline and as the major component of Sterno. It is also used for making bio-diesel, a process very similar to soapmaking. Isopropanol (isopropyl alcohol) is also known as "rubbing alcohol," the kind you can buy at the drug store. From one carbon (methyl) to two carbons (ethyl) to three carbons (propyl), the boiling point increases and the solubility in water decreases as the carbon chain gets longer. Referring to Table 7-1 (page 129), you can probably name some of the heavier alcohols and draw their structural formulas.

For alcohols with more than 10 carbons, the water solubility is so small that they are virtually insoluble. They are so insoluble, in fact, that we call them *fatty alcohols*. We have, for example, lauryl alcohol ($C_{12}H_{25}OH$) with a melting point near room

Figure 11-3. Acids, Alcohols, and Esters

acetic acid	60.05 g/mol, $HC_2H_3O_2$, HAce	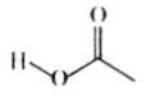
eugenol	164.20 g/mol, $HC_{10}H_{11}O_2$, HEug	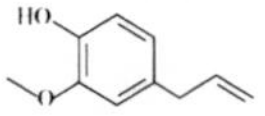

methanol	32.04 g/mol, CH_3OH, MthOH	
ethanol	46.04 g/mol, C_2H_5OH, EthOH	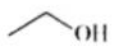
isopropanol	60.10 g/mol, C_3H_7OH, IprOH	
ethylene glycol	62.07 g/mol, $C_2H_4(OH)_2$, $Etg(OH)_2$	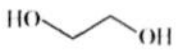
propylene glycol	76.09 g/mol, $C_3H_6(OH)_2$, $Prg(OH)_2$	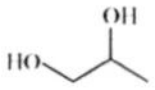
glycerol	92.05 g/mol, $C_3H_5(OH)_3$, $Gly(OH)_3$	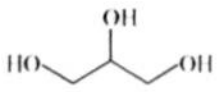

ethyl acetate	88.11 g/mol, $C_4H_8O_2$, EthAce	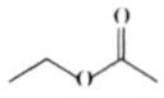
glyceryl monoacetate	134.13 g/mol, $C_5H_{10}O_4$, $GlyAce(OH)_2$	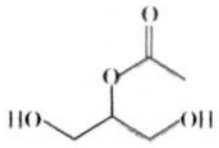
glyceryl diacetate	176.17 g/mol, $C_7H_{12}O_5$, $Gly(Ace)_2OH$	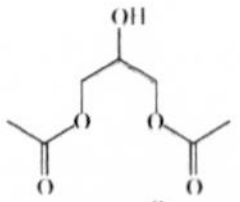
glyceryl triacetate	218.21 g/mol, $C_9H_{14}O_6$, $Gly(Ace)_3$	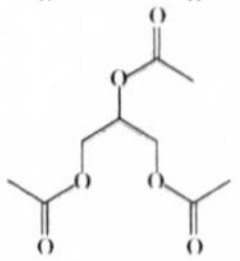

Figure 11-4. Eugenol

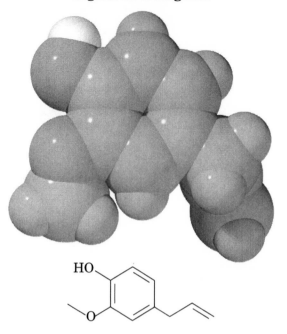

temperature. Myristyl alcohol ($C_{14}H_{29}OH$) and stearyl alcohol ($C_{18}H_{37}OH$) are both waxy solids at room temperature. What might be called *palmityl alcohol* is more commonly called cetyl alcohol ($C_{16}H_{33}OH$) because it was first isolated from whale oil.[4] All of the fatty alcohols have long, hydrophobic carbon chains and hydrophilic hydroxyl groups that give them useful properties as surfactants and emollients. They are used in a wide variety of cosmetics.

Some of the larger alcohols have strong, characteristic scents and are major components of many essential oils. Linalyl alcohol ($C_{10}H_{17}OH$) and its ester linalyl acetate ($C_{12}H_{20}O_2$) dominate the scent of lavender and many other floral oils. While linalyl alcohol does not react with NaOH, the ester may undergo hydrolysis to linalyl alcohol and sodium acetate. In the soap pot, essential oils containing alcohols and esters may become richer in the alcohols and leaner in the esters, changing the character of the scent.

---

4. *Cetus* is Latin for *whale*.

Figure 11-5. Glycerol

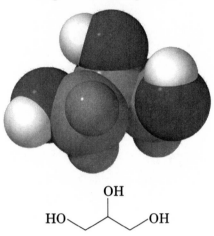

Eugenol ($HC_{10}H_{11}O_2$) is the major component of clove and cinnamon oils. Figure 11-4 shows a model that is mostly gray; we can expect eugenol to be largely non-polar, greasy, and insoluble in water. Its lone proton, however, is not to be trifled with—it has the distinction of being an *acidic* proton. The acidity of eugenol is unusual and derives from the curious six-carbon ring to which the hydroxyl group is attached. Alcohols like this are classified as phenolic[5] compounds, and they react immediately with NaOH and other alkalis. The acidity of eugenol will prove to be important in Chapter 13.

The curious chemist might wonder whether it is possible to put two hydroxyl groups on a single alcohol. Good for you. "Two-headed" alcohols are called *glycols,* two of which are shown in Figure 11-3. Ethylene glycol is the most common kind of automotive anti-freeze. Though they tell me it has a sweet taste, it is extremely toxic, making the careless disposal of anti-freeze a problem for pets and wild animals. By contrast, propylene glycol is odorless, tasteless, colorless, and generally non-toxic, though some individuals may be more sensitive than others. Propylene glycol is a common ingredient in cosmetics and is an important solvent for making transparent soap.

---

5.   Phenolic compounds get their name from phenol (C_6H_5OH), which is a weak acid.

The curious chemist will not be able to help but wonder whether a "three-headed" alcohol exists. Glycerol (glycerin, glycerine) is just such an alcohol. Soapmakers know it as a beneficial byproduct of the soapmaking process. It can also be produced from petroleum. There is no foundation to the claim that *glycerin* refers to the natural compound and *glycerol* to the synthetic. Glycerol molecules are identical to one another, regardless of source. Otherwise we would have to give them different chemical names and draw different structural formulas for them. While there is no chemical difference between natural and synthetic glycerin, some people have a legitimate preference for the natural one. I like cooked broccoli and detest raw broccoli, while my wife has the opposite preference. It would be wrong to criticize either of us for our preferences. Some of your customers will insist on natural glycerin and others will not care one way or the other. When you buy glycerin, however, you will have no way of knowing its source except by the assurance and reputation of your vendor.[6]

Figure 11-5 shows a molecular model of glycerol. One side of the molecule is hydrophobic and the other, hydrophilic. This makes glycerol extremely useful for bringing oil and water together. Like propylene glycol, glycerol is used as a solvent for making transparent soap. It is a ubiquitous ingredient in cosmetics, foods, and pharmaceuticals. It is often used as a humectant to prevent the loss of water by evaporation. It is used as a lubricant, a carrier, a solvent, and for a host of other purposes. Alas, the smallness of its hydrophobic side makes it useless as a detergent, but there are only so many uses for one little chemical. In addition to being a byproduct of soapmaking, it is produced by the manufacture of bio-diesel, where it is considered an undesirable waste product. As bio-diesel production increases, the recovery of waste glycerin will become an important challenge for those wishing to produce fuels that are ecologically responsible and economically viable.

Any of the alcohols mentioned may be used to produce esters. We have considered ethyl acetate in some detail. We can also have methyl acetate or isopropyl acetate. We can have mono- or

---

6. An analysis of the trace impurities in glycerin would be able to distinguish the natural and synthetic products. Routine analysis by the soapmaker, however, is unlikely to be cost effective.

Figure 11-6. Triacetin

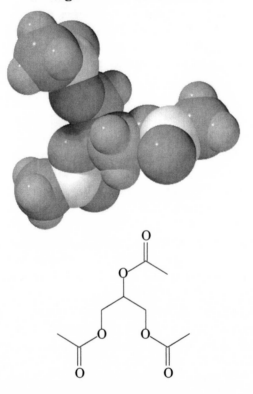

di-esters of the glycols and mono-, di-, or tri-esters of glycerol. And so far we have only mentioned the acetate esters. We can make esters by reacting any acid with any alcohol, making the variety of possible esters nearly endless. We can even combine a fatty acid with a fatty alcohol to produce, for example, lauryl laurate. In preparation for our discussion of fats, however, we'll narrow the field to the acetic esters of glycerol. Glyceryl monoacetate is a monoglyceride, glyceryl diacetate is a diglyceride, and—you guessed it—glyceryl triacetate is a triglyceride with the common name triacetin. In the next section, we'll practice on ethyl acetate, leaving the glycerides as prime targets for the practice problems.

11.4 The Hydrolysis of Ethyl Acetate

In the next chapter we'll explore the chemistry of fats and oils. We'll find that they are great big esters and that saponification is just the hydrolysis of a fat. Before we go there, however, I would like you to understand the hydrolysis of a little bitty ester so that the saponification of a great big fat does not seem so bewildering. And so we end this chapter with the hydrolysis of ethyl acetate. What follows is more of a demonstration than an experiment; while an experiment is designed to answer a question, a demonstration is designed simply to—well—demonstrate some principle. Many of the principles developed here will transfer directly to the saponification of fats.

While ethyl acetate is a relatively inexpensive chemical, it is not readily available through retail sources, and chemical supply companies have become increasingly paranoid about selling chemicals to folks who are unaffiliated with an industrial or academic laboratory. So while I will give the complete procedure for this demo, I will also describe the results for those who do not have access to the chemicals.

In this demonstration we want to practice our stoichiometric skills on the relatively manageable problem of the hydrolysis of ethyl acetate. To do this, we need the molecular weight of sodium hydroxide from Table 9-2 (page 165) and that of ethyl acetate from Figure 11-3. We also need to know how many moles of ethyl acetate react with each mole of sodium hydroxide. We get this from the balanced equation:

$$C_2H_5C_2H_3O_2 + NaOH = C_2H_5OH + NaC_2H_3O_2$$
$$EthAce + NaOH = EthOH + NaAce$$

We now ask the stoichiometric question, "How many grams of lye are required to hydrolyse, say, 5 g of ethyl acetate?"

$$? \text{ g Lye} = 5.00 \text{ g } EthAce\left(\frac{1 \text{ mol } EthAce}{88.11 \text{ g } EthAce}\right)\left(\frac{1 \text{ mol } NaOH}{1 \text{ mol } EthAce}\right)$$
$$\left(\frac{40.00 \text{ g } NaOH}{1 \text{ mol } NaOH}\right)\left(\frac{1000 \text{ g Lye}}{500 \text{ g } NaOH}\right)$$
$$= 4.54 \text{ g Lye}$$

So if we mix 5.00 g of EthAce with 4.54 g of 500 ppt NaOH, we expect all of the EthAce and NaOH to be consumed. But in order to react, the EthAce and NaOH must come into contact with one another, and we have already predicted that EthAce and water do not mix. What we need is a solvent that dissolves both in hydrophobic substances like EthAce and in aqueous solutions like lye. Can you think of such a solvent? If you guessed *ethanol* or, indeed, any of the alcohols, you can pat yourself on the back. Ethanol will be used in this demonstration to bring the hydrophobic and hydrophilic molecules together so that they may react. We will also add some additional water to prevent the NaOH from falling out of solution.

1. *Gather your materials:*
   - Goggles or glasses
   - An eyewash bottle
   - Gloves
   - A centigram balance
   - A filled 125 mL PP bottle labeled `Lye`
   - Ethyl acetate
   - 95% ethanol or denatured ethanol
   - A small glass beaker
   - A plastic weighing cup labeled `Water`
   - A 30 mL glass vial labeled `EthAce` with cap
   - Four pipets labeled `EthAce`, `EthOH`, `Water`, and `Lye`
   - Your soapmaking notebook and a pen

2. *Arrange your workspace:* Since you have not dealt with ethyl acetate before, you should summarize its MSDS in your notebook. Note in particular that ethyl acetate and ethanol are flammable.

3. *Synthetically weigh the EthAce:* Add more than 5 g of ethyl acetate to the glass ***beaker***[7] and use it as a weighing cup to synthetically weigh 5.00 g of ethyl acetate into the labeled vial.

4. *Synthetically weigh the water:* Synthetically weigh 2.27 g of water to the EthAce vial.

5. *Synthetically weigh the lye:* Synthetically weigh 4.54 g of 500 ppt NaOH from the Lye bottle to the EthAce vial.

6. *Shake:* Shake the vial to thoroughly mix the materials. After a few seconds the liquids will separate into two layers, like oil and water.

7. *Add ethanol:* Add about 1 mL of ethanol to the vial, tighten the cap, and shake it. Again, the liquids separate into two layers. Add another 1 mL of ethanol and repeat the shaking. Add a third and a fourth mL of ethanol, shaking the vial after each addition. The more ethanol you add, the longer you will find that it takes for the liquids to separate.

8. *Observe:* After the addition of the fourth mL of ethanol, you should find that the solution is getting warm. If not, shake the vial again. The heat comes from the liberated acetic acid reacting with sodium hydroxide to form sodium acetate. Once the solution is warm, you should loosen the cap after each shake to release any pressure. Continue shaking the vial until the liquids no longer separate. By that time the vial will be very nearly too hot to handle.

9. *Cleanup:* Alkaline spills may be cleaned up with household vinegar. At the conclusion of the experiment, the contents of the vial may be washed down the drain with plenty of water.

If every experiment is designed to answer a question, every demonstration is designed to make a point. Here we see that when a hydrophobic ester is made to react with sodium hydroxide, the reaction is exothermic and the resulting products are

---

7. Ethyl acetate will dissolve many plastics, so we use a glass weighing cup.

soluble in water. The same behavior will be observed when we (finally) turn to the saponification of fats and oils in Chapter 12.

Practice Problems

Answers to practice problems appear in Appendix A (page 335).

1. Draw the structural formulas for methyl acetate and iso-propyl acetate and calculate the molecular weight for each.
2. Draw the structural formula for lauryl laurate and calculate its molecular weight. Search the Internet for a manufacturer who uses lauryl laurate in a product. Why do you suspect this particular compound was chosen for this particular application?
3. Of the compounds glyceryl monoacetate, glyceryl diacetate, and glyceryl triacetate, which do you expect to be most soluble in water and which least?
4. How many grams of NaOH would be required to react completely with 1000 grams of glyceryl monoacetate?
5. How many grams of NaOH would be required to react completely with 1000 grams of glyceryl diacetate?
6. How many grams of NaOH would be required to react completely with 1000 grams of glyceryl triacetate?
7. Imagine that 1000 grams of glyceryl triacetate react completely with the stoichiometric quantity of 500 ppt NaOH, as determined in the previous problem. What percentage of the total weight of products will be made up of glycerol?
8. What do you suppose would happen if less than the stoichiometric quantity of 500 ppt NaOH were added to 1000 g of glyceryl triacetate?
9. What do you suppose would happen if more than the stoichiometric quantity of 500 ppt NaOH were added to 1000 g of glyceryl triacetate?
10. How many grams of 500 ppt NaOH would be required to react completely with 1 gram of eugenol?

Chapter 12

Saponification

*W*E have been through quite a bit of chemistry to get to this point. In Chapter 10 we learned the properties of the fatty acids, with their characteristic carboxylic acid groups (-COOH), and became familiar with the likes of stearic acid and oleic acid. In Chapter 11 we investigated the alcohols, with their characteristic -OH groups, and became friends with ethanol and glycerol. We learned that an acid can bond to an alcohol; a molecule of water is eliminated and the new, larger molecule is known as an ester. When a strong base like sodium hydroxide reacts with an ester, it is hydrolyzed into the original alcohol and the sodium salt of the original acid. In this chapter we'll explore the hydrolysis of fats and oils (saponification).

12.1 Triacylglycerides

All of the fats and oils that can be saponified are esters of fatty acids and glycerol.[1] For the most part, they are tri-esters composed of three fatty acids bonded to a single glycerol. Oil chemists refer to these as *triacylglycerides* (TAG).[2] An acyl group is just the part of the molecule that will become a fatty acid once it has been separated from the glycerol. Some oils, particularly rancid ones, will contain diacylglycerides (DAG) and monoacylglycerides (MAG) in addition to triacylglycerides. Rancid oils may also contain free fatty acids (fatty acids that are not bonded to glycerol). You can think of these rancid oils as partially saponified.

---

1.   Motor oil, mineral oil, and petroleum jelly are not esters and cannot be saponified.
2.   Triacylglycerides are often called *triglycerides* for short.

Figure 12-1. Glyceryl Trilaurate

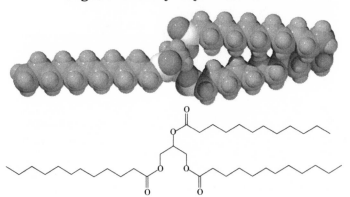

Table 12-1. TAG Makeup of Three Oils

	Percent		
	Olive	Almond	Apricot
TAG		Kernel	Kernel
GlyPlmOleOle	23	10	4
GlyStrOleOle	8	2	1
GlyOleOleOle	45	36	26
GlyPlmOleLin	4	8	5
GlyOleOleLin	10	25	33
GlyPlmLinLin	2	2	2
GlyOleLinLin	1	13	23
GlyPlmStrOle	2	0	0
GlyPlmPlmOle	3	0	0
GlyLinLinLin	0	2	5
Other	2	2	1

Plm=palmitate, Ole=oleate, Str=stearate, Lin=linoleate

Reference [80].

Figure 12-1 shows a model and structural formula for glyceryl trilaurate. The three acyl groups are easily identified. If you count the carbon atoms, you will find that each acyl group contains twelve of them, the hallmark of lauric acid. The molecule is not a rigid structure; the three acyl groups are somewhat free to move, finger-like, about the glyceryl "knuckles." There is a limit to their range of motion, however, and like fingers they have a natural rest position. The model shows that two of the acyl groups lie parallel to one another and the third points in the opposite direction. The structural formula attempts to represent this arrangement as well, but is limited in the three-dimensional information it can convey.

We can write simplified formulas for triacylglycerides. Glyceryl trilaurate, for example, is represented by GlyLauLauLau[3], glyceryl trioleate by GlyOleOleOle, and glyceryl trilinoleate by GlyLinLinLin. And there is no reason that the three acyl groups must be identical. We may have, for example, GlyOleOleLin, GlyOleLinLin, or GlyLinLauOle. Real-world fats and oils consist of a wide variety of TAGs. Table 12-1 lists the percentages of select TAGs in olive, almond kernel, and apricot kernel oils. These oils are mixtures of ten TAGs, each one an ester of oleic, palmitic, stearic, and linolenic acids in various combinations with glycerol. The percentages given in the table are representative and may vary seasonally and geographically within each oil type.

We seldom know (or need to know) the exact composition of TAGs in an oil. Chemists more often express the composition of an oil by giving the percentage of each acyl group. We can determine the fatty acid composition for an oil in Table 12-2 by multiplying the percentage of each TAG by the proportion of a given acyl group in that TAG (for example, the GlyPlmOleOle TAG is $\frac{1}{3}$ palmitate) and summing the results. Thus we find that the total palmitate composition of olive oil, for instance, is 12.33%.[4] In other words, 12.33% of the acyl groups in the various triacylglycerides are palmitic acid groups.[5] This statement might be

---

3. We could also write GlyLau$_3$. For comparison among other triacylglycerides, however, I have shown the three acyl groups individually.
4. $\frac{1}{3}(23\%) + \frac{1}{3}(4\%) + \frac{1}{3}(2\%) + \frac{1}{3}(2\%) + \frac{2}{3}(3\%) = 12.33\%$
5. Note that these percentages ignore the glyceryl moiety, which is common to all triacylglycerides.

Table 12-2. Fatty Acid Makeup of Three Oils

Fatty Acid	Percent		
	Olive	Almond Kernel	Apricot Kernel
Palmitate	7–20	4–13	4–6
Oleate	55–83	43–70	58–66
Stearate	0–5	1–10	0–1
Linoleate	3–21	20–34	29–33

Reference [80].

shortened to "olive oil is 12.33% palmitic acid," but this does *not* mean that olive oil is literally 12.33% palmitic acid. If it were, it would taste sour, smell terrible, and turn to soap immediately upon the addition of lye. No, when we express the fatty acid composition of an oil, we understand that the fatty acids are all chemically bound to glycerol and will be released only when a reaction occurs.

As with the TAG composition, the fatty acid composition varies seasonally and geographically. Table 12-2 compares the fatty acid makeup of olive, almond kernel, and apricot kernel oils. The similarity of these oils is more apparent here than it was in Table 12-1. Oleic acid is the most abundant acyl group for all three oils. Linoleic acid is next, followed by palmitic and stearic acids. The most important differences are also apparent; apricot kernel oil "contains" the highest percentage of linoleic acid; olive oil, the least. Once the oils are saponified, the resulting fatty acid salts have no memory of the particular TAGs in which they originated. This makes it possible to substitute oils with similar fatty acid composition without worrying about the TAG composition. Appendix B (page 377) groups oils with similar fatty acid compositions.

12.2 The Saponification Reaction

A triglyceride is an ester of three fatty acids with glycerol. When a TAG reacts with a strong alkali such as sodium or potassium hydroxide, the acyl "fingers" are amputated, one by one, from the glyceryl "knuckles." The reaction of glyceryl trilaurate with

Figure 12-2. The Fundamental Soap Reaction

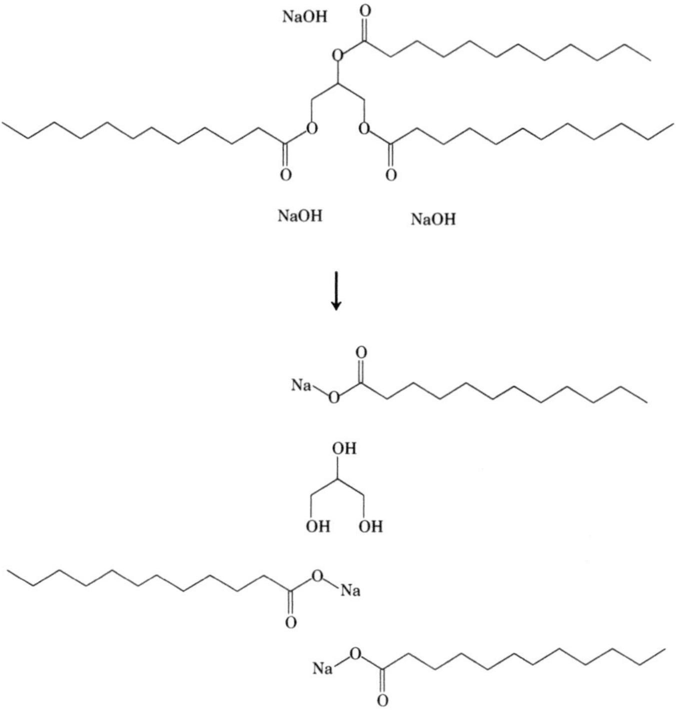

sodium hydroxide, for example, may be represented quite simply:

$$GlyLauLauLau \ + \ 3\,NaOH \ = \ Gly(OH)_3 \ + \ 3\,NaLau$$

The products are glycerol and three fatty acid salts—in this case, sodium laurate. Fatty acid salts are soaps, the *raison d'être* of the saponification reaction. This reaction is so important that it deserves to be investigated in a little more detail.

Figure 12-2 shows a structural formula for glyceryl trilaurate as it reacts with three molecules of NaOH. Among the products, we recognize three molecules of sodium laurate, each with its fat-soluble tail and its polar, water-soluble head. In addition, we find a molecule of glycerol, with its three characteristic -OH groups. The structural formulas give us more detail of the reaction than the simple equation does. But in actual fact, the

TAG reacts with one NaOH molecule at a time. This further level of detail appears in the molecular models of Figure 12-3.

In the top frame of the figure, we see a molecular model of glyceryl trilaurate surrounded by three hydroxide ions. As usual for ionic compounds, the sodium ions have dissociated from the hydroxide ions and are happily floating around somewhere else. For simplicity, these sodium ions are not shown in the figure. The hydroxide ions are colored very dark, indicating that they are negatively charged. The glyceryl trilaurate is depicted as uniformly gray, the hallmark of a non-polar, fat-soluble molecule. One can, however, make out three carbon atoms, lighter in color than the rest, indicating that they are more positively charged than the remainder of the molecule. The negative hydroxide ions are attracted to these positive atoms, and it is here that the reaction occurs.

In the second frame of the figure, we see that the first hydroxide ion has "attacked" one of the positive carbon atoms, severing the finger at the knuckle, and releasing it. The free laurate ion (left) manifests those properties that render it soapy—it has a gray, greasy, fat-soluble tail and a black-and-white, water-soluble head. Somewhere (not shown in the figure), a positive sodium ion exactly balances the charge on the negative laurate ion. If the soap were dried, this sodium ion would loosely attach itself to the laurate ion to form a molecule of sodium laurate.

The third and fourth frames of the figure show the removal of the remaining laurate fingers. We find our three laurate ions surrounding the central glycerol molecule, with its three watery hydroxyl groups. In the progression from frame one to frame four, we see the transformation from fat-soluble (glyceryl trilaurate) and water-soluble (hydroxide) reactants to products that exhibit fat-soluble and water-soluble regions. The dual nature of these products allow soap to mingle with both oil and water.

12.3 Soap Stoichiometry

It is now straightforward to answer the question, "How many grams of potassium hydroxide are required to saponify 1000 g of glyceryl trilaurate," in other words, to calculate its ***saponifi-***

Figure 12-3. Saponification

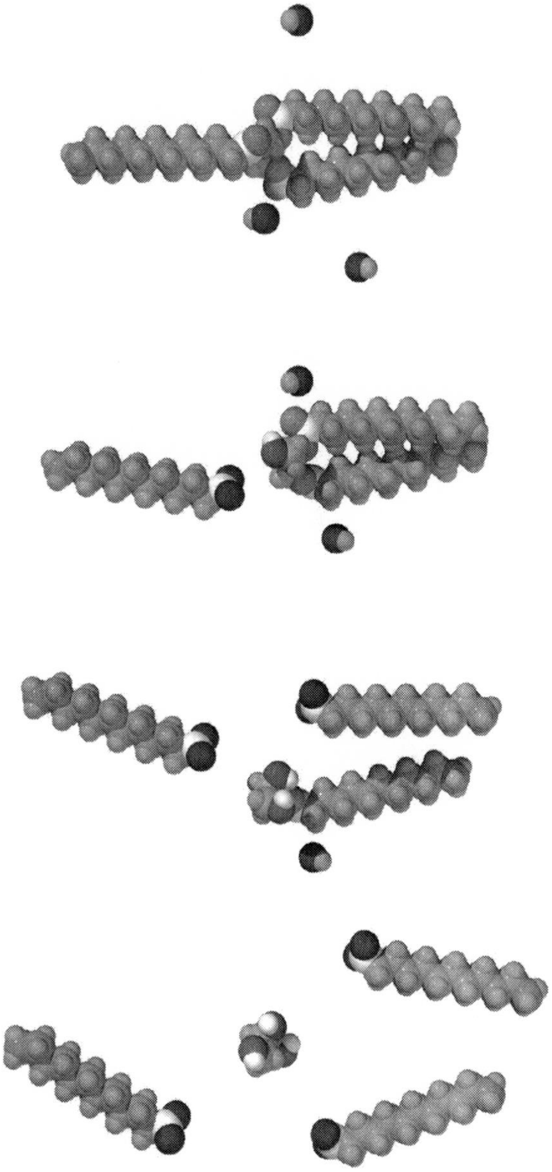

cation value (sv). The problem requires the tools developed in Chapter 9. We need a balanced equation (from the previous section) and the molecular weights of the reactants. We recall the molecular weight of KOH (56.11 g/mol) from Table 9-2 (page 165). For glyceryl trilaurate, we might painstakingly count up all of the atoms and multiply these numbers by the atomic weights of Table 9-1 (page 164). There turns out, however, to be an easier way.

We may think of glyceryl trilaurate as the product resulting from the reaction of glycerol with three molecules of lauric acid:

$$Gly(OH)_3 + 3\ HLau = Gly(Lau)_3 + 3\ H_2O$$

The molecular weight of glyceryl trilaurate, then, must be exactly the same as the molecular weight of glycerol plus three times that of lauric acid minus three times that of water. We can get the molecular weight for glycerol from Figure 11-3 (page 198), that of lauric acid from Figure 10-2 (page 184), and that of water from Table 9-2 (page 165). The molecular weight of glyceryl trilaurate is then 638.95 g/mol.[6] Once we have these molecular weights, it is an easy matter to calculate the saponification value for the triacylglyceride:

$$? \text{ g KOH} = 1000\ g\ GlyLau_3 \left(\frac{1\ mol\ GlyLau_3}{638.95\ g\ GlyLau_3} \right)$$
$$\left(\frac{3\ mol\ KOH}{1\ mol\ GlyLau_3} \right) \left(\frac{56.11\ g\ KOH}{1\ mol\ KOH} \right)$$
$$= 263 \text{ ppt KOH}$$

We may also calculate the *sodium saponification value* (ssv), the number of grams of NaOH required to saponify 1000 g of oil:

$$? \text{ g NaOH} = 1000\ g\ GlyLau_3 \left(\frac{1\ mol\ GlyLau_3}{638.95\ g\ GlyLau_3} \right)$$
$$\left(\frac{3\ mol\ NaOH}{1\ mol\ GlyLau_3} \right) \left(\frac{40.00\ g\ NaOH}{1\ mol\ NaOH} \right)$$
$$= 188 \text{ ppt NaOH}$$

---

6. 92.05 g/mol + 3(200.32 g/mol) - 3(18.02 g/mol) = 638.95 g/mol

These calculated saponification values for glyceryl trilaurate are within the range given for coconut oil in Table 4-1 (page 65), and this is no accident—lauric acid is the most abundant fatty acid in coconut oil. It is possible to calculate the saponification value for any TAG once we know its formula and hence its molecular weight. Furthermore, if we know the TAG composition of an oil, we can calculate its saponification value as well. Such a calculation is left as an exercise for the exceptionally curious student.

For the rest of us, it is best not to have our view of the forest obstructed by trees. What's most important to know is that three molecules of alkali are needed to saponify each molecule of a triacylglyceride. If we know the molecular weights of the TAG and the alkali, simple stoichiometry allows us to calculate the saponification value. The saponification value of an oil will depend on the percentages of its TAGs and their individual saponification values. In practice, the saponification value of an oil is very close to that of its most abundant TAG.

If the alkali ratio used to make a soap is higher than the saponification value of the oil used to make it, we can expect the alkali to saponify the oil completely and the soap to contain excess alkali. If, on the other hand, the alkali ratio is less than the saponification value of the oil, the alkali will be consumed and the soap will contain excess, unsaponified (or partially saponified) oil. This hypothesis will be tested in Example 15-1.

12.4 Sodium Saponification Value

We have developed the basic theory that if we add less than the stoichiometric quantity of NaOH, the NaOH will be consumed and excess, unsaponified oil will remain in the soap. If we use more than the stoichiometric quantity of NaOH, all of the oil will be saponified and there will be excess NaOH in the soap. If we can manage to add exactly the stoichiometric quantity of NaOH, both oil and lye will be consumed and our soap will contain neither of them. Using this theory, we should be able to determine that stoichiometric quantity by making a series of soaps with different alkali ratios. The maximum alkali ratio that yields a tongue-neutral soap would be a good approximation to the sodium saponification value.

We could measure alkalinity the old-fashioned way, using the tongue test. We might alternatively use a pH test strip to determine whether or not the soaps are alkaline. Neither of these tests, however, gives a result that is sensitive enough to distinguish soaps that are very close to one another in alkalinity. In this procedure, we'll dissolve our soaps in alcohol and use phenolphthalein and citric acid to determine whether or not they are alkaline. We'll be able to distinguish three levels of alkalinity: a) not alkaline, b) alkalinity less than 1 ppt, and c) alkalinity greater than 1 ppt. We'll approximate the sodium saponification value as the maximum alkali ratio that yields a soap with an alkalinity of less than 1 ppt.

Using Appendix B we can calculate minimum and maximum alkali ratios for the oil or oil blend to be evaluated. Delight, for example, would have minimum and maximum alkali ratios of 144 and 156 ppt, respectively. We would then make a series of soaps with alkali ratios intermediate between these two extremes. We might make thirteen bars of soap in 1 ppt increments, but this seems like an awful waste of oil. We might make seven bars in 2 ppt increments or five bars in 3 ppt increments. We might even make three bars at 144, 150, and 156 ppt to determine whether the ssv lies between 144 and 150 or between 150 and 156 ppt. Depending on this answer, we could then make a fourth bar intermediate between the two more alkaline soaps. In this way we could sneak up on the ssv making as few bars as possible. In Chapter 18, however, we'll learn to determine the saponification value with more precision and with less oil. For the purposes of this procedure, simply choose five alkali ratios intermediate between your calculated minimum and maximum values.

1. *Gather your materials:*
    - Goggles or glasses
    - An eyewash bottle
    - Gloves
    - A centigram balance
    - Five bars of soap with different alkali ratios
    - Ethanol
    - Five 125 mL Erlenmeyer flasks

- A soap oven (or microwave oven) and oven mitts
- A knife
- A filled 125 mL dispensing bottle labeled 5 ppt H₃Cit (Yellow)
- A plastic cup labeled Soap
- A plastic powder funnel
- 1% phenolphthalein solution

2. *Preheat your oven:* If you plan to use an oven, preheat it to 175°F or 80°C.

3. *Prepare the ethanol:* Add about 50 mL of ethanol to each Erlenmeyer flask. The exact amount is not critical. You may use the graduations on the side of the flask to measure the alcohol. Add 5 or 6 drops of 1% phenolphthalein solution and swirl the flask to mix it with the alcohol.

4. *Weigh the soap:* Place the Soap cup onto the balance and press the tare button. Use the knife to carefully shave more than 1.00 g of your first soap into the cup. Try to get the soap weight between 1.10 and 1.20 g.

   Analytically weigh the soap into the first Erlenmeyer flask using the procedure of Section 2.3 (page 25). Remember to place the funnel into the Soap cup, tare the balance, use the funnel to pour the soap into the flask, and return both the cup and funnel to the balance. The balance will now read -1.*XX* g, the exact weight that has been transferred from the cup to the flask. Weigh each of the remaining soaps into their respective flasks, taking care to label each flask with the appropriate batch code.

5. *Dissolve the soap:* You may heat the Erlenmeyer flasks in either a roaster oven[7] or a microwave oven. A laboratory hotplate may also be used. Any other heat source—such as a kitchen oven, range, or household hotplate—is a fire hazard because of the flammability of ethanol. The roaster oven is convenient if you have other things to do while the soap is heating. The microwave oven is more convenient if you want to dissolve the soap as quickly as possible.

   To use the roaster oven, place the flasks in the oven. After fifteen minutes, remove the soap from the oven and gently swirl it to help dissolve the soap. Place it back into the

---

7. See Section 1.2 (page 5).

oven for another fifteen minutes and continue the cycle of heating and swirling until the soap has dissolved.

To use the microwave oven, place the flasks into the oven and turn it on for no more than 10 seconds at a time. Swirl the flasks after each period of heating until the soap has dissolved. You should not allow the ethanol to boil, and the flasks should never become so hot that you cannot pick them up with your bare hands.

6. *Check the color:* If the dissolved soap is colorless, there is no detectable alkali in the soap. More than likely, however, there will be some detectable alkali and the solution will turn pink.

7. *Add acid:* If the dissolved soap is pink, synthetically weigh 0.32 g of 5 ppt H₃Cit into each Erlenmeyer flask. If the dissolved soap becomes colorless, the soap contains less than 1 ppt alkali. If it remains pink, it contains more than 1 ppt alkali.

8. *Cleanup:* Acid spills may be cleaned up with household ammonia. Alkaline spills may be cleaned up with household vinegar. Wipe down your balance and bring your notebook up to date.

9. *Tabulate the results:* The sodium saponification value is the highest alkali ratio that results in a soap containing less than 1 ppt alkali.

12.5 Glycerol Concentration

The glycerol produced during saponification is stoichiometrically related to the alkali ratio. We may ask the stoichiometric question, "How many grams of glycerol are produced the saponification of 1000 grams of Delight?" We start with the formula: $Delight_{1000}Lye_{288}Aq_{144}$. This tells us that for every 1000 grams of oil, we have 144 grams of NaOH. We don't need to know the detailed TAG makeup of the oil—we just need to know that for every mole of glycerol produced, three moles of NaOH are consumed:

$$oil + 3\,NaOH = Gly(OH)_3 + 3\,soap$$

A little stoichiometry gives us our answer:

$$? \text{ g Gly(OH)}_3 = 1000 \; g\text{-}oil \left(\frac{144 \; g \; NaOH}{1000 \; g\text{-}oil} \right) \left(\frac{1 \; mol \; NaOH}{40.00 \; g \; NaOH} \right)$$
$$\left(\frac{1 \; mol \; Gly(OH)_3}{3 \; mol \; NaOH} \right) \left(\frac{92.05 \text{ g Gly(OH)}_3}{1 \; mol \; Gly(OH)_3} \right)$$
$$= 110.46 \text{ g Gly(OH)}_3$$

Since the total weight of the raw soap was 1432 g, this soap will contain 7.7% glycerol when saponification is complete. As the soap cures, it will lose weight from the evaporation of water. Since glycerol is not volatile, the cured soap will contain 110.46 g of glycerol in *less than* 1432 g of soap. The concentration of glycerol will consequently increase as the soap cures.

Practice Problems

Answers to practice problems appear in Appendix A (page 335).

1. Given the triacylglyceride compositions of Table 12-1 (page 208), what are the percentages of palmitic, oleic, stearic, and linoleic acids in olive oil?

2. Given the triacylglyceride compositions of Table 12-1 (page 208), what are the percentages of palmitic, oleic, stearic, and linoleic acids in almond kernel oil?

3. Given the triacylglyceride compositions of Table 12-1 (page 208), what are the percentages of palmitic, oleic, stearic, and linoleic acids in apricot kernel oil?

4. The percentages of fatty acids calculated in the previous three questions differ from those listed in Table 12-2 (page 210). Why?

5. What are the saponification value and sodium saponification value of triolein?

6. What are the saponification value and sodium saponification value of tripalmitin?

7. Compare the saponification values of triolein and tristearin.

8. Compare the saponification values of trilaurin and tristearin.

9. What are the saponification values for each of the triacylglycerides of Table 12-1 (page 208)?

10. Given the triacylglyceride compositions of Table 12-1 (page 208) and the saponification values calculated in the previous

Example 12-1. Brute Force SSV of Delight

I wanted to measure the ssv for Delight. Using Appendix B I calculated minimum and maximum alkali ratios of 144 and 156 ppt, respectively. I then made five bars of soap with alkali ratios of 144, 147, 150, 153, and 156 ppt. I dissolved 1 g soap samples in 50 mL of ethanol and added phenolphthalein indicator. The first soap solution was colorless, the next two turned pink but cleared upon the addition of acid, and the final two remained pink even after the addition of acid. More precise alkali measurements for these soaps appear in Example 15-1 (page 250).

Batch Code	Formula	AR	Alkaline?
KMD2008.2.17A	$Delight_{1000}Lye_{288}$	144	No
KMD2008.3.22A	$Delight_{1000}Lye_{294}$	147	<1 ppt
KMD2008.3.21A	$Delight_{1000}Lye_{300}$	150	<1 ppt
KMD2008.3.22B	$Delight_{1000}Lye_{306}$	153	Yes
KMD2008.3.22C	$Delight_{1000}Lye_{312}$	156	Yes

I concluded that the ssv of this oil lies somewhere between 150 and 153 ppt. This may be compared to an ssv of 150.8 ppt NaOH, as determined in Example 18-1 (page 275).

---

question, what is the saponification value of olive oil?

11. Which contains more glycerol, a bar of soap made from 100% coconut oil, or one made from 100% olive oil?

12. What assumptions were made in the calculations of Section 12.5?

Chapter 13

Soaps and Detergents

*H*AVING mastered the first dozen chapters of this book, you know a great deal about the chemistry of fats and oils, acids and bases, and the stoichiometry of saponification. A few more topics will bring our discussion of basic chemistry to a conclusion. First, we wish to understand what soaps and detergents have in common—what makes them do what they do. Second, we would like to understand pH in a little more depth. Finally, we would like to understand the differences between soaps and synthetic detergents. By the time you finish this chapter, you will know enough chemistry to speak confidently with any chemist, to ask intelligent questions about soap, and to understand the answers that a chemist might give.

13.1 Surfactants

Some emulsions like milk or mayonnaise are stable for long periods of time; others like orange juice, salad dressing, and house paint must be shaken before use. Emulsions may be stabilized with *emulsifiers*. While there are several kinds of emulsifiers, we'll be most concerned with the ones called *surfactants*. And while there are several classes of surfactants, the first surfactant to be used as a detergent was soap. Someone unfamiliar with these definitions might say, "Soap can dissolve oil in water." But it would be more precise to say, "Soap is a surfactant that can emulsify oil and water."

We recall from Chapter 10 that a fatty acid is simply a carboxylic acid with a long, hydrophobic hydrocarbon tail. The hydrophilic carboxyl group, though soluble in water, can be made more so by neutralizing it with an alkali such as sodium, potassium, or ammonium hydroxide. The resulting alkali carboxylate is what we know and love as good old-fashioned soap.

Figure 13-1. Sodium Laurate

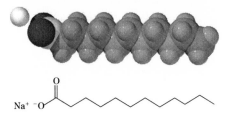

Figure 13-1 shows a molecular model of sodium laurate, the principle soap produced by the reaction of sodium hydroxide with coconut oil. In aqueous solution, the soap ionizes; a harem of water molecules seduces the positive sodium ion to abandon its laurate ion; another bevy of water molecules solvate the hydrophilic carboxylate head of the laurate ion, leaving the hydrophobic tail to sulk like a wallflower at the senior prom. Such is the life of a soap molecule at very low concentration.

Things get more interesting, however, as the soap concentration increases. As we noted in Section 7.4, solutions are transparent. But as we increase the soap concentration, there comes a point where the solution begins to look turbid or cloudy, the surface tension drops, and the electrical conductivity changes. The concentration at which these changes occur is called the *critical micelle concentration.* The reason for these changes is that when the concentration reaches this critical level, the lonely hydrophobic tails begin to find one another and the soap molecules aggregate into roughly spherical *micelles,* as shown in Figure 13-2. Like a tiny planet, each micelle has a liquid, fatty core of hydrophobic tails and a surface of hydrophilic carboxyl groups (upper figure). Above this surface is an atmosphere of sodium ions, each surrounded by a happy clan of water molecules (lower figure). Not shown in the figure is a seemingly infinite space that separates our little micellar planets. This space bustles with countless dancing water molecules, unaffiliated with sodium or laurate ions for the time being.

We can now begin to understand how soap stabilizes an oil/water emulsion. In the absence of soap, oil molecules would wander aimlessly through the solution, occasionally finding hydrophobic soulmates and coalescing into droplets. Tiny droplets would occasionally merge, forming larger and larger droplets,

Figure 13-2. Soap Micelle

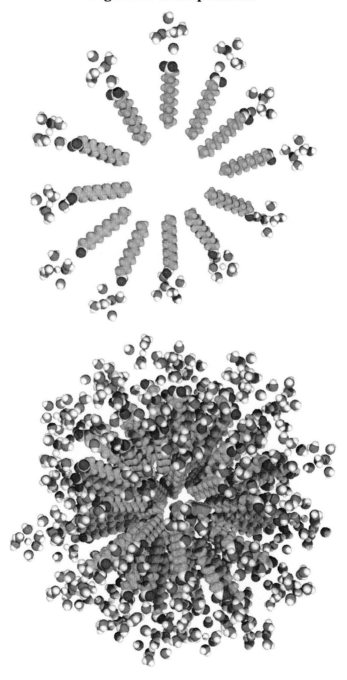

until at last only one giant glob of oil would remain. In the presence of soap, however, the hydrophobic oil molecules dissolve in the fatty liquid cores of the micelles, which swell to accommodate their new tenants. But because their surfaces are covered with negatively charged carboxyl groups, and because like charges repel one another, micelles do not merge. Instead, they keep their distance from one another, drifting endlessly through the crush of dancing water molecules. The oil molecules are happy, the soap molecules are happy, and the sodium ions and water molecules are happy—the emulsion is stable, and all is right with the world.

We now turn to the question of whether soap is the only kind of substance that can behave in this way. The essential requirement for emulsion bliss is that one end of the surfactant molecule should be soluble in oil and the other in water.[1] Alcohols have this property—short alcohols like methanol or ethanol are more soluble in water than in oil, while long alcohols like decanol or dodecanol are more soluble in oil than in water. Some emulsions are well stabilized by an alcohol with a tail length chosen to be "just right."

In Section 11.2 we found that an alcohol and a carboxylic acid may combine to form an ester. These esters were not soluble in water because the hydrophilic heads of the acid and alcohol were joined, leaving only the hydrophobic tails. But carboxylic acids are not the only acids that form esters. Sulfuric acid is a di-protic acid—it has two ionizable protons. When an alcohol combines with sulfuric acid, the resulting ester is still water soluble because of the remaining proton. If this acidic ester is neutralized with sodium hydroxide, we get a sodium alkyl sulfate.[2] Sodium lauryl sulfate, illustrated in Figure 13-3, exemplifies the alkyl sulfates. This molecule has the same hydrocarbon tail as sodium laurate, but its sulfate group is more soluble in water than the carboxyl group that heads the fatty acids. Consequently, sodium lauryl sulfate does not precipitate in the presence of acids and minerals as the soaps do. Its detergency survives hard or acidic water that would turn soap into an insoluble scum. It is largely for this reason that sodium lau-

---

1.   Such molecules are called *amphiphiles.*
2.   *Alkyl* is the generic term for the hydrocarbon tail. Though it sounds like *alkali,* the two words are unrelated.

Figure 13-3. Sodium Lauryl Sulfate

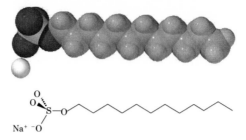

Figure 13-4. Sodium Eugenolate

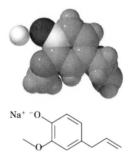

ryl sulfate and its alkyl sulfate brethren have found a home in the commodity soap industry.

We met eugenol in Section 11.3 as the principle component of clove and cinnamon oils. Technically an alcohol, eugenol's proton is more acidic than those of ethanol, glycerol, and the other alcohols. Like the fatty acids, eugenol is not very soluble in water, but its alkali salts are. Figure 13-4 shows a molecular model of sodium eugenolate. The oxygen atom of sodium eugenolate is darker (more negative) than that of eugenol, as seen in Figure 11-4 (page 199). As with the other surfactants in this chapter, the sodium cation is easily ionized, and the eugenolate anion behaves as a surfactant. This has important consequences for soaps containing clove or cinnamon oils, as we'll find in Section 13.5.

All of the surfactants of this section ionize into cations and anions. Though their cations do not participate in micelle formation, they do affect the solubility of the surfactants. Those containing sodium are the least soluble, those containing potassium are more soluble, and those containing ammonium as the cation are even more soluble. The most soluble of these surfactants employ the tetraethylammonium cation; these are often used as components of shampoos. While the cations affect solubility, the working part of these surfactants is the anion, derived from acids with non-polar hydrophobic tails. It is for this reasons that they belong to a class of surfactants known as the *anionic surfactants*.

13.2 Dynamic Equilibrium

The anionic surfactants of the previous section ionize when dissolved in water. When sodium laurate dissolves, for example, we may write:

$$NaLau = Na^+ + Lau^-$$

So far in this book, we have presumed that *all* of the sodium laurate ionizes. In fact, our stoichiometric calculations assume that all of the reactants in an equation turn completely into products. But education is an increasingly sophisticated series of half-truths. It is time to move to the next level. Not all of the sodium laurate ionizes—some of it may remain as an undissolved lump. In other words, sodium laurate has a limited solubility.

You are undoubtedly familiar with materials that, though soluble, are not completely soluble. If you add a spoonful of sugar to a glass of iced tea, it dissolves completely. A second or third spoonful of sugar may also dissolve completely, but there comes a point where additional sugar simply falls to the bottom of the glass. The solution is now saturated. Hours later, the sugar continues to sit at the bottom of the glass, and it may appear that nothing is going on, but the situation is not static. Some of the sugar is dissolving while some of the dissolved sugar falls out of solution—precipitates—and sinks to the bottom of the glass. Chemists call this *dynamic equilibrium*. The concentration of sugar remains constant even while individual sugar molecules continue to dissolve and precipitate.

Solubility is one example of dynamic equilibrium. When a little sodium laurate is added to water, it dissolves completely, ionizing into sodium and laurate ions. As more soap is added, individual laurate ions aggregate into micelles and more soap dissolves. But there comes a point where no more soap will dissolve, and any additional soap remains undissolved. As in the sugar example, however, this equilibrium is dynamic. Some laurate ions join to form new micelles; others leave existing micelles and move back into solution. Sodium and laurate ions meet, join, and precipitate as quickly as undissolved sodium laurate molecules ionize and dissolve. All of these processes happen simultaneously, continually, and quickly. We represent this intricate dance of molecules with a simple equation:

$$NaLau = Na^+ + Lau^-$$

The ionization of sodium laurate is not the only dynamic equilibrium in play in a soap solution. The laurate ion is the conjugate base of lauric acid, and as such, it may react with acid. If there are no stronger acids around, laurate ion may even react with water:

$$Lau^- + H^+ = HLau$$
$$Lau^- + H_2O = HLau + OH^-$$

In fact, these two equations are simply two ways of expressing the same basic chemistry: that any weak acid is in equilibrium with its conjugate base.

The simple equations in this section represent multiple, simultaneous, dynamic equilibria. Laurate ions are constantly entering and leaving micelles. Lauric acid molecules are ionizing and entering solution even while sodium and laurate ions are coming together and precipitating as sodium laurate. In the midst of all this, laurate ions are bumping into water molecules, picking up protons from them to produce hydroxide ions and lauric acid molecules, which may meet and become laurate ions and water once again. This is the elaborate and continuous dance that a chemist envisions, as choreographed by the deceptively sedate equations we've considered on paper.

13.3 pH

The simultaneous equilibria of the last section fundamentally link the interactions of conjugate acids and bases. When the pH is low, there are plenty of H^+ ions floating around, making it very likely that any available laurate ion will pick up a proton and become lauric acid. When the pH is high, there are very few H^+ ions, and unaffiliated laurate ions are more likely to run into water molecules than protons. When they do, they release OH^- ions into solution. Thus, acidic solutions necessarily contain more lauric acid molecules than laurate ions; alkaline solutions contain more laurate ions than lauric acid molecules. Thus the pH of a solution determines the relative amounts of lauric acid and laurate ion.

By the same token, the relative amounts of lauric acid and laurate ion determine the pH. If you mix a lot of lauric acid with a little sodium laurate, the solution will be acidic and its pH will be low. If you mix a little lauric acid with a boatload of sodium laurate, the solution will be alkaline and its pH will be high. Chemists view pH as a sliding scale, with low pH favoring lauric acid and high pH favoring laurate. If you mix equal moles of lauric acid and sodium laurate, you get to a very special place: The pH of such a mixture is called **pK_a**. Each fatty acid has a characteristic value of pK_a; for lauric acid it is 7.5.

The fatty acid/soap equilibrium explains why a soap solution must be alkaline in order to work. Under acidic conditions (pH below pK_a), the equilibrium favors insoluble lauric acid, which separates from solutions as a greasy solid. Only when the pH is relatively high (pH above pK_a) is there enough laurate ion in solution to form micelles, which do the "dirty work" for which soap is famous. In practice, the pH of a fatty acid/soap mixture must be somewhere between pK_a and the pH of a pure soap solution. Table 13-1 gives the possible pH ranges for the common fatty acids and their soaps. A mixture of lauric acid/sodium laurate, for example, must have a pH between 7.5 and 10.1. The higher the pH climbs within this range, the more laurate ion is available for cleaning. Excessively alkaline solutions, however, sting the eyes and tongue and are therefore associated with harsh, undesirable soaps. So the trick is to balance the high pH required for soap to work with the low pH valued by consumers.

Makers of commodity soap solve this problem by including detergents with low pK_a values or by mixing soap with fatty acids before pressing the resulting mixture into bars. By this means, they can precisely balance the ratio of acid to soap to get the optimum cleansing properties at the lowest possible pH.

Table 13-1. pH Ranges for Fatty Acid/Soap Mixtures

Fatty Acid	pKa	pH*	Soap
Lauric Acid	7.5	10.1	Sodium Laurate
Myristic Acid	8.2	10.4	Sodium Myristate
Palmitic Acid	8.8	10.7	Sodium Palmitate
Stearic Acid	10.2	11.4	Sodium Stearate
Oleic Acid	9.9	11.2	Sodium Oleate
Linoleic Acid	9.2	10.9	Sodium Linoleate
Linolenic Acid	8.3	10.4	Sodium Linolenate

Sources for pKa: References [64] and [65].

* pH for 1% solution of pure soap in water.

In the handcrafted soap business, however, things are not quite so simple. Hot-process soapmakers can add fatty acids (or even acetic or citric acid) to the finished soap before pressing it into the molds. Cold-process soapmakers do not have this luxury. If you add any acid to the raw soap, it will react instantly with the caustic soda, resulting in an expensive and wasteful version of lye discounting. There will be unsaponified oil in the finished soap, but it will be just as alkaline as if you had added no acid at all.[3] Any soap, be it a commodity or handcrafted product, made by the cold- or hot-process method, can only be acidified after saponification is complete.

The cold-process soapmaker has two means by which to control the pH of soap. Since the various fatty acids have different values of pK_a, a soapmaker might choose to include soaps whose fatty acids are at the low end of the pK_a scale. We would expect a coconut oil soap, high in sodium laurate, to be less alkaline than a tallow soap, high in sodium stearate. In practice, soapmakers blend oils to balance the desirable properties of the resulting soaps. Coconut and palm kernel oils, for example, contribute not only a quick lather, but a lowering of the pH in soap solutions.

The second means for controlling pH is to acidify the soap during the curing process. This happens naturally, without effort or expense, because we happen to live in an atmosphere

---

3. See Example 15-1 (page 250).

that is slightly acidic. Acidic carbon dioxide in the air slowly neutralizes alkalis in soap. It reacts with any excess sodium hydroxide to produce sodium carbonate, also known as soda ash. After consuming sodium hydroxide, it starts in on the next strongest alkali—soap. It is for this reason that aged soap has always been considered milder than fresh soap.

13.4 Soap Scum

The sodium soaps we have been considering are only one member of an extended family, which includes any combination of a fatty acid with an alkali. Ammonium and potassium soaps are the most soluble members of the family; they find use in liquid soaps and shampoos. The sodium soaps are less soluble and are commonly used for bar soaps. Lithium, barium, and calcium soaps are used in lubricating oils and greases. In this application, calcium soaps have the distinct advantage of being insoluble in water. This property, however, is problematic in soaps used for cleansing. While nobody would intentionally include calcium in a cleansing bar, calcium soaps form spontaneously when hard water is used.

Hard water is a general term used to describe water containing dissolved minerals, particularly calcium compounds. When soluble soaps meet hard water, dissolved calcium combines with soap anions to produce insoluble calcium soaps. Sodium laurate, for example, combines with calcium chloride to produce calcium laurate:

$$2\,NaLau + CaCl_2 = CaLau_2 + 2\,NaCl$$

The calcium laurate precipitates as a greasy solid. In hard water, multi-oil soaps precipitate a variety of insoluble calcium soaps including calcium palmitate, calcium stearate, and calcium oleate. We know this mixture as soap scum.

In actual use, the soap concentration is usually much higher than the calcium concentration. Calcium combines with soap anions until the calcium is consumed. The remaining soluble soap then emulsifies the greasy calcium soaps along with the oils and greases it is being used to clean. Thus, with ordinary hard water, we do not notice the formation of calcium soaps immediately. We find them as deposits that build up over time on the side of the tub or in the drain trap.

We have seen that detergents have the advantage of working at lower pH than soaps. Another major advantage is that they do not form insoluble calcium compounds. This difference between soaps and detergents is not likely to be noticeable in any but the hardest water. In the following demonstration, we use a 1% solution of calcium chloride (far more concentrated than most hard water) to illustrate the difference between soaps, detergents, and combinations of soaps and detergents. To make this solution, you may use laboratory-grade calcium chloride or a commercial ice-melting product that contains mostly calcium chloride. I used Prestone Driveway Heat, a product that lists calcium chloride as its first ingredient.

You will need examples of toilet soaps containing soaps and detergents. We want one that contains only detergents. Look for sodium lauryl sulfate and/or sodium laureth sulfate on the list of ingredients and make sure that no soaps or fatty acids appear there. Most often, these formulations appear in commodity liquid soaps. I used Dial Antibacterial Hand Soap. We want another product that contains only soap. You may use one of your soaps or a commodity soap that contains no detergents. I used Ivory Soap. We also want an example of a product that combines detergents with soaps and fatty acids. A popular combination is sodium lauroyl isethionate, stearic acid, and sodium tallowate. I used Dove Sensitive-Skin, Unscented Beauty Bar. In a classroom setting, your teacher may also provide an unknown solution for you to identify as soap, detergent, or a detergent/soap combination.

1. *Gather your materials:*
   - Distilled water
   - Calcium chloride
   - Three or four cleaning products to be tested
   - A soap oven (or microwave oven) and oven mitts
   - Three or four 125 mL Erlenmeyer flasks
   - Three or four 250 mL Erlenmeyer flasks
   - Three or four pipets, labeled with the names of the sample to be tested.
   - Your soapmaking notebook and a pen

2. *Make calcium chloride solutions:* Synthetically weigh 99.00 g of distilled water and 1.00 g of calcium chloride into each of the 250 mL flasks. Swirl each flask until the calcium chloride is completely dissolved.

3. *Make sample solutions:* Synthetically weigh 99.00 g of distilled water and 1.00 g of the first cleaning product into its labeled 125 mL flask. Repeat with the other products. Label each flask accordingly. You may heat the water in advance, or you may place the flasks in a soap oven or microwave oven to heat the solutions. Swirl the flasks until the cleaning products are dissolved. Some of the products will produce clear solutions; others may produce cloudy suspensions. Note the differences in your notebook.

4. *Add sample to the calcium chloride solutions:* Because a cloudy suspension will obscure our view of the reaction, we will add the sample solution to the calcium chloride solution, not *vice versa*. Use a labeled pipet to transfer 1 mL of the first sample solution to one of the calcium chloride flasks. Label this flask with the identity of the cleaning product added to it. Repeat with the remaining cleaning products, adding 1 mL of sample solution to a correspondingly labeled calcium chloride flask. Note the results in your notebook.

   We added only 1 mL of sample solution to start with so that we could see the reaction before the solution got too cloudy. You may now add a second, third, and fourth 1 mL portion of each sample solution to the corresponding calcium chloride flask, noting the results as you go. Finally, you may add the entire contents of each sample flask to the corresponding calcium chloride flask. If you leave the flasks undisturbed overnight, you will see any insoluble calcium soaps separate from the rest of the solution.

5. *Cleanup:* The solutions may be safely poured down the drain. Wipe down your balance, wash out your glassware, and bring your notebook up to date.

The world is a big place, full of myriad people with a variety of consumer preferences. Some people prefer detergents, which operate at a lower pH than soaps and are more or less impervious to the calcium in hard water. Others like commodity soaps, with their traditional look and feel, and their low prices. Still others value the compromises that come out of combining soaps and detergents. And the late twentieth century saw a blossoming of the handcrafted soap industry, capable of producing soaps with a wider variety of scents, colors, and combinations of oils than had been available in commodity soaps. Personally, I am glad to have lived at a point in history with such a wide variety of available cleansing products.

Properly manufactured, none of these products is dangerous. Yet at least one ad campaign for a commodity detergent/soap combination bar has portrayed soap scum as an invisible layer of nastiness that can be visualized only in an "artistic dramatization." You will judge for yourself whether, as the ad claims, a detergent/soap combination bar "does not interact with calcium in the same way that a soap would."

While makers of handcrafted soap do not have advertising budgets as large as those of giant soap companies, they have not been immune from trash talking the competition. Email chain letters circulate, claiming that sodium laureth sulfate causes cancer. Websites make detergents sound like napalm. The safety of soaps and detergents should be evaluated by those with the budgets and expertise needed to do so. References [60], [66], [67], and [68] exemplify the kinds of exhaustive reviews that are available for detergents, soaps, and common ingredients found in both. If you choose to talk about the relative safety of competing products, you owe it to yourself and your audience to understand what the literature does and does not say, and to summarize it fairly, without cherry-picking or embellishing the worst-sounding sentence fragments from these studies. Otherwise, you descend from the lofty realm of the soapmaker to the lair of the charlatan and the quack.

13.5 Trace

Soaps and detergents stabilize oil/water emulsions, not only in the tub, sink, and washing machine, but in the soap pot. The limiting factor in saponification is the degree to which oil and lye come into contact with one another. When we shake, stir, or blend oil and lye, the lye is broken up into droplets, increasing the total surface area through which oil and lye come into contact. In the absence of saponification, this emulsion would eventually separate, but the first little bit of soap that forms stabilizes the emulsion. We see this stabilization as a thickening of the emulsion—that is, an increase in its viscosity. As more soap forms, the viscosity continues to increase to the point that the soap will no longer separate and may be safely poured into the mold. A visible marker for adequate viscosity is that the surface of the raw soap no longer "heals" itself when soap is drizzled into it. A dribble of soap from a spoon or spatula leaves a mark, or *trace* on the surface, and this sign has given us the name for the condition.

If your experience in Section 4.2.4 (page 73) was anything like mine, your linoleic and linolenic soaps were very slow to trace, if they traced at all. In fact, my linoleic and linolenic soaps separated in the mold. The result was a slimy concoction that had to be scraped out of the mold with a spatula. Trace can be hastened by decreasing the amount of water, by increasing the temperature, or by adding materials that stabilize the raw soap emulsion. In Section 4.2.4 we added no extra water, so that option is not available to us. We could increase the temperature, but for this exercise we choose to add a surfactant to stabilize the raw soap emulsion. Eugenol has been identified as particularly effective in this regard. You can use clove oil. For comparison, make up a bar of linoleic soap and one of linolenic soap using 1 ppt clove oil. I made, for example:

- $\text{Safflower}_{1000}\text{Lye}_{266}\text{Clove}_1$
- $\text{Hemp}_{1000}\text{Lye}_{270}\text{Clove}_1$

If you wish, you may make up a bar of each soap without clove oil for comparison.

In Section 4.2.1 (page 64) we made olive oil soap with no extra water because additional water would have slowed saponification. We may now use clove oil to make a Castile soap with the usual amount of water without waiting an inordinate amount of time for trace:

- $\text{Olive}_{1000}\text{Lye}_{262}$
- $\text{Olive}_{1000}\text{Lye}_{262}\text{Aq}_{131}\text{Clove}_1$

The use of clove oil as a catalyst for the saponification of olive oil will allow us to study the "water discount" in Chapter 21. The chemistry of trace will be further explored in Chapter 23.

Practice Problems

Answers to practice problems appear in Appendix A (page 335).

1. Soap labels sometimes list as ingredients sodium tallowate, sodium cocoate, sodium palmate, or sodium palm kernelate. How do these differ from soaps like sodium stearate and sodium laurate?

2. Soap labels sometimes list as ingredients coconut acid and tallow acid. What do you suppose these are?

3. Sodium laureth sulfate (CAS 9004-82-4) is a popular detergent. Search for information on this compound and draw its structural formula. What makes it an effective detergent?

4. Sodium lauroyl isethionate (CAS 7381-1-3) is a popular detergent for solid cleansing bars. Search for information on this compound and draw its structural formula. What makes it an effective detergent?

5. Cocamidopropyl betaine (CAS 86438-79-1) is a popular detergent for solid cleansing bars. Search for information on this compound and draw its structural formula. What makes it an effective detergent?

6. A recent television ad claims that the cleansing system in a Dove bar is fundamentally different from soap. Examine the ingredients list on a Dove beauty bar and classify each ingredient as detergent, soap, fatty acid, or other.

7. Ivory Soap's slogan, "99-44/100% Pure," follows from an 1882 analysis by chemist W. M. Habirshaw, who found the soap to be 72.53 percent "fatty anhydrides," 9.28 percent "soda combined," and 17.63 percent "water by difference." Examine the ingredients list on an Ivory Soap bar and classify each ingredient as detergent, soap, fatty acid, or other.

8. Palmolive Soap was originally named for the oils used to make it. Examine the ingredients list on a Palmolive Soap bar and classify each ingredient as detergent, soap, fatty acid, or other.

9. Liquid soap may be made by substituting potassium hydroxide for sodium hydroxide. Commodity liquid "soaps," however, are more often made with detergents than soaps. Examine the ingredients list on several bottles of liquid soap,

and find examples that are predominantly soap or predominantly detergent.

10. Many email chain letters and websites malign sodium lauryl sulfate as a toxin and a carcinogen. One website even goes so far as to misquote, misinterpret, and fabricate portions of an extensive review of the properties of sodium lauryl sulfate [60]. A copy of the original review may be obtained by interlibrary loan. Summarize in your own words the Discussion and Conclusion sections of this review.

Part III

Quality Control

In Part I you learned how to make single bars of soap for evaluation purposes. Part III will focus on evaluating the properties of finished soap. The goal of quality control is to ensure that the product is free of defects that might render it unfit for its intended use. The American Oil Chemists' Society (AOCS) publishes methods for measuring most anything you would want to measure about oils and soap [72]. Many of the tests in this part have been adapted from AOCS methods to use materials and skills developed earlier in this book. The American Society for Testing and Materials (ASTM) also publishes methods for measuring and testing a wide variety of products, including soap [58].

Mastering the material in this part will enable you to:
- experimentally measure the moisture concentration of soap
- experimentally measure the alkali concentration in soap
- determine whether a soap is caustic

Chapter 14

Moisture

*A*LL cold-process soaps contain some moisture, even after curing. This moisture comes from the water used to make the lye, any additional water added to dilute the lye, and any moisture present in other additives, such as milk. As the soap cures, moisture evaporates and the weight of the soap decreases for a while until at last it reaches a stable value. At this point, the soap is in equilibrium with the moisture in the air around it. It picks up moisture when the relative humidity increases and releases that moisture when the relative humidity falls. We would like to know how much moisture is contained in a sample of soap. The procedures of this chapter will allow you to answer that question.

14.1 Air Oven Method

There are two reasons that the air oven method may not be ideal for measuring the moisture concentration of cold-process soaps.[1] First, these soaps contain significant amounts of glycerol, a by-product of the saponification process. The concern is that some of this glycerol may evaporate in the oven along with the water, and since we are following the weight loss, we'll fool ourselves into thinking that there was more water present than there actually was. The second concern is that any unsaturated fatty acids in the soap may oxidize during the heating process.

---

1. This method has been adapted from AOCS Official Methods Da 2-48 [72]. A similar method is provided by ASTM D 460-91 [58]. These methods specify heating the soap in an oven at 105°C (221°F), just above the boiling point of water. They note that the method is not applicable to soaps containing sodium silicate or more than 1% glycerol, or to those made from highly unsaturated oils such as linseed oil. For soaps like these, a more involved procedure (AOCS Da 2b-42) is recommended.

Equation 14-1. Calculating Moisture Concentration

$$? \text{ g Aq} = 1000 \, \cancel{g \, soap} \left(\frac{\text{YY.YY} - \text{ZZ.ZZ} \, \cancel{g \, Aq}}{\text{YY.YY} - \text{XX.XX} \, \cancel{g \, soap}} \right)$$

$$C_{Aq} = 1000 \left(\frac{\text{YY.YY} - \text{ZZ.ZZ}}{\text{YY.YY} - \text{XX.XX}} \right) \text{ppt Aq}$$

In these equations, XX.XX is from step 4, YY.YY from step 5, and ZZ.ZZ from step 7.

The method is easy, however, and as long as we are aware of these limitations, it may provide some information on the moisture concentration of soap.

The aocs method employs a desiccator, a special container designed to keep things dry. In the aocs method, an evaporating dish filled with soap is dried in an oven and then allowed to cool in a desiccator. The desiccator prevents the dish from picking up moisture from the air before it can be weighed. While this additional step might be appropriate for precision work with a milligram balance, it may not be necessary for an approximate measure of moisture concentration, particularly given the other considerations that limit the accuracy of the method.

1. *Gather your materials:*
   - Goggles or glasses
   - An eyewash bottle
   - Gloves
   - A centigram balance
   - A sample of the soap to be tested
   - A small porcelain evaporating dish
   - A soap oven and beaker tongs
   - A knife

2. *Preheat your oven:* Preheat your oven to 225°F or 105°C. The important thing is that the temperature be above the boiling point of water but not so high that the soap decomposes.

3. *Dry the dish:* Place the evaporating dish in the oven for one hour. Use beaker tongs to remove the dish from the hot oven and allow it to cool for 5 minutes.

4. *Weigh the dish:* Tare the balance and place the cool dish on it. Record the empty weight, XX.XX g, in your notebook.

5. *Weigh the soap:* Remove the dish from the balance and fill it with about 5 g of soap shavings. Return it to the balance and record the total weight, dish plus soap, YY.YY g, in your notebook.

6. *Dry the soap:* Place the filled evaporating dish in the oven for one hour. Use beaker tongs to remove the dish from the hot oven and allow it to cool for 5 minutes.

7. *Weigh the dried soap:* Return the dish to the balance and record the total weight, dish plus dried soap, ZZ.ZZ g, in your notebook.

8. *Cleanup:* Wipe down your balance and bring your notebook up to date.

9. *Calculate the moisture concentration:* Three numbers are needed to calculate the moisture concentration: the weights of the empty dish, the dish filled with moist soap, and the dish filled with dry soap. Equation 14-1 details the calculation for turning these three numbers into the moisture concentration in ppt.

In the example shown, I tested the oven method on a sample of soap with a known moisture concentration. I made one trial using a desiccator and one without. In this test the use of the desiccator did not produce more reliable results, and it would be difficult to justify the expense of a desiccator for a soapmaker who did not already have one. Both trials underestimated the moisture concentration by a few ppt, but confirmed the known moisture concentration when rounded to the nearest percent. I believe that when this level of accuracy is sufficient, the air oven method can be used to measure the moisture concentration of cold-process soap.

14.2 Calculated Moisture Concentration

The air oven method and the more involved distillation method (AOCS Da 2b-42) were developed to analyze soap with unknown moisture concentration. But in the cold process, we know exactly how much water is in the raw soap because we put it there explicitly. If we can keep track of the weight loss as the soap cures, it should be possible to calculate the moisture concentration simply from the weight of the soap. This has the additional advantage that no soap need be sacrificed in the test.

In the example from the previous section, we determined the moisture concentration of raw olive oil soap. To calculate this, we took half the weight of lye and divided by the total weigh of the raw soap. We could have done the calculation using the actual weights used to make the soap, be it a single experimental bar or a larger batch. We could also have made the calculation from the soap formula. If the soap had contained additional water or other aqueous additives, we would have included these along with half of the lye.

To determine the moisture concentration of finished soap, we start with the moisture concentration of raw soap. Consider the four-oil soap from Section 5.5:

$Olive_{390}Coconut_{280}Palm_{280}Castor_{50}Lye_{288}Aq_{144}$
We begin by calculating the total weight of the raw soap:

Olive	390 g
Coconut	280 g
Palm	280 g
Castor	50 g
Water	144 g
Lye	288 g
Total	1432 g

Now calculate the weight of any water in the formula. This includes half the lye, the additional water, and any other aqueous materials:

Example 14-1. Using Equation 14-1 to Calculate Moisture Concentration

I wanted to find out how reliable the oven method would be in determining the moisture concentration of cold-process soap. I started by making a bar of soap whose moisture concentration I would know exactly: $Olive_{1000}Lye_{262}$. Since the lye was half water, this soap contained 131 g of water per 1262 g of soap, or 104 ppt moisture. I mixed and processed the soap in the soap oven for 4 hours at 60°C (140°F), sealing it in a plastic bag to prevent the escape of moisture.

I measured the moisture concentration for two samples. Dish A was always allowed to cool for 5 minutes in a desiccator before weighing. Dish B was always allowed to cool on the countertop for 5 minutes. Soap shavings were added to each dish and they were heated in an oven at 104°C (219°F) for 1 hour, cooled for 5 minutes, and weighed. The process was repeated for 30 minutes at 105°C (221°F) and then another 30 minutes at 120°C (248°F). There was negligible weight loss (0.01 g and 0.00 g) between the final two heatings, and the samples were considered to be completely dried at this point.

Dish	Empty (g)	Full Moist (g)	Full Dry (g)	Moisture (ppt)
A	20.97	26.08	25.59	96
B	21.67	26.74	26.24	99
Formula				104

The moisture concentration for this soap turned out to be near 10%, whether calculated from the formula or determined by the oven method. I expect, then, that the oven method is a reliable one for measuring moisture concentration to the nearest percent.

This procedure took about 4 hours, though other activities were performed while the dishes were in the oven.

Water		144 g
Lye	(0.5) 288 g =	144 g
Total		288 g

Finally, divide the weight of water by the total weight and multiply by 1000 to get the moisture concentration; in this example, 201 ppt.

Suppose that we have made up a large batch of this soap and unmolded the fresh soap, which we'll assume to have the original moisture concentration. We reserve one bar of this batch for analysis, using some of it to perform any of the tests in the chapters to follow. When we have finished our analysis, we have the remnants of a bar weighing, say, 124.29 g. As this bar cures, it loses weight, and by keeping track of the weight loss, we can estimate the remaining moisture concentration. If the soap has a weight of 110.34 g after a few weeks, it has lost 112 ppt of its original weight.[2] The moisture concentration now is just the initial moisture concentration minus the moisture concentration lost—that is, 89 ppt.[3]

Practice Problems

Answers to practice problems appear in Appendix A (page 335).

1. A bar of $Palm_{1000}Lye_{286}Aq_{286}$ initially weighed 116.36 g. After curing for several weeks, it weighed 93.25 g. What were the initial and final moisture concentrations?
2. A bar of $Coconut_{1000}Lye_{348}Aq_{174}$ initially weighed 118.03 g. After curing for several weeks, it weighed 101.47 g. What were the initial and final moisture concentrations?
3. In Example 14-1, the moisture concentrations of samples A and B are lower than those computed from the formula. Why? How would you test your hypothesis?

---

2. 1000(124.29 - 110.34)/124.29 = 112 ppt weight loss.
3. 201 - 112 = 89 ppt.

Chapter 15

Alkalinity

ECAUSE fatty acids are weak acids, their sodium and potassium salts (soaps) are alkaline by nature. In aqueous solution, a pure soap such as sodium palmitate dissociates into sodium and palmitate ions. A few of the palmitate ions pick up protons from water and become palmitic acid molecules, the water molecules that lost protons become hydroxide ions, and the solution consequently becomes alkaline. Even so, for every hydroxide ion in a solution of pure sodium palmitate there is a palmitic acid molecule. If we were to mix pure sodium palmitate with sodium hydroxide, however, hydroxide ions would outnumber palmitic acid molecules, and the solution would be *excessively* alkaline. In practice, soap may contain excess alkali because too much lye was included in its formula or because saponification is not yet complete. Whatever the reason, soap chemists refer to excess alkali as ***total alkali.*** (TA)[1]

15.1 Total Alkali

As shown in Table 13-1 (page 229), the pH of a soap solution may vary over a considerable range. Consequently, pH alone will not tell us whether soap contains excess alkali. For analytical work, we need a method for precisely measuring the amount

---

1. This method has been adapted from AOCS Official Methods Da 3-48 and Da 4a-48, Da 6-48, and Da 7-48 [72]. A similar method is provided by ASTM D 460-91 [58]. Departures from the official methods are intended to use materials and skills developed earlier in this book. The adaptation uses a smaller sample and less alcohol than the official methods, and the alcohol-insoluble matter is not separated for analysis. Citric acid is used instead of hydrochloric or sulfuric acids, and the titration is performed gravimetrically with a balance rather than volumetrically with a buret. This method is suitable for the routine analysis of finished soap to check the alkali content.

of excess alkali in soap. The TA test expresses the excess alkali in ppt of NaOH, which is sufficiently precise to answer the kinds of questions we wish to ask.

When an excessively alkaline soap is dissolved in ethanol containing phenolphthalein, the solution turns pink. From this point forward, that color change will be the dividing line between "excessively alkaline" (pink) and "tongue neutral" (colorless). The total alkali may be measured by adding acid until the pink color disappears. The more acid required, the more excess alkali is present. The total alkali may then be calculated from the weight of acid required to reach the phenolphthalein endpoint.

The total alkali test may be the most useful analytical test in the whole book. It can be performed on a routine basis to check not only experimental bars of soap but representative bars from all production batches. While it takes some time to dissolve the soap to be tested, the heating of the soap solution may be multitasked with other activities so that the time spent performing the test is only about 10 minutes.

1. *Gather your materials:*
   - Goggles or glasses
   - An eyewash bottle
   - Gloves
   - A centigram balance
   - A sample of the soap to be tested
   - Ethanol
   - A 125 mL Erlenmeyer flask
   - A soap oven (or microwave oven) and oven mitts
   - A knife
   - A filled 125 mL dispensing bottle labeled 5 ppt H₃Cit (Yellow)
   - A filled 125 mL dispensing bottle labeled 5 ppt KOH (Green)
   - A plastic cup labeled Soap
   - A plastic powder funnel
   - 1% phenolphthalein solution

2. *Preheat your oven:* Preheat your oven to 175°F or 80°C.

3. *Neutralize the alcohol:* Add about 50 mL of ethanol to the Erlenmeyer flask. The exact amount is not critical. You may

use the graduations on the side of the flask to measure the alcohol. Add 5 or 6 drops of 1% phenolphthalein solution and swirl the flask to mix it with the alcohol.

The ethanol may contain a small amount of acid that must be neutralized before the soap is added. To neutralize the ethanol, you will add the 5 ppt KOH solution described in Section 8.4.1 (page 155). Add the potassium hydroxide one drop at a time, swirling to mix after each drop, until a faint pink color is just barely detectable. You may hold the flask up against a white piece of paper to view the color. The color should be as faint as you can make it, but there should be no doubt in your mind that it is pink. The ethanol is now said to be neutral to phenolphthalein—the addition of even the slightest amount of base will cause the ethanol to become vividly pink; the addition of even the slightest amount of acid will remove the pink color.

4. *Weigh the soap:* Place the Soap cup onto the balance and press the tare button. Use the knife to carefully shave more than 1.00 g into the cup. Don't waste your time trying to hit an exact target—any weight between 1.10 and 1.20 g will do.

   Analytically weigh the soap into the Erlenmeyer flask using the procedure of Section 2.3 (page 25). Remember to place the funnel into the Soap cup, tare the balance, use the funnel to pour the soap into the flask, and return both the cup and funnel to the balance. The balance will now read -1.*XX* g, the exact weight that has been transferred from the cup to the flask. Whatever the actual weight is, you must record that weight in your notebook *including all three digits.*

5. *Dissolve the soap:* You may heat the Erlenmeyer flask in either a roaster oven[2] or a microwave oven. A laboratory hotplate may also be used. Any other heat source, such as a kitchen oven, range, or household hotplate, is a fire hazard because of the flammability of ethanol. The roaster oven is convenient if you have other things to do while the soap is heating. The microwave oven is more convenient if you want to dissolve the soap as quickly as possible.

---

2. See Section 1.2 (page 5).

To use the roaster oven, place the flask in the oven. After fifteen minutes, remove the soap from the oven and gently swirl it to help dissolve the soap. Place it back into the oven for another fifteen minutes and continue the cycle of heating and swirling until the soap has dissolved.

To use the microwave oven, place the flask into the oven and turn it on for no more than 10 seconds at a time. Swirl the flask after each period of heating until the soap has dissolved. You should not allow the ethanol to boil, and the flask should never become so hot that you cannot pick it up with your bare hands.

6. *Check the color:* If the dissolved soap is colorless, there is no detectable alkali in the soap. More than likely, however, the pink color will have intensified as the soap dissolved.

7. *Titrate the soap solution:* Place the 5 ppt H₃Cit bottle onto the balance and press the tare button. Add a drop of acid to the Erlenmeyer flask and gently swirl it to mix the acid with the soap solution. If the solution loses its pink color, you have reached the endpoint. Otherwise, continue adding acid to the flask a few drops at a time, swirling the flask after each addition, until you reach the endpoint. Replace the 5 ppt H₃Cit bottle onto the balance and record the weight, Y.YY g, in your notebook. A fully saponified soap should require no more than a few drops of acid to reach the endpoint.

8. *Cleanup:* Acid spills may be cleaned up with household ammonia. Alkaline spills may be cleaned up with household vinegar. Wipe down your balance and bring your notebook up to date.

9. *Calculate the total alkali:* Two numbers are needed to calculate the total alkali: the weight of the soap, 1.XX g, and the weight of the acid needed to titrate that soap, Y.YY. Equation 15-1 details the calculation for turning these two numbers into the total alkali in ppt.

Fully saponified, properly formulated soap will contain 1 ppt or less of NaOH. A soap containing 2 ppt of NaOH may simply need to cure a little longer. Soap containing more than 3 ppt NaOH may not have saponified completely, may have been im-

---

Equation 15-1. Calculating TA

$$? \text{ g NaOH} = 1000 \, g \, soap \left(\frac{\text{Y.YY} \, g \, acid}{1.\text{XX} \, g \, soap} \right) \left(\frac{5 \, g \, H_3Cit}{1000 \, g \, acid} \right)$$

$$\left(\frac{1 \, mol \, H_3Cit}{192.12 \, g \, H_3Cit} \right) \left(\frac{3 \, mol \, NaOH}{1 \, mol \, H_3Cit} \right) \left(\frac{40.00 \text{ g NaOH}}{1 \, mol \, NaOH} \right)$$

$$\text{TA} = 3.123 \left(\frac{\text{Y.YY}}{1.\text{XX}} \right) \text{ppt NaOH}$$

In these equations, 1.XX is from step 4 and Y.YY from step 7.

---

properly formulated, or may have issues of incomplete mixing or partial separation.

15.2 Soda Ash

A common defect in handcrafted soap is the phenomenon of "soda ash," a white, powdery deposit that sometimes forms on the surface of soap. There are several possibilities as to the identity of this material, but on websites and in craft books, it is usually identified with sodium carbonate. The idea is that when raw soap is left uncovered, sodium hydroxide rises to the surface and is deposited there as the water evaporates. Over time, the sodium hydroxide reacts with carbon dioxide in the air to produce sodium carbonate:

$$2 \text{ NaOH} + CO_2 = Na_2CO_3 + H_2O$$

That's right—carbon dioxide is an acidic gas, present in ordinary air, that can combine with strong bases just like any other acid. Since the old name for sodium carbonate is "soda ash," that name has been commonly used to describe the phenomenon.

The common cure for soda ash is to cover the raw soap with plastic film until saponification is complete, and if the material formed is actually sodium carbonate, covering the soap is a reasonable prophylactic. Some soapmakers complain, however, that this does not cure their problem. The reason, I believe, is

Example 15-1. The Stoichiometric Hypothesis

Section 12.3 (page 212) introduced the stoichiometric hypothesis, that soap is expected to be tongue neutral as long as the alkali ratio is below the saponification value. I wanted to test this hypothesis. The ssv of Delight was determined in Example 12-1 (page 220) to be between 150 and 153 ppt and refined in Example 18-1 (page 275) to be 150.8 ppt. I made a series of soaps with alkali ratios ranging from 140 to 156 ppt and measured the total alkali the next day. I followed up by repeating the measurements 11 weeks later.

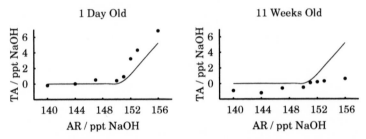

The day old data vindicated the stoichiometric hypothesis. I had expected these soaps to be tongue neutral when the alkali ratio was below 151 ppt. I had further expected that beyond an alkali ratio of 151 ppt, each 1 ppt increase in the alkali ratio would increase the total alkali by 1 ppt, as represented by the solid curve. I was surprised that the soaps beyond 151 ppt were a little more alkaline than expected, but I was satisfied by the striking increase in alkalinity when the alkali ratio exceeded the ssv.

I was further surprised when I repeated the analysis 11 weeks later—all of the soaps had total alkali below 1 ppt. In fact, those with a low alkali ratio were less alkaline than the phenolphthalein indicator (see Practice Problems 4 and 5). While there was still a change in alkalinity above 151 ppt, the magnitude of that change was much less than the stoichiometric hypothesis would lead us to expect. Can you formulate a hypothesis for this decrease in alkalinity? How would you test this hypothesis?

that the term *soda ash* is sometimes used to describe at least three different materials: sodium carbonate, sodium hydroxide, soap crystals that have separated from the main body of the soap. It may also describe some other water-soluble material that gets deposited on the surface of the soap. Until you know which material is on your soap, trying to prevent it is a shot in the dark.

The total alkali test is convenient for finding out whether a typical soap sample has fully saponified. It is incapable, however, of distinguishing between free sodium hydroxide (caustic soda) and free sodium carbonate (soda ash). In this procedure we'll learn to tell one from the other.

Let us suppose that you have a soap that exhibits a white residue of unknown identity. Collect separate samples of this residue and the soap beneath it. Perform the total alkali test on the soap, as described in the previous section. Now perform the same test on the residue up to the point that you have dissolved the residue sample in ethanol. If the entire sample dissolves, complete the total alkali test as usual. Any difference between the alkalinity of the soap and the residue may be attributed to excess sodium hydroxide in the residue. If the alkalinities of the soap and residue are close to one another (within 1 ppt), then the residue is simply soap of a different color from the rest of the soap.

If part of the residue stubbornly refuses to dissolve in ethanol, the insoluble portion *may* be sodium carbonate. Carefully decant the ethanol into a second Erlenmeyer flask, leaving behind as much of the insoluble material as possible. Complete the total alkali test on the ethanol portion in the second flask. Any difference between the alkalinity of the soap and the ethanol-soluble residue may be attributed to excess sodium hydroxide in the residue. Now add 50 mL of water to the ethanol-insoluble residue in the original Erlenmeyer flask. If the residue dissolves, it is most likely borax or sodium carbonate, and if you didn't add any borax to your soap, we can conclude with some confidence that the water-soluble, ethanol-insoluble residue is sodium carbonate. In this case, covering your soap while it is in the mold will very likely eliminate this defect.

A sodium hydroxide residue will be soluble in ethanol and much more alkaline than the soap beneath it.

A soap residue will be soluble in ethanol and will have an alkalinity similar to that of the soap beneath it.

A sodium carbonate residue will be insoluble in ethanol but soluble in water.

A residue that is insoluble in both ethanol and water must be some other impurity. Silica, clays, talcs, and other additives are often added to soap as colorants or modifiers. Check each of your soap ingredients for solubility in ethanol and water, and you will likely be able to identify the residue.

Practice Problems

Answers to practice problems appear in Appendix A (page 335).

1. A soap whose alkali ratio exceeds its saponification value is initially found to be excessively alkaline, as expected. After some time, however, it is retested and found to be tongue neutral. Formulate a hypothesis for this decrease in alkalinity. How would you test this hypothesis?

2. It takes 3.63 g of 5 ppt H_3Cit to titrate a 1.61 g sample to the phenolphthalein endpoint. What is its total alkali?

3. It takes 0.26 g of 5 ppt H_3Cit to titrate a 1.27 g soap sample to the phenolphthalein endpoint. What is its total alkali?

4. For a soap that does not turn ethanolic phenolphthalein pink, we can determine the alkali "shortage" as a *negative* total alkali. We titrate a sample with an alkaline standard like 5 ppt KOH until the solution turns pink. Derive an equation to calculate total alkali from the quantity of soap and the amount and concentration of the standard.

5. It takes 0.37 g of 4.18 ppt KOH to titrate a 1.22 g soap sample to the phenolphthalein endpoint. What is its total alkali?

6. Reference [56] lists the pH of Zest Aqua soap as 9.89 and that of Johnson's Baby soap as 11.90. Should the more alkaline soap be considered harsher?

7. Why do you suppose that the total alkali test is performed in ethanol rather than water?

Part IV

Quality Assurance

In Part III you mastered those skills required to evaluate the properties of finished soap. Part IV will focus on the process of making soap and, in particular, the properties of the raw materials that go into making soap. The goal of quality assurance is to ensure that defects in the raw materials or procedures do not lead to defects in the finished product.

Mastering this material will enable you to:
- compensate for caustic soda or lye that has absorbed moisture
- experimentally measure the acid value of an oil
- experimentally measure the saponification value of an oil

Chapter 16

Caustic Soda

*I*N all of the preceding chapters, we have made an important assumption—that the white granules you spoon out of a bottle or can labeled *sodium hydroxide* are actually pure sodium hydroxide. If you consult the MSDS for this material, it is very likely to state in section 2 that the material is 99–100% sodium hydroxide. If you are willing to spend more money, you can get very pure sodium hydroxide. Aldrich, for example, sells a product that is guaranteed to be 99.998% pure, but it costs about $200 per pound. Even though you will never use this product, it is instructive to note that even this premium grade still contains 0.002% of things that are *not* sodium hydroxide. More importantly, all sodium hydroxide, whether cheap or expensive, contains an impurity not mentioned on the label. That impurity is water.

As soon as you open that premium bottle of sodium hydroxide, it begins to absorb moisture from the air. The product you buy for soapmaking is likely to contain a fair amount of moisture even before you open the can. The amount of moisture depends on the conditions of storage, particularly the humidity at the manufacturing plant on the day the can was sealed. So when you weigh out 20 g or 20 lb of "sodium hydroxide," you are very likely weighing less than that amount.

In Section 4.1 (page 57), we drew the distinction between sodium hydroxide and lye. In this book, the word *lye* is specifically reserved for a solution of sodium hydroxide in water. Beginning in this chapter, we'll draw the further distinction between sodium hydroxide and caustic soda. These are commonly used as synonyms, but in this book, the term *caustic soda* is reserved for the real-world stuff that you actually buy from a vendor. Caustic soda contains mostly sodium hydroxide with an unknown amount of water.

Equation 16-1. Calculating NaOH Concentration

$$? \text{ g NaOH} = 1000 \; \cancel{g \; base}\left(\frac{\text{YY.YY} \; \cancel{g \; acid}}{10.\text{XX} \; \cancel{g \; base}}\right)\left(\frac{500 \; \cancel{g \; H_3Cit}}{1000 \; \cancel{g \; acid}}\right)$$

$$\left(\frac{1 \; \cancel{mol \; H_3Cit}}{192.12 \; \cancel{g \; H_3Cit}}\right)\left(\frac{3 \; \cancel{mol \; NaOH}}{1 \; \cancel{mol \; H_3Cit}}\right)\left(\frac{40.00 \text{ g NaOH}}{1 \; \cancel{mol \; NaOH}}\right)$$

$$C_{\text{NaOH}} = 312.3\left(\frac{\text{YY.YY}}{10.\text{XX}}\right)\text{ppt NaOH}$$

$$\text{AR} = \left(1000 - 624.6\left(\frac{\text{YY.YY}}{10.\text{XX}}\right)\right)\text{ppt NaOH}$$

$$\text{WR} = \left(624.6\left(\frac{\text{YY.YY}}{10.\text{XX}}\right) - 1000\right)\text{ppt Water}$$

In these equations, 10.XX is from step 5 and YY.YY from step 7 of Section 9.4 (page 169). "Base" can be either suspect lye or suspect caustic soda.

If moisture is going to cause a problem, at least it is a problem the soapmaker can live with. Far better to unintentionally use too little sodium hydroxide than too much. You might spend a lifetime without ever being aware of moisture, and the only consequence would be that your soap contained more oil than you intended. No harm done. But to make intelligent decisions about such things as alkali discounting and to evaluate whether a shipment of sodium hydroxide is suitable for making soap, you will need to be able to measure the concentration of lye or caustic soda when you suspect they may have picked up atmospheric moisture.

16.1 Titrating Suspect Lye

To determine the concentration of a suspect lye, follow the procedure of Section 9.4 (page 169), substituting the suspect lye for 5 ppt KOH and substituting 500 ppt H_3Cit for 5 ppt H_3Cit. Then use Equation 16-1 to calculate the concentration of the lye.

Lye that has absorbed moisture will have a concentration less than 500 ppt, which we can remedy by adding more NaOH.

The AR of Equation 16-1 tells us how much NaOH we should add to the dilute lye in order to bring it up to the standard concentration. We use it in the same way that we used it for determining how much NaOH to add to a given amount of oil. If, for example, we had 3518 g of dilute lye with an AR of 24 ppt NaOH, we would need an additional 84 g of NaOH to bring the lye to full strength.[1] This simple calculation will allow us to "rescue" any quantity of lye that has been compromised.

16.2 Titrating Suspect Caustic Soda

To determine the purity of suspect caustic soda, follow the procedure of Section 9.4 (page 169), substituting the suspect caustic soda for 5 ppt KOH and substituting 500 ppt H_3Cit for 5 ppt H_3Cit. Note that you will have to use the procedure of Section 2.3 (page 25) to weigh the solid caustic soda analytically. Then use Equation 16-1 to calculate the concentration of NaOH in the caustic soda. You may need to analyze several samples if the amount of contaminated caustic soda is large.

Good, dry, pure caustic soda has a concentration near 1000 ppt NaOH. A moisture-laden caustic soda will have a lower concentration. When making 500 ppt NaOH, we usually weigh dry NaOH into a container along with an equal portion of water. The water ratio (WR) of Equation 16-1 tells us how much water we should use for a compromised caustic soda. We use it in the same way that we use an AR. If, for example, we had 2431 g of caustic soda with a WR of 904 ppt, we would need 2198 g of water.[2] The resulting lye would have a concentration of 500 ppt, exactly as if we had used dry caustic soda.

16.3 Sodium Carbonate

There is a second material that may contaminate lye or caustic soda exposed to moist air. Atmospheric carbon dioxide is an acidic gas that reacts with sodium hydroxide to form sodium carbonate. While sodium carbonate is not harmful in soap,

---

1. 3518(0.024) = 84 g NaOH.
2. 2431(0.904) = 2198 g of water.

it is less alkaline than sodium hydroxide and, like water, contributes to the weight of caustic soda. Fortunately, sodium carbonate is very nearly insoluble in concentrated lye, so it is easy to spot. It may show up as insoluble white crystals when compromised caustic soda is used to make lye. It may show up as crystals floating on the surface of the lye or as a white crust around the mouth of the bottle. The formation of sodium carbonate is an unavoidable consequence of handling sodium hydroxide in air, and there is no reason to be paranoid about it.

We were once fooled into thinking that we had sodium carbonate contamination in a batch of caustic soda. A student made some lye that, days later, contained undissolved white crystals. It turned out that he had not thoroughly mixed the lye and some of the caustic soda simply sank to the bottom, where it remained as a stubborn undissolved lump. The remedy for this situation was to warm the bottle for a day in a soap oven at its lowest setting. In this way, undissolved sodium hydroxide may be distinguished from sodium carbonate; sodium hydroxide will eventually dissolve under gentle heat, but sodium carbonate will not. Both may be avoided, however, by thoroughly mixing your lye and protecting it from prolonged exposure to air.

Practice Problems

Answers to practice problems appear in Appendix A (page 335).

1. 10.23 g of a compromised lye requires 15.46 g of 500 ppt citric acid to reach the endpoint. How much sodium hydroxide is required to bring 2519 g of this lye up to 500 ppt?
2. 9.97 g of a compromised caustic soda requires 28.55 g of 500 ppt citric acid to reach the endpoint. How much water is required to produce a 500 ppt NaOH solution from 25.7 kg of this caustic soda?
3. In cleaning up the soap lab, white crystals are found under the balance. Are they more likely to be sodium hydroxide or sodium carbonate?

Chapter 17

Free Fatty Acid

Fats and oils undergo a variety of chemical changes during processing, shipping, and storage. One such change is the decomposition of the oil molecule into glycerol and free fatty acid, *free* meaning not part of a triacylglyceride. In essence, the oil has already saponified to some extent, though the fatty acid is produced rather than the sodium or potassium salt of the fatty acid. An oil with a high free fatty acid concentration is often deemed rancid, though it is not necessarily unfit for soapmaking.

The main effect of free fatty acids on soapmaking is that the oil reaches trace very quickly. This is because fatty acids react much more quickly with lye than oils do. When the fatty acid combines with sodium hydroxide, it immediately forms the sodium salt of the fatty acid—that is, a soap. This soap rapidly emulsifies the rest of the oil, which accelerates the saponification of the oil, with the result that the oil traces much more quickly than it would have without the free fatty acid.

Note that if an oil contains free fatty acid, there need not be anything wrong with the soap produced from it. Though the free fatty acid reacts quickly with lye, the product of this reaction is just soap. For this reason, it is not necessary to test every batch of oil for free fatty acid. You can perform this test only if you suspect that a high free fatty acid concentration is responsible for unusually short trace times. If you purchased a batch of rancid oil, it may be possible to negotiate a discount with your vendor.

17.1 Acid Value

The test described in this section will determine the total acidity present in an oil.[1] The ***acid value*** (AV) test is similar to the total alkali measurement of Section 15.1. When measuring TA, you add acid to an ethanolic soap solution until the phenolphthalein indicator changes from pink to colorless. In the AV test you will add standard KOH to an ethanolic oil solution until the indicator changes from colorless to pink. In some sense, the AV test is the opposite of the TA test, measuring the amount of acid present rather than the amount of base. Procedurally, however, the two tests are very similar.

The oil to be tested is dissolved in ethanol and a few drops of phenolphthalein indicator are added. This solution is then titrated with our standard 5 ppt KOH until the indicator changes from colorless to pink. We'll express the AV as the weight of potassium hydroxide needed to neutralize 1000 g of oil. An oil with an AV of more than a few ppt is considered rancid.

1. *Gather your materials:*
   - Goggles or glasses
   - An eyewash bottle
   - Gloves
   - A centigram balance
   - A soap oven (or microwave oven) and oven mitts if the sample is solid
   - Ethanol
   - A 125 mL Erlenmeyer flask
   - A filled 125 mL dispensing bottle labeled   `5 ppt KOH` `(Green)`
   - A 125 mL dispensing bottle labeled `Oil` containing at least 2 g of the oil to be tested
   - 1% phenolphthalein solution

---

1. This method has been adapted from AOCS Official Methods Ca 5a-40 [72]. Departures from the official methods are intended to use materials and skills developed earlier in this book. The adaptation uses a smaller sample and less alcohol than the official methods. Potassium hydroxide is used instead of sodium hydroxide, and the titration is performed gravimetrically with a balance rather than volumetrically with a buret. This method is suitable for the routine analysis of oils and fats to check the acid content.

2. *Melt the sample:* If the sample is solid, melt it in your soap oven or in a microwave oven.

3. *Neutralize the alcohol:* Add about 50 mL of ethanol to the Erlenmeyer flask. The exact amount is not critical. You may use the graduations on the side of the flask to measure the alcohol. Add 5 or 6 drops of 1% phenolphthalein solution and swirl the flask to mix it with the alcohol.

    The ethanol may contain a small amount of acid that must be neutralized before the soap is added. To neutralize the ethanol, add 5 ppt KOH solution one drop at a time, swirling to mix after each drop, until a faint pink color is just barely detectable. You may hold the flask up against a white piece of paper to view the color. The color should be as faint as you can make it, but there should be no doubt in your mind that it is pink. The ethanol is now said to be neutral to phenolphthalein—the addition of even the slightest amount of acid will remove the pink color.

4. *Weigh the oil:* Place the `Oil` bottle onto the balance and press the tare button. Transfer *more than* 1.00 g (about 30 drops) into the Erlenmeyer flask. Don't waste your time trying to hit an exact target—any weight between 1.10 and 1.20 g will do. Return the `Oil` bottle to the balance, which will now read -1.XX g, the exact weight that has been transferred from the bottle to the flask. Whatever the actual weight is, you must record that weight in your notebook *including all three digits.*

5. *Dissolve the oil:* Gently swirl the contents of the flask until the oil has dissolved. If the oil contains any detectable acid, the pink color will disappear. If the solution remains pink, the oil contains no detectable acid and the experiment is complete.

6. *Titrate the oil solution:* Place the `5 ppt KOH` bottle onto the balance and press the tare button. Transfer a drop of KOH to the flask and give it a gentle swirl to mix the base with the oil. If the solution loses its pink color, you have reached the endpoint. If the solution remains pink, continue adding KOH one drop at a time, swirling the solution between additions, until the endpoint is reached. When the solution remains colorless for at least 30 seconds, place the `5 ppt`

Equation 17-1. Calculating AV

$$? \text{ g KOH} = 1000 \, \cancel{g \text{ } oil}\left(\frac{\text{YY.YY } \cancel{g \text{ } standard}}{1.\text{XX } \cancel{g \text{ } oil}}\right)\left(\frac{4.\text{ZZ g KOH}}{1000 \, \cancel{g \text{ } standard}}\right)$$

$$\text{AV} = \left(\frac{\text{YY.YY}}{1.\text{XX}}\right) 4.\text{ZZ ppt KOH}$$

In this equation, 1.XX is from step 4 and YY.YY from step 6. 4.ZZ is the *actual* concentration of your 5 ppt KOH, as determined using the procedure of Section 9.4 (page 169).

KOH bottle back onto the balance and record the weight, Y.YY g, in your notebook.

7. *Cleanup:* Acid spills may be cleaned up with household ammonia. Alkaline spills may be cleaned up with household vinegar. Wipe down your balance and bring your notebook up to date.

8. *Calculate the acid value:* Three numbers are needed to calculate the AV: the weight of the oil, 1.XX g, the weight of 5 ppt KOH needed to titrate that oil, Y.YY g, and the exact concentration of your 5 ppt KOH as determined in the procedure of Section 9.4 (page 169), 4.ZZ. Equation 17-1 details the calculation for turning these three numbers into the acid value in ppt.

The astute reader will note that we have taken less care in measuring the AV than we did with the SV. For one thing, we performed only one titration instead of six. Because the AV is almost always small, we can afford to be a little bit lax in its determination. Simply knowing that the oil contains acid is more important than the precise AV. Even so, it may seem peculiar to express free *acid* in terms of KOH, a base. Since no single acid accounts for the total acidity, we have chosen to express AV in terms of the base needed to neutralize that acidity. In the next section, we'll use this to estimate the free fatty acid (FFA).

Example 17-1. Using Equation 17-1 to Calculate AV

A soapmaker sent me some coconut oil that traced inconveniently quickly. I titrated 1.17 g of this oil to the phenolphthalein endpoint using 21.20 g of 4.18 ppt KOH. Using Equation 17-1 we have:

$$AV = \left(\frac{21.20}{1.16}\right) 4.18 \text{ ppt KOH}$$
$$= 76 \text{ ppt KOH}$$

To put this number in perspective, non-problematic coconut oil from my lab had an AV of only 4 ppt. This test took me 10 minutes to perform.

17.2 Free Fatty Acid

The AV tells us how much free acid is present in an oil. A reasonable question would be "What percentage of my oil consists of free fatty acids—that is, those not bonded to glycerol?" If we make two reasonable assumptions, we can calculate this value without any additional experiments. First, we assume that the only acids present are fatty acids. If the oil had been somehow contaminated with vinegar or other acids, this would be a poor assumption. But if all of the acidity present comes from the natural degradation of the fats present, then the only acids present will be fatty acids. Second, we need a molecular weight for the fatty acid.

Different oils, of course, contain different proportions of fatty acids. One solution to this problem would be to choose the molecular weight of the most abundant fatty acid for the oil in question. This could get complicated for oils that contain a variety of fatty acids, so in practice we choose to express the FFA *as* lauric, palmitic, or oleic acid. We might, for example, express FFA "as lauric acid" for either coconut or palm kernel oil, "as palmitic acid" for tallow, palm oil, or any of the hard fats, and "as oleic acid" for any of the soft, unsaturated oils. Equation

---

Equation 17-2. Calculating FFA

$$? \text{ g lauric acid} = 1000 \, g\text{-}oil\left(\frac{\text{AV } g\text{ } KOH}{1000 \, g\text{-}oil}\right)\left(\frac{1 \, mol\text{ } KOH}{56.11 \, g\text{ } KOH}\right)$$

$$\left(\frac{1 \, mol\text{ } lauric\text{ } acid}{1 \, mol\text{ } KOH}\right)\left(\frac{200.32 \text{ g lauric acid}}{1 \, mol\text{ } lauric\text{ } acid}\right)$$

$$\text{FFA} = 3.570 \, (\text{AV}) \text{ ppt lauric acid}$$

$$? \text{ g palmitic acid} = 1000 \, g\text{-}oil\left(\frac{\text{AV } g\text{ } KOH}{1000 \, g\text{-}oil}\right)\left(\frac{1 \, mol\text{ } KOH}{56.11 \, g\text{ } KOH}\right)$$

$$\left(\frac{1 \, mol\text{ } palmitic\text{ } acid}{1 \, mol\text{ } KOH}\right)\left(\frac{256.42 \text{ g palmitic acid}}{1 \, mol\text{ } palmitic\text{ } acid}\right)$$

$$\text{FFA} = 4.570 \, (\text{AV}) \text{ ppt palmitic acid}$$

$$? \text{ g oleic acid} = 1000 \, g\text{-}oil\left(\frac{\text{AV } g\text{ } KOH}{1000 \, g\text{-}oil}\right)\left(\frac{1 \, mol\text{ } KOH}{56.11 \, g\text{ } KOH}\right)$$

$$\left(\frac{1 \, mol\text{ } oleic\text{ } acid}{1 \, mol\text{ } KOH}\right)\left(\frac{282.46 \text{ g oleic acid}}{1 \, mol\text{ } oleic\text{ } acid}\right)$$

$$\text{FFA} = 5.034 \, (\text{AV}) \text{ ppt oleic acid}$$

In these equations, AV is the acid value calculated in Equation 17-1. Express FFA in terms of lauric, palmitic, or oleic acid, depending on the oil being tested.

17-2 shows the conversion from AV to FFA for each of these fatty acids.

Most oils will have an AV of 0 ppt and an FFA of 0 ppt. Unless you are having a problem, you need not perform this test on a regular basis. If you suspect an oil of being rancid, however, the AV test is quick and easy. If your AV is more than a few ppt, it is probably a good idea to measure the SV as well, using the procedure of Chapter 18. Armed with this information, there is nothing wrong with using the rancid oil for soapmaking. You may, however, want to limit the percentage of rancid oil used if the trace time is inconveniently short.

Example 17-2. Using Equation 17-2 to Calculate FFA

Because the oil in our example was coconut oil, I chose to express the FFA as grams of lauric acid per 1000 g of oil. Taking the AV as 76 ppt, we have:

$$FFA = 3.570 \ (76) \ \text{ppt lauric acid}$$
$$= 271 \ \text{ppt lauric acid}$$

The soapmaker who sent me this oil did so because she noted that it came to trace very rapidly and wondered what might cause this. The FFA test was able to show that approximately 27% of the oil was free fatty acid. When mixed with lye, these fatty acids convert almost immediately into soap. This "instant" saponification releases heat more rapidly than usual and the resulting soap emulsifies the rest of the oil, hastening its saponification. These two effects in combination account for the rapid tracing of this oil.

I also noted that this oil had a strong smell—presumably the smell of the free lauric acid—that vanished after saponification. As was the case for acetic acid in Section 10.1 (page 175), fatty acid salts do not vaporize as easily as the fatty acids themselves.

I concluded that this rancid coconut oil was perfectly acceptable for making soap, particularly if combined with oils that are slow to saponify.

Practice Problems

Answers to practice problems appear in Appendix A (page 335).

1. It took 3.50 g of 4.72 ppt KOH to titrate 1.17 g of an unknown oil to the phenolphthalein endpoint. What was its acid value?

2. An unknown oil has an AV of 6 ppt KOH. Express the FFA "as lauric acid," "as palmitic acid," and "as oleic acid." How might you decide which expression would be most suitable?

3. We have used the AV to characterize oils, but it may also be used for pure acids. Calculate the AV for pure oleic acid. Hint: What is the FFA of pure oleic acid?

4. Derive an equation relating AV to FFA "as stearic acid."

Chapter 18

Saponification Value

*S*OAP made with too much alkali will be excessively harsh; that made with too little will contain unsaponified or partially saponified oil. Had Goldilocks encountered soap-making bears, she would rightly have insisted that the amount of alkali be "just right." We have come to rely on tabulated alkali ratios to determine the amount of NaOH to use with a given weight of oil. But how are these tabulated values determined? How do they compare to the saponification values of the oils we actually have in inventory? Is it possible to measure saponification values ourselves in order to better control the soapmaking process?

In Chapter 12 we learned what *just right* means for an oil of known molecular weight. But real-world oils are complex mixtures of triglycerides, from glyceryl tricaprate to glyceryl triarachidate. If we knew the exact percentages of each triglyceride in the oil, it would be a simple matter to calculate the saponification value. But in real life we never know these percentages exactly. Palm oil differs from coconut oil and olive oil. More than that, the composition of any oil may vary from vendor to vendor and even from one shipment to the next. For all these reasons, it would be useful to be able to determine saponification values for ourselves. This new skill will allow us to use new oils and to diagnose problems with vendors should they arise.

The determination takes place in three stages. First, we make up a solution of KOH in ethanol. Then we use an excess of this solution to make a liquid soap. Next we titrate both the original ethanolic solution and the final soap solution to get the amount of KOH remaining in each. Finally, by subtracting one from the other, we get the amount of KOH that was actually consumed by the saponification process. A mere student will be satisfied to determine a single saponification value. But a soapmaker might actually care enough about the answer to determine the sv three times to make sure the results are consistent.

18.1 Ethanolic KOH Solution

The determination of saponification values starts with a solution of KOH in ethanol. The exact concentration of this solution is not as important as the use of identical portions of the solution in each run of the experiment. Because the exact concentration is not important, we don't need to be particularly careful in weighing out the materials. 40 g of KOH added to 600 g of ethanol will produce enough solution for one complete sv determination.[1]

1. *Gather your materials:*
   - Goggles or glasses
   - An eyewash bottle
   - Gloves
   - A decigram or gram balance
   - KOH
   - Denatured ethanol
   - A clean, dry 2000 mL PP bottle labeled `6% Ethanolic KOH` with cap
   - A plastic powder funnel (optional)
   - A plastic weighing cup
   - A plastic spoon

2. *Arrange your workspace:* Potassium hydroxide deserves your respect. You *must* wear safety goggles or glasses for eye protection and you *ought* to wear gloves. Note that this is one of the few occasions in this book where you can use a decigram or gram balance. Your notebook should be opened to a new page with your pen at the ready.

3. *Approximately weigh the KOH:* The exact concentration of the KOH solution is not important. Tare a plastic weighing cup and pour 80–81 g of KOH into it. Pour this KOH into the bottle labeled `6% Ethanolic KOH`.

---

1. To make enough solution for three complete sv determinations, you can dissolve 80 g of KOH in 1200 g of ethanol using a plastic bottle with a volume of 2000 mL.

4. *Approximately weigh the ethanol:* Tare a plastic weighing cup and pour 1200–1201 g of ethanol into it. Pour this ethanol into the bottle labeled `6% Ethanolic KOH`.

5. *Dissolve the KOH:* Screw the cap onto the bottle and gently swirl it to dissolve the KOH. The solution is ready to use once all of the KOH has dissolved.

6. *Cleanup:* Alkaline spills may be cleaned up with household vinegar.

18.2 SV Determination

The sv test employs the 6% KOH solution of the previous section to make a liquid soap.[2] We can save significant time by coordinating three phases of the experiment. In the first phase, we carefully weigh out six identical portions of 6% KOH. We add the oil of interest to three of these portions and place them in the soap oven to saponify. While the soap is cooking, we titrate the three *blanks,* those portions of 6% KOH that contain no oil. When the soap has finished cooking, we titrate the three soaps. The total time needed for one complete determination is about two hours on the clock, but about one hour of active work.

1. *Gather your materials:*
   - Goggles or glasses
   - An eyewash bottle
   - Gloves
   - A centigram balance
   - An oil to be tested
   - 6% ethanolic KOH solution
   - A filled 125 mL dispensing bottle labeled `500 ppt H₃Cit (Red)`
   - Six clean 500 mL Erlenmeyer flasks labeled `Blank A, Blank B, Blank C, Soap A, Soap B,` and `Soap C`
   - Three watch glasses
   - Two plastic weighing cups labeled `Oil` and `Base`

---

2. This method has been adapted from AOCS Official Methods Ca 3-25 [72]. Departures from the official methods are intended to use materials and skills developed earlier in this book. Citric acid is used instead of hydrochloric or sulfuric acids, and the titration is performed gravimetrically with a balance rather than volumetrically with a buret. This method is suitable for the routine analysis of soapmaking oils.

- Two pipets labeled `Oil` and `Base`
- A soap oven and oven mitts
- 1% phenolphthalein solution

2. *Preheat your oven:* Preheat your oven to 160°F or 70°C.

3. *Synthetically weigh KOH solution:* Use the `Base` weighing cup and `Base` pipet to synthetically weigh 100.00 g of 6% ethanolic KOH solution into the `Blank A` flask. Then weigh identical portions into the other five flasks. What matters here is that the contents of the six flasks are as close to identical as possible. Within limits, the concentration of the solution doesn't matter. What does matter is that the six flasks contain exactly the same weight of KOH solution.

4. *Synthetically weigh oil:* Use the `Oil` weighing cup and `Oil` pipet to synthetically weigh 20.00 g of the oil to be tested into the `Soap A` flask. Then weigh identical portions into the other two `Soap` flasks. If these are not quite identical, note the exact weight, 20.XX g, that went into each flask. The oil will dissolve in the alcohol and immediately begin to saponify. Since we are making liquid soap, however, it will not trace. Furthermore, we have used an excess of KOH so that when saponification is complete, there will be excess alkali. Gently swirl the soap solutions until they are completely mixed. Cover the three flasks with watch glasses[3] and place them into the soap oven for 1 hour to ensure complete saponification.

5. *Prepare the blank solutions:* While the soap is cooking, you can titrate the blank solutions (the ones with no oil in them). Add about 100 mL of distilled water to the three `Blank` flasks. The exact amount of water is unimportant, so you can use the graduations on the sides of the flasks to measure the water. We'll now titrate these solutions to determine exactly how much KOH they contain. Add 5 or 6 drops of 1% ethanolic phenolphthalein solution to each `Blank` solution and swirl to mix; the solutions will turn pink.

6. *Titrate `Blank A`:* Place the `500 ppt H₃Cit (Red)` dispensing bottle onto the balance and tare it. Squirt about

---

3. A watch glass is a small curved dish used here to prevent the ethanol from boiling away. We do not stopper the flasks because a sealed, heated container may explode. The watch glass will cover the flasks without tightly sealing them.

10 g of acid into the `Blank A` flask and return the dispensing bottle to the balance, which shows the weight of acid transferred. Give the flask a gentle swirl to mix the acid with the base. The solution should remain pink, but if it fades slightly, you can add another drop of phenolphthalein solution. Squirt another 10 drops of acid into the flask and give it another swirl. Continue adding acid to the flask, 10 drops at a time, swirling the flask after each addition, until suddenly the solution changes from pink to colorless. Return the dispensing bottle to the balance and note the weight of acid transferred. Whatever the endpoint is, it is less than this amount. In this first titration, we have gone past the endpoint by as many as 10 drops, but in the next two titrations we'll be more careful.

7. *Titrate flasks* `Blank B` *and* `Blank C`*:* Place the `500 ppt` H_3Cit `(Red)` dispensing bottle onto the balance and tare it. Titrate flask `Blank B` as before, but this time, when you get to within about 1 g of the endpoint, add acid to the flask one drop at a time. Drop, swirl, drop, swirl. When the solution in the flask changes from pink to colorless, return the `500 ppt` H_3Cit `(Red)` bottle to the balance and record the weight, YY.YY g, in your notebook. Then proceed to titrate flask `Blank C` in the same way. If you are careful, the endpoints for flasks `Blank B` and `Blank C` should be within just a few drops of one another.

8. *Prepare the soap solution:* Especially your first time out, your blank titrations may occupy the entire hour that the soap is cooking. With practice, though, you will have time for a coffee break. When an hour has elapsed, remove the `Soap` flasks from the soap oven and add about 100 mL of distilled water. As with the blanks, the exact amount of water used is not important, and you may use the graduations on the sides of the flasks to measure the water. Add 5 or 6 drops of 1% ethanolic phenolphthalein solution to the `Soap` flasks and swirl to mix; the solutions will turn pink.

9. *Titrate* `Soap A`*:* We will now use `Soap A` to approximate the endpoint of the soap solutions, just as we used `Blank A` to do this for the blank solutions. Place the `500 ppt` H_3Cit `(Red)` dispensing bottle onto the balance and tare it. Squirt 10 drops of acid into the `Soap A` flask and give it a gentle

swirl to mix the acid with the soap. The solution should remain pink, but if it fades slightly, you can add another drop
of phenolphthalein solution. Squirt another 10 drops of acid
into the flask and give it another swirl. Continue adding
acid to the flask, 10 drops at a time, swirling the flask after each addition, until suddenly the solution changes from
pink to colorless. Return the dispensing bottle to the balance and note the weight of acid transferred. Whatever the
endpoint is, it is less than this amount. As in the first blank
titration, we have gone past the endpoint by as many as 10
drops, but in the next two titrations we'll be more careful.

10. *Titrate flasks* Soap B *and* Soap C*:* Place the 500 ppt
H₃Cit (Red) dispensing bottle onto the balance and tare
it. Titrate flask Soap B as before, but this time, when you
get to within about 1 g of the endpoint, add acid to the flask
one drop at a time. When the solution in the flask changes
from pink to colorless, return the dispensing bottle to the
balance and record the weight of acid transferred, ZZ.ZZ g,
in your notebook. Then proceed to titrate flask Soap C in
the same way. If you are careful, the endpoints for flasks
Soap B and Soap C should be within just a few drops of
one another.

11. *Cleanup:* Acid spills may be cleaned up with household ammonia. Alkaline spills may be cleaned up with household
vinegar. The flasks and cups can be washed immediately.
Wipe down your balance and bring your notebook up to
date.

12. *Calculate the* sv: Only three experimental numbers are
needed to determine the saponification value: the weight of
the oil (20.XX), the endpoint for the blank (YY.YY), and the
endpoint for the soap solution (ZZ.ZZ). The result is given
by the simple calculation shown in Equation 18-1. You can
get both the NaOH and KOH sv from the same set of data.
Each sv may be calculated twice—once using Blank B and
Soap B, and once using Blank C and Soap C. Label the
oil being tested with the average of these two values.

A student measuring an sv for a course may be satisfied with
the preliminary blank and soap titrations. But a soapmaker is
going to actually use the results to make large quantities of
soap. A few hundred grams of material and a couple of hours

of work may save hundreds of pounds of materials later on. If you actually care about the ***precision*** of your answer, you will want to run the experiment multiple times. Fortunately, a preliminary run and two precision runs of the experiment can be done in about the same time as a single precision run. For one thing, all three soaps can cook at the same time. For another, since the preliminary titrations give us ballpark values for the endpoints, we can add enough acid to quickly get close to the endpoints of the precision titrations.

The astute reader will notice that we might just as well calculate the sv for `Soap B` using the endpoint for `Blank C`. This is quite correct. The endpoints for either of the two blanks may be used with the endpoints for either of the two soaps. As a matter of fact, if you are determining svs for several oils using the same ethanolic KOH solution, you only need two blank runs for as many oils as you wish. The only caveats are that the blank runs must be done on the same ethanolic KOH solution used to make the soaps and that the blanks should be run on the same day as the soaps. Using your notebook to keep the data straight, you can save a lot of time by determining svs for several oils at a time.

18.3 The Lye Discount

Our stoichiometric hypothesis holds that if the AR is less than the ssv, all of the NaOH will be consumed and excess oil will remain in the soap. Conversely, if the AR is greater than the ssv, all of the oil will be consumed and excess NaOH will remain in the soap. For most soapmakers, however, the ssv is an unknown quantity, making it difficult to ensure a tongue-neutral soap. Since the ssvs found in tables and lye calculators are average values, the possibility exists that the ssv of a real-world oil might be greater or less than average. If greater, no problem. But if less, we run the risk of making excessively alkaline soap. To counter this possibility, many soapmakers employ a ***lye discount,*** usually expressed as a percentage of the tabulated ssv.

In this book I have advocated an alternate approach. We use an AR at the very bottom of the ssv range, thus ensuring that our soap contains no excess alkali. Nevertheless, we might choose

---

Equation 18-1. Calculating SSV and SV

$$? \text{ g NaOH} = 1000 \; g\text{-}oil\left(\frac{\text{YY.YY} - \text{ZZ.ZZ} \; g\text{-}acid}{20.\text{XX} \; g\text{-}oil}\right)\left(\frac{1 \; g \; H_3\text{Cit}}{2 \; g\text{-}acid}\right)$$

$$\left(\frac{1 \; mol \; H_3\text{Cit}}{192.12 \; g \; H_3\text{Cit}}\right)\left(\frac{3 \; mol \; NaOH}{1 \; mol \; H_3\text{Cit}}\right)\left(\frac{40.00 \text{ g NaOH}}{1 \; mol \; NaOH}\right)$$

$$\text{SSV} = 312.3 \left(\frac{\text{YY.YY} - \text{ZZ.ZZ}}{20.\text{XX}}\right) \text{ ppt NaOH}$$

$$? \text{ g KOH} = 1000 \; g\text{-}oil\left(\frac{\text{YY.YY} - \text{ZZ.ZZ} \; g\text{-}acid}{20.\text{XX} \; g\text{-}oil}\right)\left(\frac{1 \; g \; H_3\text{Cit}}{2 \; g\text{-}acid}\right)$$

$$\left(\frac{1 \; mol \; H_3\text{Cit}}{192.12 \; g \; H_3\text{Cit}}\right)\left(\frac{3 \; mol \; KOH}{1 \; mol \; H_3\text{Cit}}\right)\left(\frac{56.11 \text{ g KOH}}{1 \; mol \; KOH}\right)$$

$$\text{SV} = 438.1 \left(\frac{\text{YY.YY} - \text{ZZ.ZZ}}{20.\text{XX}}\right) \text{ ppt KOH}$$

In these equations, 20.XX is from step 4, YY.YY from step 7, and ZZ.ZZ from step 10.

---

to use even less alkali to provide a greater quantity of unsaponified or partially saponified oil in the soap. We'll express this as a lye discount for consistency with established practice. The only difference is that we'll discount the actual, measured value of the ssv rather than an average tabulated value.

In Example 18-1, for example, I found the ssv of Delight to be 150.8 ppt NaOH. Throughout the book, however, we have used the formula Delight$_{1000}$Lye$_{288}$Aq$_{144}$ with an AR of 144 ppt NaOH. For this formula, the AR was 95% of the ssv, so we would say that we had discounted the lye by 5%. If we wanted to use a 3% discount, the AR would be 97% of the ssv, or 146 ppt NaOH; we would make Delight$_{1000}$Lye$_{292}$Aq$_{146}$. Some of the practice problems explore the difference between using measured ssvs and tabulated ones.

Example 18-1. Using Equation 18-1 to Calculate SSV and SV

I wanted to determine the saponification value for the oil blend of Example 6-2 (page 103). I collected the following data:

	KOH Soln (g)	Oil (g)	Acid (g)
Blank A	100.00	0.00	12.85
Blank B	100.01	0.00	12.95
Blank C	100.00	0.00	12.91
Oil A	100.01	20.00	3.29
Oil B	100.01	20.00	3.27
Oil C	100.00	20.00	3.28

Using Equation 18-1 we have for `Soap B`:

$$SSV = 312.3 \left(\frac{12.95 - 3.27}{20.00} \right) \text{ ppt NaOH}$$
$$= 151.2 \text{ ppt NaOH}$$

And for `Soap C`:

$$SSV = 312.3 \left(\frac{12.91 - 3.28}{20.00} \right) \text{ ppt NaOH}$$
$$= 150.4 \text{ ppt NaOH}$$

As in the case of our lye concentration, half of the sum of the two values gives us the average:
½(151.2 + 150.4) = 150.8 ppt
Half of the difference between the two values gives us the precision in the measurement:
½(151.2 - 150.4) = ±0.4 ppt
If your precision is smaller than one ppt, your ssv is precise enough for the experiments ahead. The oil tested in this example should be labeled 150.8±0.4 ppt NaOH.

The potassium sv can be computed in the same way from the same data. In this example, the oil should be labeled 211.5±0.6 ppt KOH.

Practice Problems

Answers to practice problems appear in Appendix A (page 335).

1. It takes 13.05 g and 4.01 g of 500 ppt H_3Cit to titrate the blank and soap solutions, respectively, for a 20.05 g sample of tallow. What are the sv and ssv for this oil?

2. An oil is known to contain free fatty acids. How will this affect the determination of sv and ssv?

3. sv and av have the same units. How do they differ from one another?

4. It takes 13.05 g and 10.23 g of 500 ppt H_3Cit to titrate the blank and soap solutions, respectively, for a 19.97 g sample of hemp oil. What are the sv and ssv for this oil?

5. Pure coconut oil may be used to make a soap that is effective even in salt water. Its tabulated ssv ranges from 176–189 ppt NaOH. What is the lye discount for $Coconut_{1000}Lye_{352}Aq_{176}$?

6. The average ssv for coconut oil is 183 ppt NaOH. A soap-maker without knowledge of the actual ssv for the oil at hand might apply a 5% lye discount. Under what circumstances might this practice lead to the production of excessively alkaline soap?

7. The average ssv for emu oil is 137 ppt NaOH. A soapmaker without knowledge of the actual ssv for the oil at hand might apply a 5% lye discount. Under what circumstances might this practice lead to the production of excessively alkaline soap?

8. Why is it necessary to measure the sv for every oil you buy?

9. Imagine that after receiving a new batch of palm kernel oil, you start producing excessively alkaline soap. It takes 14.12 g and 4.67 g of 500 ppt H_3Cit to titrate the blank and soap solutions, respectively, for a 21.07 g sample of this oil. What might the problem be?

Part V

Research and Development

In Part III you mastered those skills required to evaluate the properties of finished soap. In Part IV you learned how to determine the properties of the raw materials that go into making soap. This part documents several extended experiments designed to answer questions or solve problems.

The chapters in this part address the following questions or problems:

- the causes of dreaded orange spots and steps that can minimize or eliminate their appearance
- the purpose and effectiveness of lye discounting
- the difference between superfatting and lye discounting
- the so-called water discount and the curing process
- the effect of temperature and moisture concentration on saponification
- the factors that affect the thickening of raw soap prior to trace

Chapter 19

The Dreaded Orange Spots

*T*HE soap was perfect. It had traced and poured without incident, it had unmolded easily, and its creamy color and texture spoke to my unrivaled saponifactory skill. After curing for four weeks, it was gentle on the skin and pleasing to the nostrils. All was right with the world. Then *they* showed up. Small at first—unnoticeable, really, to anyone but an anal-retentive lavanteur—they took up residence on a few bars that would now be destined for my own personal use. Not that there was anything wrong with the soap—goodness no! The blemished bars would perform every bit as well as their fair-complexioned siblings. But when I send my soaps out into the world, I want them to make the best possible first impression, so best to keep the spotty ones at home in the cupboard—no harm done! But as these bars lost the blush of youth and entered their adolescence, most of them developed orange zits of one kind or another. Unlike human teenagers, however, they would never outgrow them. I have come to understand through reading, both in the commodity and the craft literature, that the dreaded orange spots (DOS) are caused by the oxidation of unsaturated (soft) oils like olive oil. Makers of commodity soap have largely given up on soft oils in favor of coconut oil and tallow. But the diversity of modern handcrafted soaps owes much to the availability of a dozen or more soft oils that are routinely used to lend their specific properties to soap. In the fall of 2004, my students and I began investigating the causes and cures for DOS.[1]

---

1. This study was conducted by Brad Benedetti, Stephen Diegelman, Shea Duerring, Stephen English, Alex Garcia, Michael Kraemer, Jamie Rock, William Slack, Kevin Thompson, and Keith Williams under the direction of Kevin M. Dunn at Hampden-Sydney College. It was originally published as an article in the *Journal of the Handcrafted Soap Makers Guild* [101].

Figure 19-1. Sample Holder and Vial

19.1 Experimental Method

Makers of commodity soap use a variety of techniques for measuring the rancidity of oils, chiefly the rancimat method. But I wanted a method that most makers of handcrafted soap could use without expensive or specialized equipment. We used an ordinary flat-bed scanner and a free computer program called the GNU Image Manipulation Program (GIMP) [99].

The scanner would be used to acquire digital images of our soaps over several weeks and the GIMP would measure their color. To speed up the arrival of the spots, we stored our soaps in an incubator at 60°C (140°F). For each of our soaps, we monitored the color of two samples: one stored in a vial of oxygen and the other in a vial of nitrogen. Comparing these two samples would reveal the role of oxygen in the development of soap rancidity. A specialized holder was developed that left the soap in contact with the gas in each vial while allowing the soap to be scanned without removing it from the vial. A disposable transfer pipet[2] was formed into a soap holder. The bulb of the dropper was snipped off and the remaining cavity filled with a one gram sample of soap. A plastic collar allowed the sample holder to slide up and down within the vial without sticking to the sides. The sample holder was placed in a small vial filled with

2.   Cynmar [9] part number 132-24513.

Figure 19-2. Olive vs Coconut Oil

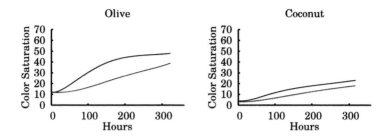

either oxygen or nitrogen gas, as shown in Figure 19-1. During incubation, the vials were stored cap down, leaving the soap in contact with the gas in the vial. For scanning, however, the vial was placed right-side up on the scanner, making it possible to scan the soap sample without removing it from the vial.

When cooking or soapmaking, it is human nature to give free reign to our creative impulses. Though we may be careful to follow a tried-and-true recipe for production-grade soap, we may develop new recipes by making several variations at the same time. To answer questions scientifically, however, it is best to change only one thing at a time. In the present investigation, all soaps are subtle variations of one soap recipe. Each of the soap samples was prepared from 100.0 grams of olive oil, 13.0 grams of sodium hydroxide, 26.0 grams of distilled water, and 0.1 grams of any chosen preservatives. Sodium hydroxide was dissolved in water, allowed to cool and added to the oil. After 15 minutes of continuous shaking, the raw soap mixture was poured into a mold and placed in an incubator for 4 hours at 60°C (140°F). Previous tests had shown that saponification is complete at the end of this incubation. One-gram samples of each soap were then placed in vials as described above, and the soap was artificially aged by incubating it for several weeks while scanning it on a daily basis to record its color. The color was measured using the GIMP "color picker" tool, set to measure "color saturation." Soap is noticeably orange when its color saturation is above about 30%.

Figure 19-3. Lye Discount

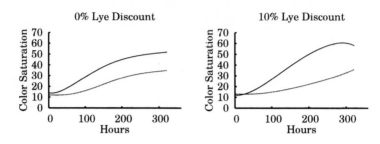

19.2 Results

The first question to ask is "Can you produce orange spots under these conditions?" Two curves are shown on the color-saturation graph for pure olive oil soap, Figure 19-2 (left). The color saturation curves show what happens to the color of the soap as it ages. The lower curve is for soap stored in nitrogen, the upper curve for soap stored in oxygen. The lower curve is for soap stored in nitrogen, the upper curve for soap stored in oxygen. The lower curve shows that soap stored in nitrogen becomes gradually more colorful (orange) during incubation, rising to 38% saturation after 300 hours. The upper curve shows that soap stored in oxygen turns orange more rapidly than soap stored in nitrogen. Of particular note is a rapid increase in color saturation at about 75 hours. The time at which such a rapid increase occurs is referred to as the *induction period*. A soap that turns orange rapidly is said to have a short induction period; a soap that stays white for a long time has a long induction period.

The color saturation curve for coconut oil soap shows that it is relatively resistant to rancidity, as seen in Figure 19-2 (right). For one thing, there is little difference between the color of soaps stored in oxygen versus nitrogen—neither soap rises above 23% saturation. If all of our soaps behaved as coconut oil soap does, we would never see orange spots. Now that we know how to measure orange spots, we can try to prevent them by changing one thing at a time in the soapmaking process and seeing how these changes affect the induction period and the final color saturation.

Figure 19-4. EDTA vs ROE

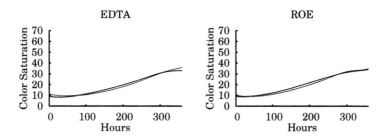

It is sometimes asserted that an excessive lye discount causes orange spots. We therefore made two soaps identical to our standard soap except that in one case the lye discount was 10%, in the other, 0%, as shown in Figure 19-3. From the color saturation curves we can see that, indeed, the 10% discount soap does eventually become more orange than the 0% discount soap. But looking more closely, we also see that the induction period is about the same, 75 hours. Even at 0% discount the soap becomes noticeably orange in about the same time as at 10% discount. Since our goal is to prevent orange spots altogether, we should not look to changing lye discount as a cure for them.

Handcrafted soap books and websites suggest several additives as preventatives for orange spots. We tested the most commonly suggested preservatives, using 0.1 grams of each per 100.0 of oil, i.e., 1 ppt of the oil weight. The test results showed that the color saturation curves for grapefruit seed extract, vitamin C, vitamin E, and sodium citrate are virtually identical to that for olive oil soap with no additive. They showed no prophylactic effect in our tests. Two other preservatives, rosemary oleoresin extract (ROE) and tetrasodium ethylenediamine tetraacetate (EDTA) showed almost identical performance, as shown in Figure 19-4. Both lengthened the induction period beyond 300 hours (the limits of our test) and held the eventual color saturation below 30%. In our tests using each preservative alone, we found ROE and EDTA to be the most effective. Also effective as a preservative for handcrafted soap was butylated hydroxytoluene (BHT), which lengthened the induction period to 150 hours, twice the induction period of olive oil soap with no additive.

Figure 19-5. Combined Additives

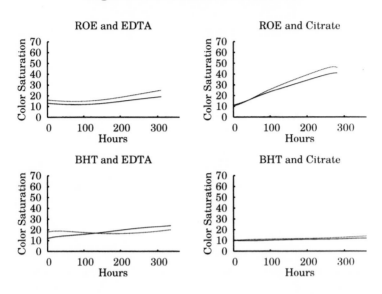

We next looked at combinations of preservatives. Vitamin E (1 ppt) with sodium citrate (1 ppt) performed slightly better than vitamin E alone—that is to say, it did not perform very well. The combination of ROE and sodium citrate actually performed worse than ROE alone. Three combinations, however, performed dramatically better than any single preservative. When combined with either BHT or ROE, EDTA lengthened the induction period beyond 300 hours and held the eventual color saturation below 25%. The best combination in our tests, however, came from BHT with sodium citrate. Used together they lengthened the induction period beyond 300 hours and held the eventual color saturation to about 10%, the same color as fresh soap.

All of our initial work tested preservatives at 1 ppt concentration. In the final round, we altered the concentrations to determine how little of each preservative would be effective. Since ROE is a natural product with variable composition, we separately tested its active ingredients, rosemarinic acid and carnosic acid. We found rosemarinic acid to be the active ingredient, somewhat effective when added to the oil at a concentration of 0.3 ppt or 0.6 ppt. Only at 1.2 ppt, however, did it lengthen the induction period beyond 300 hours. Thus, the minimum effective concentration of ROE would depend on its rosemarinic acid content. We found BHT to be effective when added to the lye at 0.7 ppt. The most potent preservative was EDTA, lengthening the induction period beyond 300 hours when added to the lye at a rate of as little as 0.3 ppt. This final round of testing confirmed that ROE (added to oil), BHT (added to oil), or EDTA (added to lye) provide protection against the oxidation of unsaturated fatty acids and the subsequent development of DOS.

We now turn to the question of *why* these preservatives are effective. Rosemarinic acid and BHT are anti-oxidants, and since oxygen shortened the induction period in our tests, we can presume that they work by protecting the soap from atmospheric oxygen. Sodium citrate and EDTA are often used to bind metal ions in solutions. We wondered whether metals played a role in the formation of spots. We made soap intentionally spiked with small concentrations of several metals and found that calcium and copper shortened the induction period. Since these metals may be present as impurities in tap water or caustic soda, we presume that sodium citrate and EDTA prevent spots by binding to metals that catalyze the oxidation of soft oils. Combinations like ROE with EDTA or BHT with sodium citrate pack a double punch—protecting soap from oxygen and binding to any metals that may catalyze oxidation.

19.3 Conclusions

Makers of handcrafted soap now have at their disposal several options for preventing soap rancidity. They may minimize the use of soft oils, those that are most susceptible to oxidation. They may use distilled or de-ionized water to minimize the presence of catalytic metal ions. If problems remain, preservatives may be used to extend shelf life. Depending on your experience, you may scale the preservative weights up or down to provide the protection you desire at minimum cost. Typical formulas would be:

- $\text{Delight}_{1000}\text{Lye}_{288}\text{Aq}_{144}\text{ROE}_1$
- $\text{Delight}_{1000}\text{Lye}_{288}\text{Aq}_{144}\text{BHT}_1$
- $\text{Delight}_{1000}\text{Lye}_{288}\text{Aq}_{144}\text{BHT}_1\text{NaCit}_1$
- $\text{Delight}_{1000}\text{Lye}_{288}\text{Aq}_{144}\text{EDTA}_{0.5}$

The issue of preservatives often takes on quasi-religious overtones.[3] While I, personally, have no qualms about the use of artificial preservatives, there are many in the handcrafted soap community who do. In particular, many of your customers may value natural ingredients, perhaps even insisting on them. I believe that one of your chief advantages over the commodity soap manufacturer is the ability to tailor soap recipes to the preferences of individual customers. If your client base is heavily tilted toward natural ingredients, you may extend the shelf life of your soap by adding 1–2 ppt of high-rosemarinic ROE to your oil. If, on the other hand, your client base is indifferent to the natural/artificial distinction, you may add 1 ppt of cosmetic-grade BHT to your oil, or 0.5 ppt of cosmetic-grade EDTA to your lye or water portions.[4]

Whatever you decide to do regarding preservatives, I would urge you to accurately label your soaps.[5] People have myriad reasons for their preferences—some due to medical conditions, some due to allergies, some due to crackpot theories or personal whims. They have a right to those preferences, whatever their reasons. Your choice is whether or not to serve customers with those particular preferences.

---

3.   There is an element of society that equates "natural" with "safe" and "artificial" with "dangerous, evil, cancer-causing, and poisonous." A list of natural products that are not necessarily safe would include nicotine, cocaine, ricin (from our beloved castor bean), and many of the essential oils used to lend their fragrances to soap. And no reasonable definition of "natural" could include sodium hydroxide, while excluding BHT and EDTA. Both of these preservatives have undergone exhaustive scientific testing, as documented in references [66] and [67]. Soapmakers need not apologize for the use of these preservatives, but they must use only cosmetic grades, those that are free of harmful impurities.

4.   If you wish to pre-dissolve EDTA in your water portion, you could dissolve 3.5 g EDTA per 1000 g of water and keep this on hand for making soap. 144 g of this solution would contain 0.5 g of EDTA.

5.   *Soap & Cosmetic Labeling* [53] discusses labeling issues for makers of handcrafted soaps and cosmetics.

Chapter 20

Superfatting

*H*ANDCRAFTED soap, whether hot- or cold-process, involves the addition of fats and oils to one of the caustic alkalis, sodium or potassium hydroxide. If excess alkali remains in the finished soap, it will be harsh and perhaps even dangerous. To prevent this possibility, soapmakers generally add more oil than can be saponified by the available alkali, or, conversely, they add less alkali than would be required to saponify the available oil. The first practice is called **superfatting** and the second, lye discounting. While the two practices are similar, there may be subtle differences in emphasis and procedure between the two. This past year, my students and I have explored these differences and have tried to quantify them.[1]

20.1 Saponification

There are many similarities between cooking and soapmaking. Fats and oils are combined in pots and melted on stoves. Stick blenders are used for mixing, and measuring cups for measuring. It is not surprising that soapmakers with a cooking background often approach soapmaking as just another recipe. In making the transition from cooking to soapmaking, however, the soapmaker must realize some important differences between cake recipes and soap recipes. First and foremost, sodium and potassium hydroxide are far more hazardous than any ingredient employed by Betty Crocker, and the soapmaker must

---

1. This research was performed during the 2006–2007 academic year at Hampden-Sydney College by students Mick Robbins, Robbie O'Cain, and Andrew McLeod under the direction of Kevin M. Dunn. It was originally published as an article in the *Journal of the Handcrafted Soap Makers Guild* [103].

be prepared to handle them cautiously and safely. A close second, however, is the concept that soap is not just a mixture of oil and lye.

When sugar, flour, and butter are combined, all three ingredients remain in the finished cake. If a cook uses more sugar than called for in the recipe, the cake will simply be sweeter than it would have otherwise been. When oil and lye are combined, however, both are consumed in a chemical reaction called saponification. Each molecule of oil may react with as many as three molecules of sodium hydroxide to produce as many as three molecules of soap. This three-to-one ratio means that there is a definite relationship between the weight of oil used in a soap recipe and the amount of sodium hydroxide needed to turn it completely into soap. If the soapmaker adds "too much" lye, three molecules of sodium hydroxide react with each molecule of oil until the oil is completely consumed and turned into soap, and the excess sodium hydroxide remains in the soap. Unlike the cake example, the soap is not simply a little more alkaline—it is caustic and potentially dangerous.

We cannot dole out lye and oil one molecule at a time, but because each molecule has a specific weight, we can determine the weight of sodium or potassium hydroxide required to exactly saponify a given weight of oil. This is generally expressed as the number of milligrams of potassium hydroxide required to saponify one gram of oil completely. Because different oils contain different oil molecules, the saponification value (sv) for palm oil differs from that for coconut oil or olive oil. Worse than that, it may differ from one sample of palm oil to another; the values tabulated in soapmaking books are simply averages over many samples of each kind of oil.

As a concrete example, consider the palm oil we used in the present study. Our supplier lists the sv of palm oil as 203 mg KOH/g oil. When we measured the sv of the oil we received, however, it turned out to be 196 mg KOH/g oil, about 3% lower than the stated value. It would not be fair to blame the supplier—the sv of palm oil might be anywhere between 190 and 209 mg KOH/g oil [80]. The supplier simply reports an average value. The fact of the matter is that the svs of real-world oils may be higher or lower than the reported average values, and the soapmaker must deal with this reality.

To cope with the fundamental uncertainty in the sv, soapmakers engage in two related practices: lye discounting and superfatting. While these terms are sometimes used interchangeably, there is a subtle distinction between the two. When soapmakers discount their lye, they generally use the average sv to calculate the amount of lye required to saponify the oil completely. They then deduct a percentage of the calculated lye portion as a safety precaution. If, for example, 100 oz of lye are indicated, they will use only 95 oz and will say that they discounted the lye by 5%. In the case of our palm oil, this discount would have been large enough to cover the (usually unknown) difference between the actual sv and the average one.

There is another way to look at the problem, however. We might use the average sv to calculate the amount of lye needed to saponify the oil to be used, but instead of discounting the lye we could simply add more oil. If we added 5% more oil than was used to calculate the lye portion, we would say that we superfatted by 5%. So far, there is not much difference between discounting and superfatting, and they both address the fundamental uncertainty in the sv.

A difference arises, however, when the soapmaker claims to have superfatted with some particular oil. He may, for example, make soap using 20% coconut oil, 60% palm oil, and 20% olive oil. He will calculate the lye needed for this oil blend and begin to make soap using the calculated lye amount. At trace, however, he adds 5% shea oil and believes that he has "superfatted with shea oil." He is assuming that the last oil added to the soap is the oil that will remain unsaponified in the finished soap. It is this assumption that we set out to test. Let us call it the *superfatting hypothesis:*

> In a superfatted soap, some oil remains unsaponified. This unsaponified oil consists mostly of the last oil added, usually at trace.

If the superfatting hypothesis is true, then the soapmaker can control the makeup of unsaponified oil by adding the superfatting oil at trace. This will generally be a relatively expensive oil whose presence in the finished soap is deemed desirable. If the hypothesis is false, however, the soapmaker makes his life harder by attempting to incorporate the superfatting oil at a time when the clock is literally ticking. Not only would he work harder than he has to, but the superfatting oil may be incompletely mixed when the soap is poured. If this happens, some bars will contain more oil and others less. Those that contain less oil may, in fact, contain excess lye, and one of the major benefits of superfatting will be lost.

20.2 Analysis of Discounted and Superfatted Soaps

We addressed the superfatting hypothesis by making soaps that were identical in composition and differed only in the order in which the oils were added. In the *discounted* soaps, all of the oils were blended before adding the lye. In the *superfatted* soaps, one of the oils was held back when the other oils and lye were mixed. The superfatting oil was then added at trace, just before the soap was poured into the mold. The discounted and superfatted soaps were then held at 70°C (158°F) for 4 hours to ensure complete saponification. Samples of each soap were then boiled in ether to extract the unsaponified oils. The unsaponified oils were analyzed using NMR spectroscopy to determine their compositions. If the superfatting hypothesis were correct, we would expect to see a difference between the oils extracted from discounted and superfatted soaps.

The first combination of oils to be tested was 91% coconut oil and 9% olive oil. This rather peculiar combination was chosen because the oleic acid in olive oil is easily distinguished from the saturated fatty acids present in coconut oil. The discounted and superfatted soaps used identical quantities of the oils and lye, which was discounted by 5%. In the discounted soap, the coconut and olive oils were mixed before the lye was added. In the superfatted soap, the olive oil was added at trace.

Our analysis found that the oils extracted from the discounted and superfatted soaps were virtually identical. The blend of coconut and olive oil used to make both soaps contained approximately 7% oleic acid, the remainder being saturated oils. The oils extracted from the discounted and superfatted soaps each contained 22% oleic acid. Thus the unsaponified oil contained more of the unsaturated oleic acid than did the original oil blend. We supposed that the unsaturated oils in olive oil react more slowly with lye than do the saturated oils that predominate in coconut oil. The resulting soap contained a higher-than-expected concentration of unsaturated oil, regardless of whether the olive oil was added at trace.

The second combination of oils was 90% palm oil and 10% castor oil. In this case, the unsaturated ricinoleic acid of castor oil is easily distinguished from the fatty acids present in palm oil. A 10% lye discount was taken to provide a greater quantity of unsaponified oil for analysis. While the original oil blend contained 9% ricinoleic acid, the unsaponified oils extracted from the discounted and superfatted soaps each contained 4% ricinoleic acid. We supposed that castor oil reacts more rapidly with lye than palm oil, resulting in a lower percentage of unsaponified castor oil. As in the case of the coconut/olive combination, it made no difference whether or not the castor oil was added at trace.

The third combination of oils studied was 90% palm oil and 10% grapeseed oil. The unsaturated linoleic acid of grapeseed oil was easily distinguished from the fatty acids present in palm oil. Again, a 10% lye discount was taken and the soaps were processed as in the previous combination. While the original oil blend contained 9% linoleic acid, the discounted soap contained 19% and the superfatted soap 17% linoleic acid. As in the case of the coconut/olive combination, we supposed that the unsaturated grapeseed oil reacted more slowly with lye than the saturated palm oil. We expected the finished soap to contain a greater percentage of unsaturated oil than did the original oil blend. Once again it made little difference whether or not the grapeseed oil was added at trace.

20.3 Conclusion

We have so far studied only three combinations of oils, chosen for ease of analysis rather than as representatives of the kinds of blends usually chosen by soapmakers. These combinations have included oils containing oleic, linoleic, and ricinoleic acids. In no instance was the superfatting hypothesis supported. For our continuing research we have adopted the *kinetic hypothesis:*

There appears to be no real difference between discounting lye and superfatting. The composition of unsaponified oil in finished cold-process soap does not depend on the order in which the oils are added. The oil component that reacts most slowly with lye will be more concentrated in the unsaponified oil than in the original oil blend.

What this means for the maker of cold-process soap is that you may discount or superfat your soap as you please. If you have been trying to incorporate superfatting oils at trace, however, you may have been working harder than you needed to. I would suggest that you thoroughly mix all of your oils before adding the lye. If you find that the quality of your soap is unchanged or improved, you will save yourself time and effort. If you do find a difference, however, between discounted and superfatted soap, I would really like to hear about it. Send me your formulas and procedure and a sample of each soap. Who knows—your observations may point us toward our next research project.

Chapter 21

The "Water Discount"

*A*LL soapmakers are familiar with the notion of a lye discount. In order to prevent the possibility of excess alkali in the finished soap, less lye is used than would be needed for complete saponification. The amount needed for complete saponification is calculated using a table of average saponification values contained in a book or in a lye calculator. We choose to discount the lye because, in reality, saponification values vary from one sample of oil to the next and may differ from those average values.

The notion of a discount implies that there is a correct value to be discounted. While you might not know the exact saponification value of a sample of oil, it does in fact have a particular saponification value. In Chapter 18 we even learned a method for determining this value. We understand that saponification values exist because of the reaction between three molecules of alkali with each molecule of oil. Thus we know that there is a normal, correct, standard amount of sodium hydroxide to be used, and it makes sense to talk about a discount from that amount.

The same cannot be said of water because it does not appear in the saponification reaction. There is no fixed number of molecules of water needed for a molecule of oil. Water is simply used to dissolve the sodium hydroxide so that it can react with the oil. Where, then, do we get the notion that there is a normal, correct, or standard value for the amount of water to be used in a soap formula?[1]

I surveyed the soap recipes from four books in my collection. The earliest, Ann Bramson's *Soap: Making it, Enjoying It* [51], may be considered the founding document of the handcrafted

---

1. This research was originally published as an article in the *Journal of the Handcrafted Soap Makers Guild* [104].

soap movement and has introduced countless soapmakers to
the craft. Published in 1972, it lacks any discussion of the chemistry of saponification, but the recipes imply that there are correct amounts of both sodium hydroxide and water. While an
examination of the recipes shows that they were correctly formulated with regards to sodium hydroxide, the book does not
show how these amounts were determined. The amount of water in the recipes resulted in lye that ranged from 25–27% sodium hydroxide, the average being 26%.

Susan Cavitch's 1997 *The Soapmaker's Companion* [52] includes an extensive discussion of chemistry, including the use of
saponification values. Cavitch also discusses the amount of water to be used and understands that the amount may be varied,
depending on circumstances such as the mixing temperature.
She recommends a lye concentration of 30% NaOH as a starting point. In her recipes, however, she tends to be somewhat
lower, ranging from 26–29%, with an average concentration of
27%. In fact, 21 of the 26 recipes use lye concentrations of exactly 27%. Both Bramson and Cavitch adopt concentrations of
26–27%, and this may be the reason that many lye calculators
use 27% as the normal, correct, standard lye concentration.

Later books have trended toward higher lye concentration.
Robert McDaniel's 2000 *Essentially Soap* [54] uses concentrations between 33 and 38%, with an average of 34%. Anne
Watson's 2007 *Smart Soapmaking* [55] uses concentrations between 30 and 37%, with an average of 33%. Watson briefly discusses the choice of concentration, claiming that saponification
and curing are faster when less water is used. She also says
that it is harder to dissolve the sodium hydroxide at higher concentrations and that the solution may give off more fumes.

I have undertaken to explore the effect of lye concentration
on the saponification process. I made a series of soaps that were
processed identically except for the lye concentration and then
measured their weight, hardness, alkalinity, and moisture concentration over an 8-week curing period. I made single-oil soaps
from coconut, palm, and olive oils. I also made a four-oil soap
from a blend of coconut, palm, olive, and castor oils. All soaps
were prepared using a 500 ppt sodium hydroxide solution, with
extra water added to some soaps to bring the sodium hydroxide
concentration to 333 ppt and 250 ppt. The soaps consequently

span a range of lye concentration from 50% (higher than most soapmakers use) to 25% (lower than most soapmakers use).

21.1 Experimental Soap Processing

All of the soaps in this study were prepared identically except for the effective lye concentration. 500 ppt NaOH was prepared by mixing equal weights of sodium hydroxide and de-ionized water. This lye was prepared in advance and used as needed. Each bar of soap was prepared from 100.00 g of oil, a standard weight of 500 ppt NaOH, and a water portion designed to dilute the lye to a particular concentration. For each oil or oil blend, three bars of soap were produced. The three coconut oil soaps, for example, had formulas:

$Coconut_{1000}Lye_{348}$ (low water)
$Coconut_{1000}Lye_{348}Aq_{174}$ (medium water)
$Coconut_{1000}Lye_{348}Aq_{348}$ (high water)

The water portion was chosen to provide effective lye concentrations of 500, 333, and 250 ppt NaOH for the low-water, medium-water, and high-water soaps, respectively.

For each bar of soap, 100.00 g of oil was weighed into a 500 mL polypropylene bottle. This was followed by the water, if needed, and then the lye. The lid was screwed onto the bottle, which was placed on a modified Blair Tornado II electrical paint shaker, where it was shaken vigorously for 15 seconds. The soap was gently swirled in the bottle for 2-5 minutes until thickened, poured into a single-bar mold from Upland Soap Factory, and placed into a roaster oven set to 60°C (140°F) for four hours. This time and temperature had been previously determined to be sufficient for complete saponification.

The day after mixing, each bar was removed from the mold and tested for alkali concentration, expressed as parts per thousand (ppt) of NaOH. This was determined by dissolving 1–2 g of soap in ethyl alcohol and titrating with a standard citric acid solution, using phenolphthalein as an indicator. Some soaps did not turn the indicator pink. These were titrated with a standard KOH solution to the phenolphthalein endpoint in order to determine the amount of acid (presumably fatty acid) present. This was expressed as a *negative* alkali concentration,

Figure 21-1. The Soil Penetrometer

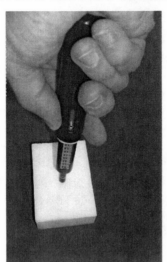

expressed as ppt NaOH for consistency with the other alkali measurements. An alkali concentration less than 1 ppt should be considered safe for use, and most soaps eventually had negative alkali concentrations, meaning that they were less alkaline than the phenolphthalein indicator. For each bar, the alkali concentration was measured independently for the top and bottom of the bar to check for possible separation of the soap.

Each soap was then weighed about once per week for a period of at least 8 weeks. In addition, the hardness of each bar was measured using a soil penetrometer, as shown in Figure 21-1. This penetrometer has a spring-loaded *foot* with a diameter of 0.25 inch. The penetrometer foot is pressed into the soap to a depth of 0.25 inch, and the hardness can then be read from a scale that records the force used to press the foot into the soap. The hardness ranges from 0–4.5 kg/cm^2. For harder soaps, I devised a 0.125 inch foot that slips over the standard foot. From measurements on numerous soaps, I determined a scale factor of 2.9 to convert measurements from the smaller foot to the larger one. Thus I was able to measure soap hardness from 0–13 kg/cm^2.

The soap cured on a chrome-plated rack and lost weight as water evaporated. Since I knew the initial moisture concentration and the weight of the water lost to evaporation, it was possible to calculate the moisture concentration of each bar from week to week without removing additional samples. At the end of the curing period, the alkali concentration was determined at the top and bottom of the bar for comparison with the initial values. The final alkali test marked the end of the study for each bar.

21.2 Palm Oil Soap

Palm oil was the first oil I investigated. Figure 21-2 shows the data for three palm oil soaps, each containing an identical amount of sodium hydroxide but different amounts of water. Soap A was the low-water soap, B the medium-water soap, and C the high-water soap. The low-water soap had the least amount of moisture, both at the beginning and at the end of the 60-day study period. The low-water soap had an initial moisture concentration of 111 ppt. The medium-water soap cured for 14 days and the high-water soap for 31 days before reaching this concentration. As shown in the first graph, however, the moisture decreased steadily over this period, and it would appear that eventually all three soaps will contain the same amount of moisture. If you were to make medium-water soap rather than high-water soap, you would save about 2 weeks of curing time. If you were to make low-water soap, you would save another 2 weeks.

As the moisture concentration decreased, the hardness increased. The low-water soap had an initial hardness of 4.5, and it took the other two soaps 16 and 25 days, respectively, to attain this hardness. While the low-water soap was initially much harder than the other two, by the end of the study period the gap had closed to the point that all three soaps were very hard indeed. As in the case of moisture, it would appear that eventually they will have the same hardness. And it would appear that using less water saves about 2 weeks of curing from one soap to the next.

All three of the soaps were alkaline when removed from the mold 1 day after mixing. The bottom of the low-water bar was most alkaline, but after 60 days all three bars had accept-

Figure 21-2. Palm Oil Curing

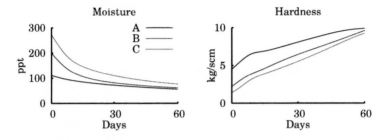

Batch Code KMD2007.12.27	Moisture (ppt)		Alkali (ppt NaOH)			
	Initial	Final	Initial		Final	
			Top	Bottom	Top	Bottom
A Palm$_{1000}$Lye$_{286}$	111	54	1.8	4.9	0.3	0.9
B Palm$_{1000}$Lye$_{286}$Aq$_{143}$	200	60	1.8	1.4	-1.7	-0.2
C Palm$_{1000}$Lye$_{286}$Aq$_{286}$	273	74	0.5	0.3	-1.7	-0.1

able alkali concentrations on the top and bottom of each bar. The medium- and high-water bars, in fact, had negative alkali concentrations, meaning that they were less alkaline than the phenolphthalein indicator. The low-water palm bar was the only one to remain alkaline after 60 days. In retrospect, it may be that less lye should have been used, but even for this bar the total alkali concentration was lower than the recommended threshold (1 ppt) given by many commodity soap books.

In the case of palm oil, the amount of water used to make soap has the greatest impact on the time required for curing. Less water at the beginning translates into a harder bar containing less moisture. There appears to be no danger in using less water, though it may be that for this oil less water translates into a slightly more alkaline bar.

21.3 Coconut Oil Soap

Many of the observations on palm oil soap carry over to coconut oil (Figure 21-3). The low-water soap was harder and contained less moisture and more alkali than the other two. The coconut oil soaps lost moisture less rapidly, however, than the palm oil soaps, even though they were cured on the same rack over approximately the same time period. The medium- and high-water soaps remained significantly softer than the low-water soap, even after 60 days. It took 25 and 46 days, respectively,

Figure 21-3. Coconut Oil Curing

Batch Code KMD2008.1.8	Moisture (ppt)		Alkali (ppt NaOH)			
	Initial	Final	Initial		Final	
			Top	Bottom	Top	Bottom
D Coconut$_{1000}$Lye$_{348}$	129	41	0.4	0.5	-0.6	-0.3
E Coconut$_{1000}$Lye$_{348}$Aq$_{174}$	229	88	-0.1	-0.2	-1.7	-1.0
F Coconut$_{1000}$Lye$_{348}$Aq$_{348}$	308	109	0.1	0.2	-1.8	-0.4

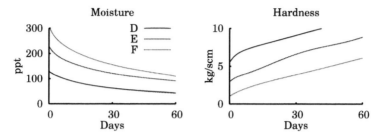

for the medium- and high-water soaps to attain the initial moisture concentration of the low-water soap. It took 19 and 52 days for them to attain the initial hardness of the low-water soap. All of the coconut oil soaps contained less then 1 ppt alkali 1 day after mixing. By the end of the study period, they were all less alkaline than the phenolphthalein indicator and were safe for use. Because coconut oil soaps take longer to lose moisture than do palm oil soaps, the advantages of using less water are more pronounced for these soaps.

21.4 Olive Oil Soap

My initial tests of olive oil soaps ran into trouble. While the low-water soap reached trace within a few minutes, the medium- and high-water soaps did not. Eventually, I got tired of waiting and processed them as usual, but these two soaps separated in the mold and were obviously unsatisfactory. A chalky, lye-heavy soap settled to the bottom of each mold and unsaponified oil rose to the top. Rather than give up on these soaps, I decided to accelerate trace by adding 1 gram of clove oil to each soap. This produced solid bars for all three moisture levels, but there was still some obvious separation of the high-water soap. The original clove-free low-water soap is included in Figure 21-4 for comparison.

Figure 21-4. Olive Oil Curing

Batch Code KMD2008		Moisture (ppt)		Alkali (ppt NaOH)			
		Initial	Final	Initial		Final	
				Top	Bottom	Top	Bottom
1.7A	$Olive_{1000}Lye_{264}$	104	36	0.3	0.2	-3.2	-0.4
3.5A	$Olive_{990}Clove_{10}Lye_{259}$	103	43	-0.4	-0.7	-0.7	-0.7
3.5B	$Olive_{990}Clove_{10}Lye_{259}Aq_{130}$	187	61	-0.4	-0.4	-0.8	-0.7
3.5C	$Olive_{990}Clove_{10}Lye_{260}Aq_{260}$	256	67	-0.7	6.2	-1.1	-0.2

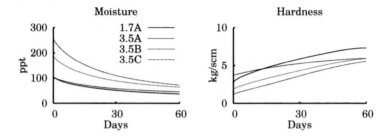

The olive oil soaps followed the usual trends in hardness and moisture concentration. It took 19 and 32 days for the medium- and high-water soaps to reach the initial moisture level of the low-water soap. It took 12 and 19 days for them to catch up in hardness. The two low-water soaps, with and without clove oil, were almost identical in moisture and very close to one another in hardness. Only the high-water soap had an unacceptably high alkali concentration when removed from the mold—a consequence of its partial separation.

21.5 Four-Oil Soap

The single-oil soaps may give us some insights into the role of water in saponification and curing, but handcrafted soap is generally made from a blend of oils. To complete the study, I chose our old friend, Delight, first encountered in Section 5.5.

The moisture concentration of the three Delight soaps followed the usual pattern. While the hardness increased as expected, the Delight soaps started and remained softer even than the olive oil soaps. This is not to say that they were soft—just softer, and had a consistency typical of what I expect of handcrafted soap. It took 36 and 57 days for the medium- and high-water soaps to reach the initial low-water moisture level. It took 12 and 36 days for them to catch up in hardness. As in

Figure 21-5. Delight Curing

Batch Code KMD2008.2.17	Moisture (ppt) Initial	Final	Alkali (ppt NaOH) Initial Top	Bottom	Final Top	Bottom
A Delight$_{1000}$Lye$_{288}$	112	48	-0.2	0.2	-1.0	-0.4
B Delight$_{1000}$Lye$_{288}$Aq$_{144}$	201	89	-0.4	0.3	-3.1	-0.9
C Delight$_{1000}$Lye$_{288}$Aq$_{288}$	274	104	-0.9	0.9	-3.7	-1.3

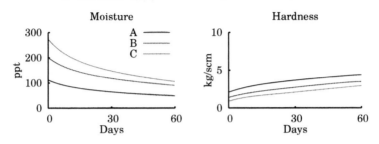

the case of the single-oil soaps, time may be saved in curing this soap by using less water at the beginning.

While all three Delight bars were solid, there was noticeable separation of the high-water soap: the surface of this soap was oily. Upon further investigation, the oil was found to be olive oil that had separated in the mold. While not as pronounced as in the pure olive oil soap, the separation is evident in the initial alkali concentration: acidic on the oily top of the bar and alkaline at the bottom of the bar. By the end of the study period, all three soaps were less alkaline than the phenolphthalein indicator, but the difference in alkalinity remained evident between the top and bottom of the high-water bar. For this oil blend, we can save time in curing by using less water. Using too much water may result in separation of the soap.

21.6 Conclusion

As I began this study, I expected that low-water soaps would start out harder than high-water soaps but that they might eventually reach the same hardness. This expectation was realized in all of the soaps studied. I worried that perhaps the low-water soaps might not have enough water to ensure that the oil was thoroughly saponified. This fear was not borne out in practice; all of the soaps were low in alkali, most of them immediately upon unmolding. What I did not expect was that there might be such a thing as "too much" water. When olive oil was present, it tended to separate from high-water soaps, leaving the bar underneath more alkaline than it would otherwise have been. I also found that saponification and curing are not synonymous and that they take place on very different time scales: most of the saponification occurred in the first 24 hours for all of these soaps, but most of them were continuing to lose moisture after 60 days.

I am *not* about to recommend that all soap should be made with 50% sodium hydroxide solutions. I *am* suggesting that you may use such a concentration if you wish. Starting with this lye, you are then free to add additional water or milk to increase the initial moisture concentration. A low-water bar can be expected to be initially harder than a high-water bar, which would be helpful in removing soaps from cavity molds. A high-water formula would be more appropriate for soap that must be cut into bars. A low-water soap generally traces faster and is more resistant to separation than a high-water soap. If you have a problem with slow trace or separation, reducing the amount of water may solve your problem. In none of my experiments did I find that the low-water soap was dangerous. I believe that you can safely experiment with low-water soaps up to and including lye concentrations of 50%. As usual when developing a formula, start out with relatively small batches and increase your batch size as you gain experience with the new formula.

Chapter 22

Time and Temperature

*S*OAPMAKING is a far more nuanced undertaking than I would have imagined when I began studying the process. Oil and lye—how hard can it be? The blend of oils, of course, determines many of the properties of the finished soap. Lauric oils contribute lather, while oleic oils are gentle on the skin. The alkali ratio must be chosen to be no greater than the saponification value of the blend, but we may choose to superfat our soap, either to ensure that it is not alkaline or to provide desirable oils, fatty acids, or partially saponified oils to the finished bar. The amount of water, too, may be varied to produce soap that is soft and easy to cut or hard and easy to unmold, according to our wishes. We have yet to explore, however, two extremely important and inter-related variables: time and temperature.[1]

What is the time scale for the saponification process? Does it take minutes, hours, days, or weeks for the alkali to be consumed? What role does temperature play in the saponification reaction? Why does soap sometimes gel to a Vaseline-like consistency and other times remain the consistency of cookie dough? These are the questions to be addressed in this chapter.

---

1. This research was performed during the 2008–2009 academic year at Hampden-Sydney College by students John Campbell, Andrew Basinger, Tyler Bowman, Drake Huzek, and William Eskridge under the direction of Kevin M. Dunn. It was originally published as an article in the *Journal of the Handcrafted Soap Makers Guild* [105]. The foundations for the project were laid by John Booker (2007) and David Wehunt (2004). Differential scanning calorimetry and x-ray diffraction experiments were performed by Jody Aiken, Steve Sealschott, David Bohlen, Kassy Pelzel, and Pauline Vu at Procter and Gamble.

22.1 Method

In order to study the effects of time and temperature, we need to hold some things constant to avoid being fooled by variations in materials and techniques. The same basic formula was used for all of the soaps in this study: $Delight_{1000}Lye_{288}Aq_X$, where X was varied from 0 to 288 ppt. We might expect the low-water soap (0 ppt Aq) to be harder initially than the high-water soap (288 ppt Aq), as explored in Chapter 21. By the method of Chapter 18, we determined the ssv of this oil to be 150.8 ppt. Since the lye portion was 288 ppt and the lye concentration was 500 ppt, the lye discount was 5%.[2] All of these soaps were produced from 100.00 g of oil and the appropriate amounts of lye and de-ionized water.

It will be seen that the water concentration dictates much of the behavior of a saponifying oil. Our soap formula expresses the water portion in ppt, as if the water portion is a separate ingredient from the lye. But it is possible to calculate the equivalent lye concentration that would be necessary to produce the same soaps from oil and dilute lye. It is also possible to express the moisture concentration as a fraction of the total soap weight. A survey of several handcrafted soap books revealed that the recommended lye concentration averaged between 260 and 340 ppt.[3] For this study, five water portions were used, with equivalent lye concentrations between 250 and 500 ppt. Table 22-1 shows the equivalent lye concentrations and moisture concentrations for these soaps.

Ingredients for each soap were added to a 500 mL polypropylene bottle, which was then shaken for 15 seconds using a modified Blair Tornado II paint shaker. The raw soap was then poured into a nest of 6–8 Styrofoam coffee cups fitted with a Styrofoam lid, observation window, and thermometer. The nest of coffee cups attempted to simulate the conditions of a large block mold, insulating the soap and preventing it from losing heat to the surroundings. Soaps were mixed at several starting temperatures, and the temperature of each soap was recorded as a function of time.

---

2. See Section 18.3 (page 273).
3. See Chapter 21 (page 293).

Table 22-1. DSC Samples

Formula	Effective Lye Concentration (ppt)	Moisture Content (ppt)
$Delight_{1000}Lye_{288}Aq_0$ (Low-Water)	500	112
$Delight_{1000}Lye_{288}Aq_{72}$	417	159
$Delight_{1000}Lye_{288}Aq_{144}$ (Medium-Water)	333	201
$Delight_{1000}Lye_{288}Aq_{216}$	292	239
$Delight_{1000}Lye_{288}Aq_{288}$ (High-Water)	250	274

22.2 Phases

Ice, water, and steam exemplify the common phases: solid, liquid, and gas. If you were to drink a cup of hot chocolate, you would have no trouble distinguishing the phases involved. You would say that the cup in your hands is a solid, the hot chocolate in that cup is a liquid, and the steam wafting its way to your nose is a gas. But what about the marshmallows? When in the bag, they maintain their apparently solid shapes. When placed into the hot chocolate, they gradually slump into apparently liquid goo. Placed into a microwave oven, they expand like balloons. The phase structure of the marshmallow is more complicated than you might have thought. The phase structure of soap is no less so.

Like a marshmallow, a bar of soap would appear to be a solid. We know from previous chapters that the lower the moisture concentration, the harder that bar of soap will be. If you place that bar into a bowl of water, however, two phases are in evidence. The bar picks up some water and softens; the water picks up some soap and becomes cloudy. The softened soap may contain 15% water and the soapy water may contain 1% soap, the exact proportions depending on the relative sizes of the bar and the bowl. You would still have no trouble saying that the bar is a solid and the soapy water a liquid. But what if the soap were to become so soft that it slumped into a goo at the bottom of the bowl? What if the water became so thick with soap that it could no longer be poured from the bowl?

Soap chemists have identified many, many phases of soap—some that are clearly solid, others that are clearly liquid, and some that seem to cross the boundary between solid and liquid [85]. Two phases in particular are central to our discussion of time and temperature. The first, which you know as a solid bar of soap, actually consists of as many as three subtly-different solid phases at room temperature. Soapmakers refer to this mixed solid phase as **soap curd.** When heated, soap curd melts into a gelatinous phase called **neat soap,** which looks something like petroleum jelly. The temperature at which soap curd melts into neat soap depends on the moisture concentration.

Figure 22-1 shows the phases present under the conditions of temperature and moisture found in the soap pot. At low temperature, soap appears as soap curd regardless of its moisture concentration. At high temperature, it appears as neat soap. The "melting point," however, is very dependent on moisture concentration. Low-water soaps melt at temperatures near the boiling point of water; high-water soaps melt at significantly lower temperatures. Medium-water soaps like $Delight_{1000}Lye_{288}Aq_{144}$ begin melting at about 60°C (140°F), but the phase change is not complete until about 70°C (158°F). Between these two temperatures, both phases are present—pockets of interspersed neat and curd soap. It might be said, then, that soap curd begins melting at one temperature and finishes at another (higher) temperature. Similarly, neat soap begins freezing at one temperature and finishes at another (lower) temperature. A high-water soap, however, melts and freezes at approximately the same temperature. Studying Figure 22-1 will allow us to understand the phase changes that occur in the soap pot during saponification.

22.3 Temperature

Saponification is an exothermic reaction—it releases heat. Some of this heat is absorbed by the raw soap, and its temperature rises. Some of the heat is lost to the mold and to the room; their temperatures also rise. And if the temperature of the soap is in the appropriate range, some of the heat is absorbed as the raw soap melts. In thinking about time and temperature, it will help us to remember that the heat produced will either raise the temperature of the soap and its surroundings or change the soap from one phase to another.

Figure 22-1. Delight/Water Phases

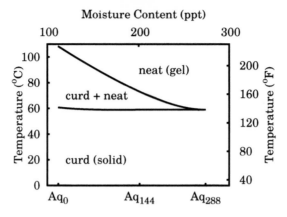

Figure 22-2. Low-Temperature Saponification

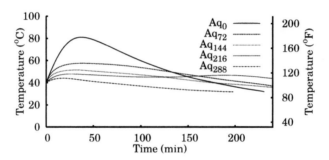

Let us imagine that we mix the oil and lye for a low-water formula at a relatively low temperature. Let us imagine, as well, that the container is so well insulated that we may initially neglect heat lost to the mold and the room. As the saponification reaction proceeds, the heat produced raises the temperature of the raw soap. At the same time, however, the oil and lye are consumed, and the reaction eventually slows as they are depleted. At some point, heat will be lost to the mold and room at the same rate that it is produced by the reaction; the temperature will stop rising and, as the rate of heat production falls further, the soap will begin to cool. We can see this behavior in Figure 22-2. The highest curve tracks the temperature of $Delight_{1000}Lye_{288}Aq_0$ with the oil and lye mixed at 40°C (104°F). After 37 minutes in the mold, the temperature peaked at 84°C (183°F). If the mold had been better insulated, it might

Figure 22-3. Low-Water Saponification

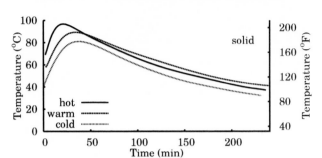

have peaked later and at a higher temperature. But even this peak temperature is nowhere near the melting point of this low-water soap, so the temperature simply rises for a while, peaks, and falls.

The lowest curve in Figure 22-2 tracks the temperature of a high-water soap, $Delight_{1000}Lye_{288}Aq_{288}$. The temperature of this soap rises only to 45°C (113°F) a mere 24 minutes after mixing. Clearly, this high-water soap must saponify more slowly than its low-water cousin. Because they contain the same quantities of oil and lye, both reactions must release the same amount of heat, but the low-water soap does so in a short amount of time while the high-water soap releases heat gradually over a longer period. $Delight_{1000}Lye_{288}Aq_{216}$ is particularly interesting. It maintains a nearly constant temperature for a long period of time. The lesson of Figure 22-2 is pretty clear: low-water soaps saponify more quickly than high-water soaps.

What happens if we increase the temperature of the oil and lye before they are mixed? Figure 22-3 tracks the temperatures of three soaps, all $Delight_{1000}Lye_{288}Aq_0$, identical except for their mixing temperatures. The soap labeled *cold* was mixed at 40°C (104°F), that labeled *warm* at 58°C (136°F), and that labeled *hot* at 65°C (150°F). The lowest curve of this graph is identical to the highest curve of Figure 22-2. From these curves we can see that the warmer the starting temperature, the sooner and higher the temperature peaks. This trend indicates that warmer soaps saponify more quickly than cooler ones. Coupled with the information from the previous figure, we can say that warm, low-water soaps saponify more quickly than cool, high-

Figure 22-4. Medium-Water Saponification

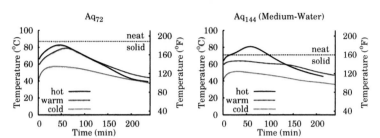

water soaps. This would be the end of the story were it not for the possibility of a phase change during saponification.

Before we consider this possibility, however, I must point out that the melting points of Figure 22-1 were determined by heating finished soaps, not raw ones. The technique used to produce this phase diagram, Differential Scanning Calorimetry, would be much more complicated were we to use it while the soap was still saponifying. In the following discussion, we make the simplifying assumption that soap is produced as oil and lye react and that the melting behavior of this oil/soap/water mixture is similar to that of a soap/water mixture. Let us see how far this assumption can take us in understanding soaps that undergo phase changes during saponification.

Figure 22-4 tracks the temperature for two soaps, Delight$_{1000}$Lye$_{288}$Aq$_{72}$ and Delight$_{1000}$Lye$_{288}$Aq$_{144}$, each at three starting temperatures. In each graph, a horizontal line shows the boundary between soap curd and neat soap.[4] The Aq$_{72}$ soap behaves much like a low-water soap. The temperature of the hot soap rises quickly to a peak and then cools relatively rapidly. The cold soap warms more slowly and stays warm longer, indicating that the saponification is slower at low temperature. Even the hot soap, however, is just shy of the boundary between curd and neat soap. Given our simplifying assumption, we expect that this soap solidifies after mixing and remains solid throughout the saponification. This is exactly what was

---

4. Recall from Figure 22-1 that these soaps begin melting at about 60°C (140°F). The boundaries shown here are the temperatures at which the melting is complete.

Figure 22-5. High-Water Saponification

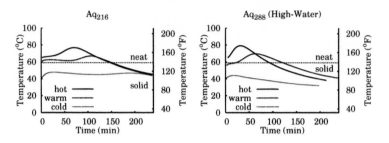

observed for this soap. We suppose that if the soap had been a little warmer, it would have entered the neat phase.

The Aq_{144} soaps mixed at the lowest two starting temperatures behave as we might expect. They warm and cool more slowly than their low-water cousins and their peak temperatures are lower. At the highest temperature, however, the peak temperature is nearly as high as that of Aq_{72} at the same starting temperature. Moreover, the peak temperature of this soap is higher than its melting point. We would expect to see this soap enter the neat phase, and that is exactly what was observed. A small spot of darker, gelatinous soap grew larger and larger until the entire soap looked like Vaseline. The increase in temperature as the soap melted indicates that the rate of saponification is higher in the neat phase than in the curd. We are also vindicated in our simplifying assumption—the observed phase change in the raw soap coincides with that in finished soap of the same composition.

Given our earlier observations, it is easy to explain the behavior of the high-water soaps detailed in Figure 22-5. The boundary between curd and neat soaps is approximately the same for both soaps. Soaps that begin at or above this temperature enter the neat phase, though some earlier than others. When they enter the neat phase, the temperatures of these soaps increase as the rate of saponification increases. Soaps started at a low temperature, however, warm only slightly and stay warm for a long period of time, never entering the neat phase. We may expect high-water soaps to enter the neat phase as long as their starting temperatures are sufficiently high.

We may now generalize about the phase behavior of soap during saponification. For soaps that begin at the same temperature, low-water soaps saponify more quickly than high-water soaps and, as a consequence, reach higher peak temperatures. The peak temperatures of low-water soaps, however, are below their melting points, and we do not expect them to enter the neat phase. The neat phase is attained only by high-water soaps heated to sufficiently high initial temperatures. We may conclude that a soap may be forced into the neat phase by simultaneously raising its temperature and its moisture concentration. The exact temperature required, however, will depend on the size and shape of the mold, on the mix of oils, and on the presence of any scents or additives that hasten or retard saponification.

We have yet to consider whether or not neat soap is desirable. Three of our formulas produced soaps that melted at the highest initial temperature, but not at the lowest. We compared the hot and cold varieties of Aq_{144}, Aq_{216}, and Aq_{288} but found no differences in appearance, alkalinity, or texture between soaps of the same formula. Only in one respect did we find a difference between soaps that had melted and those that had not. Following an experiment described in reference [62], we cut cylinders of finished soap and suspended them in cups of water for a period of 6 hours. In each case, the soaps that had melted swelled less than those that had not. Figure 22-6 shows five Aq_{216} soaps with starting temperatures ranging from 40°C (104°F) to 70°C (158°F). The three leftmost soaps remained solid during saponification while the two rightmost ones melted during saponification. Even between the soaps started at 60°C (140°F) and 65°C (150°F), there is a striking difference in swelling between the soaps that did and did not melt. We might wonder whether hot soaps swell less than cold ones, regardless of whether they melted. Hot and cold varieties of low-water soaps (none of which melted) showed no difference in swelling behavior, so we believe that melting, not temperature alone, is responsible for this difference. While we might expect the melted soaps to maintain their shapes better in the soap dish, the difference is so subtle that we can find little reason to prefer soaps that have melted over those that have not. Within a partially melted soap, however, there may be a visible boundary between the areas that

Figure 22-6. The Soak Test

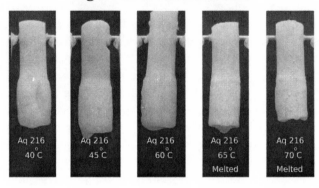

melted and those that did not. For this reason, soapmakers may prefer to make soap that has melted completely or not at all.

22.4 Neat Soap

We have explored the conditions under which neat soap forms, but we have not yet discussed what makes it neat. Neat soap is a lamellar, lyotropic, liquid-crystalline phase of soap and water. Perhaps we should take each adjective in reverse order. Neat soap is a liquid-crystalline phase of soap and water. Usually, crystalline materials are solids; the molecules vibrate about regularly spaced lattice points but they do not slide past one another. Molecules in a liquid do slide past one another more or less at random. Molecules in a liquid crystal are free to slide around, but not randomly. There is a long-range order to their positions, even though those positions are constantly changing. Liquid crystals, then, combine the long-range order of a crystalline solid with the fluidity of a liquid.

A lyotropic liquid crystal is a mixture of two or more materials, one of which is usually polar. In neat soap, the two components are soap and water. The soap molecule has an ionic head, soluble in water, and a greasy, hydrophobic, hydrocarbon tail. In the liquid crystal, the ionic head group contains a sodium or potassium ion surrounded by water molecules. The watery head groups tend to aggregate together to the exclusion of the greasy tails, and this accounts for the long range order of the liquid crystal. The properties of the liquid crystal depend on

Figure 22-7. Neat Soap

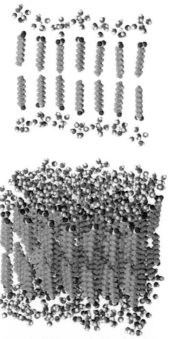

the relative concentrations of soap and water, as we have seen in the previous section.

In Section 13.1 (page 221), we saw that soap molecules assemble into micelles when the soap concentration is above a certain limit, the critical micelle concentration. The structure of a micelle allows the greasy tails to be isolated from their watery surroundings. We imagine these micelles surrounded by water molecules, their fatty interiors dissolving dirt and grease so that they may be washed down the drain. But in neat soap, there is more soap than water; there simply is not enough water to keep the micelles separated from one another. We may imagine one micelle merging with another, and another, until they are no longer isolated spherical globs, but larger structures. One such structure consists of sheets of soap molecules separated by sheets of water molecules. This kind of liquid-crystalline structure is called a lamellar structure.

Figure 22-7 shows a model of neat soap. In the top panel, we see fourteen soap molecules, their greasy tails back-to-back to minimized contact with the water molecules above and below them. In the second panel we expand this structure into a two-dimensional sheet, and in the third panel we stack these alternating sheets of soap and water to produce the full three-dimensional structure of neat soap. This structure, however, is far from static; the molecules are in constant motion, the greasy tails sliding past one another, changing places with one another, the water molecules dancing frenetically about their sodium ions, the greasy and watery layers flexing and shifting like blankets on a water bed.

As neat soap cools, it begins to solidify into curd. The constant jostling slows to the point that the soap molecules no longer slide past one another, but vibrate gently about fixed positions within the soap sheet. It is as if a nation of earthworms has settled down for a long winter's nap. We may say that the fatty layers have solidified, frozen, or crystallized. The watery layers, however, remain in constant motion until the temperature drops below the freezing point of water. It is as if soap curd consists of alternating layers of solid fatty material and liquid water. This not-quite-solid state accounts for the softness of bar soap compared to other solids like salt, sugar, or ice. Indeed, if

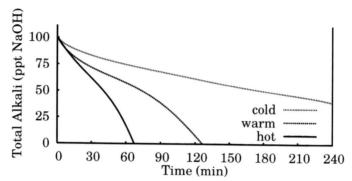

Figure 22-8. Total Alkali vs Time

we cool the soap sufficiently, the watery layers freeze and the soap becomes as hard as a brick.

22.5 Total Alkali

Throughout this study we have followed the saponification reaction by monitoring the temperature of the raw soap. While temperature plays a critical role in the phase history and ultimate structure of a soap, we can gain a little more insight by considering the reaction rate more directly. Figure 22-8 shows the total alkali of a typical soap as a function of time. We made a medium-water soap (Delight$_{1000}$Lye$_{288}$Aq$_{144}$), sucked samples into disposable plastic pipets, and kept them at a constant temperature prior to analysis. One set of samples was kept at 50°C (cold), another at 60°C (warm), and a third at 70°C (hot). For each sample, we measured the total alkali using the method of Section 15.1 (page 245) and recorded the time elapsed since the soap was mixed.

The graph shows that saponification proceeds most rapidly at high temperature and least rapidly at low temperature. Moreover, we find that for this medium-water soap, the reaction is essentially complete after an hour at 70°C. This coincides roughly with the time at which the temperature peaked for the "hot" medium-water soap of Figure 22-4 (page 309). The comparison is not perfect because the temperatures of Figure 22-8 were held constant while those of Figure 22-4 were allowed to rise and fall. Nevertheless, the coincidence lends credence to our hypothesis that the temperature begins to fall once the reaction is complete.

22.6 Conclusions

This study has focused on a single, unscented oil blend. The temperature boundary between neat and curd soap will be different for other blends. The rate of heat loss, and hence the peak temperature, will also depend on the size and shape of the mold. For this reason, we can make no dogmatic claim in favor of one particular starting temperature or moisture concentration. But we expect the relationship between temperature, moisture concentration, phase behavior, and time to be similar for other oil blends. If you have a blend that melts in a particular mold at a particular starting temperature, you may expect that decreasing the temperature and the water portion may prevent the next batch from melting. If you have a blend that does not melt, increasing the temperature and water portion may cause the next batch to melt. And if you have a blend that melts partially, you may adjust the temperature and moisture to ensure that the next batch behaves as you wish. For delicate scents, you may prefer a soap that stays warm without getting too hot. A soap that has melted, however, may maintain its shape better in the soap dish. The results of this study will allow you to choose the conditions of temperature and moisture that best suit your needs.

Chapter 23

Time to Trace

SOAP thickens. From the moment the lye hits the oil, the clock is ticking. The soapmaker must ensure that all of the ingredients are thoroughly blended before the soap becomes too thick to pour into the mold. Failure to blend the ingredients will result in soap that varies from one spot to another in alkalinity, consistency, color, or scent. Occasionally, soap thickens so quickly upon the addition of lye that it can be poured into the mold only with difficulty. Soapmakers say that the soap has **seized.** What are the factors that cause one batch to take forever to trace while another must be chipped out of the soap pot with a chisel? How can we hasten or retard trace in problematic oil blends? These are the questions to be answered in this, the final chapter.[1]

23.1 Introduction

Let us begin our exploration with a review of the history of soap, the cold process, and trace. While soap is often supposed to be ancient in origin, the historical record does not support that theory. We find no references to soap in the ancient sources that ought to mention it if, indeed, it were in common use.[2] The *Stockholm Papyrus,* of the second century AD, for example, contains an extensive discussion of laundering techniques but

---

1. This research was performed during the 2009–2010 academic year at Hampden-Sydney College by students J. Benjamin Cook, James R. Oliver, Jr., and Henry Skiba under the direction of Kevin M. Dunn. The groundwork for this study was laid by James Baldwin and Kevin M. Dunn during the 2006–2007 academic year.
2. An oft-repeated story is that soap originated in animal sacrifices at Sapo Hill in Rome. Though the story is sometimes attributed to Pliny the Elder, there is no mention of it in any of his works. I have yet to track down the original source of this story.

makes no mention of anything we would recognize as soap [61]. The earliest known use of the word *sapo* appears in Pliny the Elder's *Natural History,* written in the first century [90]. There Pliny describes soap not as an item of common commerce but as an exotic pomade used by Germans to make their hair red. *Sapo,* says Pliny, is made from suet and ash and comes in two varieties, thick and liquid. In the second century, Galen describes soap made from goat tallow and ashes as a material that is good for washing things [81]. These early references make it clear that soap was introduced to the Latin-reading public some time around the second century, but subsequent references to soap and soapmaking in works from the first millennium are both brief and vague.

The earliest complete description of the soapmaking process appears in the *Mappae Clavicula,* written circa 1130 AD [92]. The author describes the extraction of lye from wood ashes, the addition of lime to make it more caustic, and the necessity of boiling to remove excess water. Oil (olive or tallow) is then added to the boiling lye, and the mixture is cooked until it becomes thick. Upon cooling, the soap separates from the excess lye, floats to the top of the container, and is skimmed off. From that point down to the present day, the dominant soapmaking process has involved the boiling of fats and oils with lye.

The earliest reference to the cold process may come from an English patent granted in 1622 to Andrew Palmer and Roger Jones:

> The misterie, arte, way, and means of makinge of hard soape, comonly called by the name of Venice or castile soape, without the vse of anie fire in the boyling or makinge thereof, and with a materiall comonly called or known by the name of berilla, and The art, misterie, way and means of makinge of softe soape without the vse of fire in the boylinge and makinge thereof. [93]

The new soap, however, could not compete with that made in the traditional way, and there ensued a bitter and expensive attempt by soapmakers at Westminster to establish a royal monopoly to make soap by the new method and prevent London soapmakers from carrying on their trade [87]. After suffering persecution, fines, and imprisonment, the London soapmakers bought out those in Westminster and returned to their traditional methods [91].

Soap boiling continued to dominate the trade for the next two hundred years. Writing in 1807, the eminent chemist Chaptal summarized the status of the cold process:

> It has always been a desideratum with manufacturers to form soap without the aid of heat. Even at the present day this object is still regarded as worthy of attention. But though we have succeeded, by various processes, in manufacturing soaps of excellent quality in this way, yet the method usually employed has not hitherto been abandoned, which clearly proves that no great advantage has resulted from preparing them without heat. [74]

Chaptal gives full particulars for the cold process. In one description, two parts of almond oil are mixed with one part of lye with a specific gravity of 1.375, corresponding to a concentration (if pure NaOH) of about 340 ppt. Though the stoichiometry of saponification had not yet been worked out, this formula translates to an alkali ratio of 170 ppt NaOH, somewhat higher than the sodium saponification value of almond oil (134–143 ppt NaOH). Chaptal advises that if this soap is caustic, more oil should be added. Hindsight being 20/20, we can understand why this might have been necessary.

In 1823 Chevreul brought an unprecedented scientific approach to the study of fats, oils, and soaps [75]. Chevreul identified and named glycerin and many of the fatty acids, determined that oils are esters of fatty acids with glycerin, measured the fatty acid content of a wide variety of oils and fats, and concluded that soaps are alkali salts of fatty acids.[3] He made the earliest attempts at determining scientifically the amount of alkali required to completely saponify a given amount of oil. Without this information, makers of cold-process soap had been working in the dark, with the result that their soaps were often found to be more caustic than those produced by boiling.

The cold process achieved some commercial success beginning in the second quarter of the nineteenth century. Writing in 1847, Morfit devotes an entire chapter to the cold process [83]. His recipe for almond oil soap calls for lye boiled down to a density of 36° Baumé. Twelve parts of lye are mixed with twenty-five

---

3. It was not until 1854 that Berthelot discovered natural fats to be *tri*esters of fatty acids with glycerin [59]. He coined the names tristearin, triolein, and tripalmitin to reflect this fact.

of almond oil for an alkali ratio of 144 ppt NaOH, only slightly above the modern sodium saponification value (134–143 ppt NaOH). Kurten's manual of 1854 provides alkali ratios for coconut oil, lard, and tallow: 168, 144, and 155 ppt NaOH, respectively (modern ssvs: 176–189, 135–145, and 135–143 ppt NaOH, respectively) [82].[4] From this point forward, it became possible to consistently produce non-caustic cold-process soap.

While soapmakers had determined the proper ratio of lye to oil by trial and error, it was not until 1879 that chemists began to measure precise saponification values. The aim of these measurements was not to produce better soap, but to detect the adulteration of butter with coconut oil [69]. The determination of saponification values soon became a routine test in the edible oil trade. Saponification values did not enter soapmaking books, however, until 1888 [73].

As the nineteenth century continued, cold-process soap became established as the red-headed stepchild of the soap boiling industry. Used by small firms to produce specialty toilet soaps, the cold process remained uncompetitive for producing soap in large quantities. Commodity soap books of the twentieth century, by and large, regard the cold process as a quaint alternative that might be appropriate for firms lacking the capital required to boil soap on a large scale. Given this attitude, it is not surprising that as soap chemistry advanced, few resources were committed to studying problems peculiar to the cold process.

One such peculiarity is the notion of "trace." The earliest descriptions of the cold process simply say that soap should be mixed until it is thick. Writing in 1867, Adolph Ott says that cold-process soap should be stirred until a ring can be drawn on its surface with a spatula [88]. In 1872 William Dick provides a similar description:

> 583. To Make Soap by the Cold Process. Incorporate by degrees 50 pounds concentrated caustic lye of 36° Baumé, into

---

4. Lye of that era was available only as a solution whose strength was measured by its density (using the Baumé scale). Morfit and Kurten gave alkali ratios in terms of 36° Baumé lye, which would have corresponded to 300 ppt NaOH if the lye had contained only NaOH and water. Because of impurities in the lye, however, the density provided only an approximate measure of its concentration. The use of solid caustic soda did not become economically feasible until about 1896 [93].

> 100 pounds fat at a temperature not higher than 104° Fahr.
> (see No. 523 (Beef Tallow)); continue to stir thoroughly with a
> broad wooden paddle, until a complete ring can be drawn on its
> surface with the paddle. [78]

These descriptions imply that the extent of saponification may
be judged by observing the surface of the soap.

Webb's description of 1927 fleshes it out a little more:

> Crutching or mixing is continued until the mass thickens. The
> desired degree of thickness is judged by withdrawing the crutch
> (hand crutch) from the soap, and noticing the impression the
> runnings off the crutch make upon the surface of the soap. If
> they leave a dent or impression the thickness required has been
> obtained, if they do not, but mingle at once with the mass, the
> crutching should be continued until this condition is obtained.
> [94]

Webb is writing for makers of commodity soap whose scale of
operation may be small compared to that of a soap boiler, but
large compared to that met with in the modern handcrafted
soap industry.

Webb's description of the soap surface sounds very much like
that provided by Ann Bramson at the dawn of the handcrafted
soap era:

> The mixture is ready to pour when it has the consistency of a
> thick pea soup, and when dripped from a spoon, traces across
> the surface or leaves a trail. If the drops just drop in and dis-
> appear, if they don't remain temporarily in relief, if you can't
> draw a star or line or whatever and clearly see a trace of it on
> the surface of the soap, it has not thickened sufficiently. [51]

I have found no earlier use of the word *trace* to describe the phenomenon, and I believe we can thank Bramson for introducing
the word into our vocabulary.

Since commodity soap books tend to be dismissive of the
cold process, they do not directly address the trace phenomenon.
Some studies, however, have employed the cold process to evaluate the effects of *catalysts* (compounds that increase the rate
of a reaction) on saponification. The experiments of Davidsohn
and Better, for example, measured the time required for cold-
process coconut oil soap to thicken when the oil contained 2 ppt
of an additive [77]. They found that phenolic compounds such
as thymol (from thyme) and carvacrol (from thyme or oregano)

markedly accelerated the thickening of cold-process coconut oil soap. The most pronounced acceleration was found for aromatic compounds containing a single -OH group and hydrocarbon side chains. We encountered just such a molecule, eugenol, in Section 11.3 (page 197).

Ahmad *et al.* studied catalysis in the cold-process saponification of coconut and cotton seed oils [57]. They found that either 7.5 ppt salicylaldehyde (from meadowsweet) or 6 ppt eugenol (from clove or cinnamon) accelerated the thickening of cold-process soap. They speculated that these additives stabilize the oil/lye emulsion, thus shortening the initial (slow) step of saponification.

The purpose of the present study is to determine how the thickening of cold-process soap depends on such factors as water content, temperature, and the presence of catalysts. Before we can do so, we need to find out how to measure viscosity.

23.2 Viscosity

Section 13.5 (page 233) established that additives such as clove oil may be used to accelerate the thickening of soap. So far, however, we have no way to quantify this thickening. Viscosity is the technical term for "thickness," and it is usually expressed in centipoise (cP). At 20°C, for example, the viscosities of water, olive oil, castor oil, and glycerol are 1 cP, 84 cP, 986 cP, and 1490 cP, respectively. For most materials, the viscosity decreases as the temperature increases—warm honey pours more easily than cold honey.

There are many types of viscometers available, most of them too expensive or too fragile for our purposes. You may already own, however, a device that serves as a primitive and inexpensive viscometer—a disposable, graduated transfer pipet.[5] We used this marvelous item as a sample holder in Section 19.1. The body of the pipet has a mark denoting a volume of 1 mL. We can use a stopwatch to measure the time it takes to "suck" 1 mL of raw soap into the pipet. This time will be proportional to the viscosity.

---

5. Cynmar [9] part number 132-24513.

Figure 23-1. Poor Soapmaker's Viscometer

To use this *poor soapmaker's viscometer,* squeeze the pipet bulb, insert the tip into the fluid to be evaluated, prepare a stopwatch, and simultaneously release the bulb and start the watch. When the fluid reaches the 1 mL mark, stop the watch and record the time, henceforth in units of pipet-sec. Since a used pipet might be wet or clogged, use each pipet only once. In our preliminary studies, we measured the time taken to suck 1 mL of olive oil, castor oil, and glycerol. Taking six measurements for each liquid, the times were 3.29±0.18 pipet-sec, 25.32±9.51 pipet-sec, and 46.62±11.99 pipet-sec, respectively. There were substantial variations in these times from one attempt to the next, probably due to manufacturing variations in the bulbs themselves. Nevertheless, it was possible to reliably distinguish the viscosities of liquids as different as olive oil and castor oil.

To calibrate our pipets, we divided the known viscosity of each liquid by the time required to suck 1 mL in each of eighteen measurements. The resulting calibration factor was 33.99±12.11 cP/pipet-sec, rounded to 34 cP/pipet-sec. Multiplying this factor by the time taken to suck 1 mL of a fluid gives us

Figure 23-2. Palm Oil Soap Viscosity

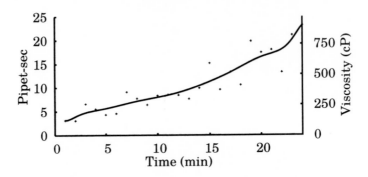

an estimate of the fluid's viscosity. We can gauge the accuracy of the viscometer by applying the calibration factor to the data from the previous paragraph to give viscosities for olive oil, castor oil, and glycerol of 112 cP (+33% error), 861 cP (-13% error), and 1585 cP (+6% error), respectively.

Armed with this viscometer, we measured the viscosity of $Palm_{1000}Lye_{280}Aq_{140}$ (starting at 40°C) as a function of time, as shown in Figure 23-2. The individual data points are shown to emphasize the considerable scatter of these points relative to a smooth line through them. We observed a thin trace on the surface of the soap beginning at 12 minutes (287 cP), a more pronounced trace at 19 minutes (674 cP), and a heavy trace at 23 minutes (717 cP). This preliminary study established the possibility of measuring the viscosity of raw soap in real time as it approaches trace.

While there is considerable scatter in the calibration data and in the viscosity measurements of Figure 23-2, the poor soapmaker's viscometer just might make a useful addition to the soapmaker's toolkit. It might be overkill to continually monitor the viscosity while mixing production soap, but it would be easy to record a single measurement—the pour viscosity—as part of the batch record. For a study of the factors affecting trace, however, we will need a more reliable device to measure viscosity, as described in the next section.

Figure 23-3. Shell Cup Viscometer

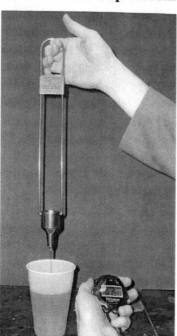

23.3 Experimental Method

The present study is essentially a carefully controlled variation
on the preliminary work of the previous section. Because temperature and moisture concentration affect the rate of saponification, as explored in Chapter 22, we supposed that the time
required to reach trace would depend on these factors as well.
In addition, we supposed that additives might hasten or retard
the onset of trace. Consequently, we measured the viscosity as
a function of time for a variety of soap formulas at a variety of
temperatures.

For viscosity measurements, we chose the Norcross Shell
cup #6.[6] The Shell cup looks something like a stainless steel funnel with a handle. It is immersed into the fluid to be evaluated,
lifted vertically from the fluid, and a stopwatch is started the
moment that the rim breaks the surface. The watch is stopped

---

6. www.Viscosity.com [24], 2007 price $160.

when the cup is empty, and the time is recorded in Shell cup-sec. A calibration graph provided by Norcross converts Shell cup-sec into cP. There is a knack to using the Shell cup—each experimenter practiced on olive oil to develop this knack. The Shell cup is very rugged, impervious to alkali, and produces reliable viscosity measurements between 200 and 800 cP.

The oil blend known as Delight had the formula $Olive_{390}Palm_{280}Coconut_{280}Castor_{50}$. Coconut, palm, pomace olive, and castor oils were provided by Columbus Foods.[7] Food-grade caustic soda was purchased from AAA Chemicals.[8] Eugenol was purchased from Sigma-Aldrich.[9] All chemicals were used without further purification.

Any soapmaker knows that mixing has a marked effect on the time required to reach trace. If lye is poured into oil with no attempt to the two, the lye settles to the bottom and the oil rises to the top. Given enough time, however, the oil will saponify. Mixing brings the oil and lye into intimate contact, hastening saponification. Since well-mixed soap saponifies more rapidly than poorly mixed soap, it is imperative to establish a mixing protocol to avoid being fooled by variations in mixing from one batch to the next.

The soaps in this study were made from 200.00 g of oil, the appropriate amount of lye as calculated from Table 4-1 (page 65), and the desired quantity of de-ionized water. The lye and water portions were mixed in one polypropylene bottle, the oil (and eugenol if required) in another. Both bottles were placed into a circulating temperature bath and equilibrated to the desired temperature. The lye was then poured into the oil bottle, which was shaken on a modified Blair Tornado II paint shaker for 45 seconds to mix the oil and lye. The raw soap was then poured into a nest of Styrofoam cups, and the temperature and viscosity were measured approximately once per minute until the onset of trace.

Popular wisdom has it that soap must be poured at trace to avoid the possibility of separation in the mold. To test this hypothesis, we mixed two identical soaps using the method of Section 6.7 (page 116). The oil, lye, and water portions were

---

7.   www.SoapersChoice.com [7].
8.   www.AAA-Chemicals.com [1].
9.   www.SigmaAldrich.com [37].

Figure 23-4. Viscosity and Temperature

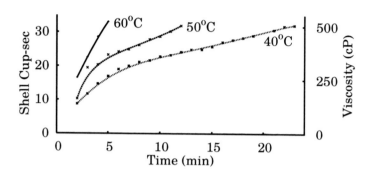

shaken vigorously in 1 gal jugs until thoroughly mixed. These soaps were poured at different viscosities into vertical wooden molds with inside dimensions 5.8 cm × 8.9 cm × 58.9 cm tall (2.3 in × 3.5 in × 22.0 in tall). To check for separation, we measured the total alkali of the top and bottom bars of each batch using the method of Section 15.1 (page 245). If the top and bottom bars were within 1 ppt NaOH of one another, we considered that no separation had taken place.

23.4 Results

Figure 23-4 shows viscosity vs time at several starting temperatures for raw $Delight_{1000}Lye_{288}Aq_{144}$. Notice how closely the individual data points hug the line through them, reflecting the improved precision of the Shell cup over the poor soapmaker's viscometer used in Figure 23-2. At each temperature, the viscosity increases steadily as time passes. We observed visible trace at a viscosity of about 500 cP for this and other soaps in the study and henceforth adopted 500 cP as our threshold for trace.

We might expect the viscosity to depend on temperature for two conflicting reasons. First, the viscosity of oil decreases with increasing temperature, so we might expect the viscosity of an oil/lye mixture to do the same. Second, oil saponifies more quickly at high temperature than low, so we might expect the viscosity of raw soap to increase more rapidly at high temperature

Figure 23-5. Viscosity and Water Content

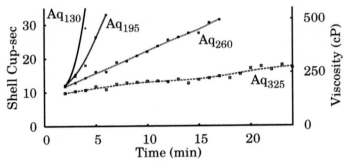

than at low temperature. From the figure, we can see that this second effect dominates the behavior of raw soap. While warm oil may have a lower viscosity than cold oil, the rapid formation of soap at high temperatures leads to stabilization of the oil/lye emulsion and rapid thickening of the raw soap.

In addition to Delight, we looked at the dependence of viscosity on time and temperature for single-oil soaps. Like that of Delight soap, the viscosity of olive oil soap increased with time, but the rate of increase did not depend on starting temperature. Palm oil soap showed the same temperature dependence as Delight soap except at the lowest temperature. In some trials, the viscosity increased more slowly at 40°C than at 50°C; in other trials, the viscosity increased more rapidly at 40°C than at 60°C. We supposed that in some of these trials the temperature was low enough for solid fat to form, increasing the viscosity of the mixture. Some soapmakers refer to the phenomenon of "false trace," and we believe that this was observed in these trials.

Figure 23-5 shows the viscosity of raw $Olive_{1000}Lye_{262}$ as a function of time using several different water portions. We expected viscosity to rise most rapidly with low water content, and this is precisely what was observed for olive oil soap. The pattern was not as evident, however, for palm oil and Delight soaps. Generally, low-water soaps thickened quickly and high-water soaps slowly, but there was no clear pattern for the soaps in the middle. It may be that some uncontrolled factor prevented us from getting reproducible results in this part of the study.

Figure 23-6. Viscosity and Eugenol Content

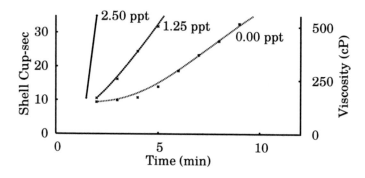

As it stands, we cannot recommend using water concentration to control the rate of viscosity change in raw soap.

When $Olive_{1000}Lye_{262}Aq_{232}$ contained as little as 1.25 ppt eugenol, the viscosity rose more rapidly than for soap made without eugenol, as shown in Figure 23-6. With 2.5 ppt eugenol, the soap reached trace in less than 2 minutes. In separate experiments, we found that eugenol reacts instantly with lye to form a nearly odorless, yellow solid (sodium eugenolate). Raw soap containing eugenol also took on a yellow color and became odorless as soon as lye was added. We concluded that sodium eugenolate (not eugenol itself) was responsible for the rapid thickening of the soap. We would expect eugenol-containing essential oils such as clove or cinnamon to hasten trace without imparting much in the way of scent.

Finally, we come to the question of whether it is important for soap to come to trace before it is poured. Two batches of $Delight_{1000}Lye_{288}Aq_{288}$ (2 ducks each) were poured into vertical wooden molds, one at a viscosity of 143 cP and the other at 282 cP. Both were poured at a temperature of 44°C. They were removed from the molds after two days and remained wrapped in waxed paper until they could be analyzed. All four samples turned out to be less alkaline than the phenolphthalein indicator. For the log poured at 282 cP, the top and bottom bars each had total alkali -0.3 ppt NaOH. For the log poured at 143 cP, the top and bottom bars each had total alkali -0.6 ppt NaOH. For these soaps, there were no separation issues despite the fact that they were poured well before the onset of trace (500 cP).

23.5 Conclusions

The biggest hurdle in the early stages of saponification is bringing the oil and lye into intimate contact with one another. The
most effective way to promote this contact is to break the oil and
lye into small droplets that can co-mingle with one another. The
biggest variable at this stage is the degree of mechanical mixing, which affects the size of oil and lye droplets, the total area
of the oil/lye surface, and the stability of the emulsion. Slow and
gentle mixing will delay trace; violent agitation will hasten it.
Once soap begins to form, soap molecules assemble at the surfaces of the droplets, bridging the interface between oil and lye.
The soap thickens as the droplets become smaller and the area
of contact between them increases. As the rate of saponification
increases, the temperature rises and the soap solidifies. If the
temperature rises high enough, the soap may re-melt into neat
soap (gel phase), further increasing the rate of saponification.
The present study has focused on the early period of the reaction leading up to trace.

Only when we were able to control the degree of mechanical
mixing were we able to explore the other factors which affect
the initial rate of saponification. By subjecting each soap to 45
seconds of violent agitation in an electric paint shaker, we made
every effort to ensure that every soap in the study was mixed
identically. Even so, there was some variation in the viscosity
curve for soaps that ought to have been identical. We attribute
these variations to the difficulty of precisely controlling the mixing process.

In spite of these variations, some factors affecting trace may
be clearly identified. Soap mixed at 60°C reached trace (viscosity 500 cP) more quickly than those mixed at 50°C. Those mixed
at 40°C reached trace more slowly, except in those cases where
it was likely that solid fats had precipitated, a condition known
in the trade as "false trace." For most soaps, we believe that
trace may be hastened by increasing the mixing temperature
and retarded by decreasing it.

Increasing the amount of water in the soap formula generally slowed the onset of trace, but the data were less reproducible
than for the temperature effect. Consequently, we believe that
the water portion should be chosen for such factors as whether

or not it is desirable for the soap to gel (melt) in the later stages of saponification. We do not believe that control of the water portion is a reliable means of controlling the time to trace.

For oils and oil blends that are slow to trace, essential oils such as clove and cinnamon oils may be added to hasten the onset of trace. At concentrations of 1 ppt, these eugenol-rich oils can decrease the time to trace without significantly affecting the scent of the finished soap. Eugenol is particularly effective in stabilizing oil/water emulsions [71], and it is presumably this stabilization that leads to its catalytic effect on saponification.

Trace is a challenging concept for novice soapmakers. Descriptions of the phenomenon are somewhat subjective, and photographs do not do it justice. As generations of soapmakers have done before them, modern makers of cold-process soap develop a knack for knowing when to pour. The current study provides some relief to those who agonize over spotting trace. First, the poor soapmaker's viscometer (or its upscale cousin, the Shell cup) may be used to determine the viscosity of raw soap in advance of any visible signs on the surface. Second, the specter of separation does not appear to pounce mercilessly on soaps poured prior to trace. Delight soaps poured well in advance of trace turned out to be equally tongue-neutral on the top and bottom bars of our vertical logs. While we cannot promise that the same will be true for all soap formulas, at all pour temperatures, and in all molds, we can give you permission to relax a little bit—to curl your lips into a gentle, confident smile as you stir the pot—and to pour at your convenience if a visible sign from the soap gods is not forthcoming.

We have hypothesized that soap thickens when soap molecules accumulate at the oil/lye interface, thereby decreasing the sizes of droplets and stabilizing the emulsion. It would be useful to further examine the role that small amounts of soap might play in the period leading up to trace. Oils might be spiked, for example, with known quantities of fatty acids (which react instantly with lye to form soap) to determine their effect on the viscosity of oil/lye mixtures. We are in the early stages of such a study, but you need not wait for our results—you can participate in the joy of scientific soapmaking yourself.

23.6 Scientific Soapmaking

Makers of commodity soap enjoy a wealth of information about oil, soap, and the processes they use to turn one into the other. Technical books detail analytical techniques for answering just about any conceivable question regarding oils, fats, soaps, and detergents. Technical journals continually add to this wealth of knowledge. Unfortunately for makers of handcrafted soap, many of these techniques employ equipment that is beyond their means, and many of the results are couched in language that is inaccessible to them. Moreover, commodity soap is rarely made from the soft, unsaturated oils prized in the handcrafted soapmaking community, and the cold process rarely receives more than a paragraph or two in technical soap books. This leaves makers of handcrafted soap at the mercy of hearsay, with little guidance in distinguishing fact from fiction.

The book in your hands is not the *Bible* of soapmaking.[10] It was never meant to deliver the Truth with a capital *T*, to dogmatically lay down laws to be accepted unquestioningly, or to contain all the answers to every imaginable question about soap. I wrote it, in part, to bridge the gap between the technical and craft literatures and make the language of commodity soapmaking more accessible to the handcrafted soapmaking community. I have modified some of the analytical techniques to use equipment and supplies that are widely available at modest cost. Most of all, however, I have provided examples of interesting questions and have demonstrated the kinds of experiments that could be used to answer them.

Five years ago Jackie Thompson invited me to lecture at the annual convention of the Handcrafted Soapmakers Guild, and that was the beginning of this journey. I realize now how little I knew then. In the years since, soapmakers have brought me their questions and their problems, and my students and I have attempted to provide answers and solutions. But more often than not, the questions have turned out to be far more

---

10. In the course of editing this book, Alex Santic remarked that while soapmakers can be grumpy, they seldom resort to violence when their cherished beliefs or traditions are called into question. He assured me that I would not end up like Salman Rushdie, with a fatwa on my head. Upon further reflection, he suggested that I change the title to *The Saponic Verses*. I didn't.

complex than I first imagined, and the problems far more persistent. This book documents the beginning of our explorations, not the end. I hope that its publication will widen the circle of soapmakers engaged in a spirit of honest inquiry, that these soapmakers will become a community with a shared technical language, and that together we can blend art and science with the best traditions of our craft.

Appendix A

Practice Problems

If this book were a mystery novel, would you read the last page first? Collected here are all the practice problems and my answers to them. You will benefit most if you check the answers *after* working the problems for yourself.

Chapter 1

1. What hazards should be anticipated in making soap?

The principle hazard is the possibility of splashing lye in the eyes. Safety glasses must be worn in the lab and a filled eyewash bottle should be kept in a convenient location. A telephone should be available in case of emergency.

    Chemicals should be stored securely and in such a way that spills may be contained. Children and pets should be protected from accidental exposure to hazardous materials.

Care must be taken in the choice of space heaters, ovens, and hotplates. Open flames should be avoided and a fire extinguisher should be kept in the vicinity of heating appliances.

2. What are the capacity and readability of a scale or balance?

The capacity of a balance is the maximum weight it can register. The readability of a balance is the smallest increment it can register. A centigram balance has a readability of 0.01 g and can distinguish, for example, 27.33 g and 27.34 g.

3. Why is an oven used for experimental cold-process soap?

While a large mold retains enough heat to ensure rapid saponification, a smaller, single-bar mold may not do so. In experimental soapmaking we keep the soap in a warm (not hot) oven to simulate the environment that would be found in the middle of a larger, insulated mold. The oven also allows us to control the temperature so that we can investigate the effect that temperature has on saponification.

4. Why does this chapter list prices, which are likely to be out of date by the time the book is published?

Prices are given to provide some indication of the relative costs of the materials. While the market prices of palm and olive oil may be expected to fluctuate, olive oil is likely to remain more expensive than palm oil.

5. Why is it better to draw a line through a notebook error rather than erasing it?

Occasionally, an "error" is later found to have been correct, after all. A line through an error marks it as an error but allows the information to be recovered if necessary.

6. What fire precautions are appropriate when making soap?

Alcohols, essential oils, and fragrance oils are volatile, meaning that they are easily evaporated. Because their vapors may be flammable, it is important to be mindful of ignition sources, such as electrical equipment, space heaters, ovens, and hotplates. Smoking should not be allowed in the soap laboratory.
The fixed oils, though not volatile, may ignite when heated. Oil fires may be smothered or extinguished with a chemical fire extinguisher.

7. What kind of ventilation is appropriate to a soap laboratory?

Alcohols, essential oils, and fragrance oils are volatile, meaning that they are easily evaporated. Because their vapors may be toxic in large quantities, the soap lab should be equipped with a ventilation fan to maintain a healthy working environment.

8. How should chemicals be stored?

Sodium and potassium hydroxides should be stored separately from other chemicals. If possible, there should be separate storage space for acids, solvents, oils, and essential or fragrance oils. Keeping chemicals in separate polyethylene bins provides an additional level of protection against leakage. Cabinets should be equipped with child-proof locks and unsupervised access to the soap lab should be limited for children and pets.

9. Why is the family kitchen an inadequate substitute for a dedicated soapmaking area?

Eye protection and awareness of hazardous materials are essential for safe soapmaking. Family members who are not participating in a soapmaking session could unexpectedly wander into the family kitchen without adequate knowledge or protection. Furthermore, the soapmaker might be tempted to use pots and utensils for food preparation and for soapmaking. While this might not be a problem once the utensils are cleaned, those waiting to be cleaned could pose a hazard to family members.

10. What does it mean to "think bad in the lab"?

We imagine the worst thing that could happen in a given procedure and prepare for that potential problem. Eye protection must be worn in the lab, an eyewash bottle should be at hand, a telephone or intercom should be available, and working alone should be avoided if possible.

Chapter 2

1. A balance has a capacity of 200 g. What is its capacity in ounces?

This question is equivalent to "How many ounces are equal to 200 g?" You will need to construct hotdogs from the following information. 1 lb = 454 g. 1 lb = 16 oz.

$$? \text{ oz} = 200 \, g \left(\frac{1 \, lb}{454 \, g} \right) \left(\frac{16 \text{ oz}}{1 \, lb} \right)$$
$$= 7.0 \text{ oz}$$

2. A balance has a capacity of 7 kilograms. What is its capacity in pounds?

This question is equivalent to "How many pounds are equal to 7 kilograms?" You will need to construct hotdogs from the following information. 1 lb = 454 g. 1 kg = 1000 g.

$$? \text{ lb} = 7 \, kg \left(\frac{1000 \, g}{1 \, kg} \right) \left(\frac{1 \text{ lb}}{454 \, g} \right)$$
$$= 15.4 \text{ lb}$$

3. How many minutes are there in a year?

You will need to construct hotdogs from the following information. 1 year = 365 days. 1 day = 24 hours. 1 hour = 60 minutes.

$$? \text{ min} = 1 \, \cancel{yr} \left(\frac{365 \, \cancel{days}}{1 \, \cancel{yr}} \right) \left(\frac{24 \, \cancel{hrs}}{1 \, \cancel{days}} \right) \left(\frac{60 \text{ min}}{1 \, \cancel{hrs}} \right)$$
$$= 525600 \text{ min}$$

4. A soap mold filled with 1.2 ducks of raw soap produces 11 bars
of finished soap. How many ducks of raw soap are needed to
produce 24 bars of soap using the same mold?

You will need to construct hotdogs from the following information. 1.2 ducks = 11 bars. Note that you can work the problem
without even knowing what a duck is.

$$? \text{ ducks} = 24 \, \cancel{bars} \left(\frac{1.2 \text{ ducks}}{11 \, \cancel{bars}} \right)$$
$$= 2.62 \text{ ducks}$$

5. A mole of NaOH weighs 40 g and a mole of KOH weighs 56 g.
1000 g of an oil reacts with 144 g of NaOH. 1 mole of KOH
reacts with the same amount of oil as 1 mole of NaOH. How
many grams of KOH are needed to react with 100 g of the
same oil?

As in the previous problem, you do not even need to know what a
mole is. You will need to construct hotdogs from the following
information. 1 mol NaOH = 40 g. 1 mol KOH = 56 g. 144 g
NaOH = 1000 g oil. 1 mol NaOH = 1 mol KOH.

$$? \text{ g KOH} = 100 \, \cancel{g \, oil} \left(\frac{144 \, \cancel{g \, NaOH}}{1000 \, \cancel{g \, oil}} \right) \left(\frac{1 \, \cancel{mol \, NaOH}}{40.0 \, \cancel{g \, NaOH}} \right)$$
$$\left(\frac{1 \, \cancel{mol \, KOH}}{1 \, \cancel{mol \, NaOH}} \right) \left(\frac{56 \text{ g KOH}}{1 \, \cancel{mol \, KOH}} \right)$$
$$= 20.2 \text{ g KOH}$$

6. Suppose you want to pump $10.00 worth of gasoline but slow reflexes result in an actual charge of $10.12. What are the relative error and uncertainty?

The relative error is $0.12 divided by $10.00, which is 0.012, or 12 ppt. The gasoline has a value between $10.11 and $10.13, so the relative uncertainty is ±$0.01 divided by $10.12, or ±1 ppt. If you had hit the target "exactly," you would have eliminated the error but not the uncertainty.

7. Suppose you want to weigh 10.00 g of water but overshoot the target by 1 drop, resulting in an actual weight of 10.05 g. What are the relative error and uncertainty?

The relative error is 0.05 g divided by 10.00 g, which is 0.005, or 5 ppt. The actual weight is between 10.04 g and 10.05 g, so the relative uncertainty is ±0.01 g divided by 10.12 g, or ±1 ppt. *10.04*

8. Consider that in weighing a liquid you can hit the target weight to within 1 drop using a centigram balance. How large must a liquid weight be if you want the relative error to be within 1 ppt of the target?

0.05 g is 1 ppt of 50.00 g. Weighing at least 50.00 g of a liquid to within 1 drop of the target will achieve a relative error of 1 ppt.

9. You want to weigh 759 g of water. How far can you stray from the target and still be within ±1 ppt? What kind of readability do you need from your balance?

Your actual weight can be anywhere between 759.7 and 758.3 g. A balance with a readability of 0.1 g would be adequate for this task.

10. You have two balances: one with a capacity of 50 g and a readability of 0.01 g, and the other with a capacity of 7000 g and a readability of 1 g. If your goal is to weigh 5000 g of water, will you get better uncertainty using the first balance or the second?

To use the first balance you will need to weigh 40 g one hundred and twenty-five times. The water is sure to weigh between 4998.75 and 5001.25 g, so the relative uncertainty is ±0.3 ppt. To use the second balance you need to weigh 5000 g only once. The water is sure to weigh between 4999 and 5001 g, so the relative uncertainty is ±0.2 ppt. In this case better uncertainty is achieved with the "less precise" balance.

Chapter 3

1. Why should an employer keep MSDSs on file for access by employees?

In the US this is an OSHA requirement. The intention of the law is to ensure that employees are properly educated in the safe handling of the materials they use in the workplace. While the sheets usually provide lots of information, it is sometimes couched in jargon that might need to be explained to employees.

2. What is the CAS registry number?

Since a given material is often known by several names, materials are assigned Chemical Abstracts Registry Numbers in order to uniquely identify them. You can think of them as "social security numbers" for chemicals. When searching for information, the CAS number can help avoid errors in identification.

3. What statistic can be used to estimate the relative toxicities of materials?

The LD_{50} is a rather gruesome statistic, giving the amount of material that can be expected to kill half of a test population. The smaller the number, the more hazardous the material. LD_{50}s are specific to particular animals and so may not strictly apply to humans.

4. Find an MSDS for citric acid. Is this material hygroscopic or deliquescent?

Anhydrous citric acid has a CAS number 77-92-9. That of citric acid monohydrate is 5949-29-1. Some sheets list them as slightly hygroscopic or deliquescent, but most do not. These materials should be protected from moist air but there is no need to be paranoid about it.

5. Find an MSDS for sodium chloride using the CAS number 7681-52-9 as one of your keywords. How does the information differ from that provided in this chapter?

7681-52-9 is the CAS registry number for sodium hypochlorite, the principle agent in laundry bleach. It just happens that laundry bleach also contains some sodium chloride. Since you would not want to confuse safety information on laundry bleach and table salt, it is important to look at Section 2 to confirm that it is for the material in which you are interested.

6. Find an MSDS for sodium lauryl sulfate. What is the CAS number for this material?

151-21-3 is the CAS number for sodium lauryl sulfate. Note that you can find the registry number from any MSDS that contains it. You can then add the registry number to your search keywords to refine your search.

7. Find an MSDS for phenolphthalein. Is this material flammable?

77-09-8 is the CAS number for phenolphthalein. Some sheets give its NFPA fire rating as 0 or 1, others as 3 or 4. If you look at Section 2, you will find the reason for this discrepancy. Pure phenolphthalein is a dry, white, nonflammable powder. It is often sold, however, as a solution in alcohol and this solution is quite flammable. Always check Section 2 before you take the rest of the sheet to heart.

8. Find an MSDS for tetrasodium EDTA. How does the health hazard for this material compare to those for sodium chloride and sodium hydroxide?

64-02-8 is the CAS number for tetrasodium ethylenediaminetetraacetic acid. Its NFPA health rating is 1, which is comparable to that for sodium chloride. Like sodium hydroxide, however, it is an eye irritant. Some sheets list it as a carcinogen, others do not. The reason for the discrepancy can be found in Section 2—some grades of EDTA contain nitilotriacetic acid as an impurity. It is this compound that is a suspected carcinogen and if it is present, even in small quantities, the MSDS lists the warning in Section 11. Cosmetic grades of EDTA do not contain this material, so the warning is not applicable to these grades.

9. Find MSDSs for ethanol and clove oil. Which of these materials is more toxic?

The CAS numbers are 64-17-5 and 8000-34-8, respectively. The sheets found at www.Sciencelab.com [34] give the LD_{50}s (oral, rat) as 7060 mg/kg and 2650 mg/kg, respectively. Thus clove oil is about twice as toxic to rats as ethanol (grain alcohol), but both numbers are rather large. The sheet for ethanol gives its NFPA health rating as 0, but its HMIS health rating as 2, representing a difference of opinion between the health hazards in a fire and in the laboratory. The sheet for clove oil gives its NFPA and HMIS health ratings as 2, making clove oil more hazardous than sodium chloride, but less hazardous than sodium hydroxide.

10. Find MSDSs for sodium lauryl sulfate and caffeine. Which of these materials is more toxic?

The CAS numbers are 151-21-3 and 58-08-2, respectively. The sheets found at www.Sciencelab.com [34] give the LD_{50}s (oral, rat) as 1288 mg/kg and 192 mg/kg, respectively. Thus caffeine is more toxic than sodium lauryl sulfate, but both numbers are rather large. These materials share an NFPA health rating of 2, making them more hazardous than sodium chloride, but less hazardous than sodium hydroxide.

Chapter 4

1. Palm and palm kernel oils have similar names, which can lead to confusion. What would be the consequence of using the recommended AR for palm oil for a soap produced from palm kernel oil?

Since the recommended AR for palm oil is smaller than that for palm kernel oil, this mistake would result in using less than the recommended amount of lye. We would expect the soap to be incompletely saponified and to contain some excess oil.

2. What soap formula would describe a soap made only from palm kernel oil, 500 ppt NaOH, and water?

Because the recommended AR for this soap is 163, it would have the formula $PalmKernel_{1000}Lye_{326}Aq_{163}$. An experimental bar of this soap would require 100.00 g of palm kernel oil, 32.60 g of lye, and 16.30 g of water.

3. Most soapmaking books advocate using lye with a concentration of 25–30%. What advantage is there to using lye with a concentration of 50% (500 ppt)?

With 50% lye we can always add more water to get the same effect as using less concentrated lye. If the AR is 140, for example, we can use 28.00 g of 500 ppt NaOH per 100.00 g of oil. We can also use 28.00 g of 500 ppt NaOH and 28.00 g of water, which would be exactly the same as using 56.00 g of 250 ppt NaOH. In either case we are adding the same amount of NaOH (14.00 g) but different amounts of water.

4. One bottle of lye was produced from 142.88 g of NaOH and 142.88 g of water. 225.78 g of this lye was used to make soap, and then 135.33 g of NaOH and 135.33 g of water were added to the same bottle. What was the final concentration of the lye?

The initial concentration was 500 ppt. When some lye was used to make soap, the concentration of the remaining lye was still 500 ppt. The fresh lye added to the bottle was also 500 ppt, so the final concentration remained 500 ppt.

Another way to look at this is that a total of 278.21 g of NaOH and 278.21 g of water were added to the bottle. When 225.78 g of lye were removed, this included 112.89 g of NaOH and 112.89 g of water. So the net weights of NaOH and water were 165.32 g and 165.32 g, respectively. Any way you cut it, the concentration comes out to 500 ppt.

5. An employee insists that tasting soap is dangerous. How would you answer this employee's concerns?

No one should be forced to taste something against their will. That employee should be instructed to use pH test strips instead.

6. You discover that you left the lid off of your lye bottle overnight. What would be the consequences of using this lye for making soap?

You might think that some water would evaporate and the lye would be more concentrated than when it started. Amazingly, concentrated lye absorbs water from the air, becoming more dilute in the process. You should not take my word for this. Weigh a bottle of lye before and after leaving its lid off and see whether it gains weight.

Since a given weight of dilute lye contains less NaOH than the same weight of concentrated lye, using this lye to make soap would produce a soap that contains excess oil. While this would not be a catastrophe, it might fool you into thinking that your soap formula did not call for enough lye.

7. Why was extra water included in the formulas for the palmitic, lauric, and ricinoleic soaps?

These oils saponify more quickly than the oleic, linoleic, and linolenic oils. Extra water is added to slow the saponification reaction to give us enough time to thoroughly mix the raw soap before pouring it into the mold.

8. Many people would prefer not to wear gloves when making lye and soap. Considering the properties of the oils discussed in this chapter, what practice might protect skin from chemical burns without the use of gloves?

The linoleic and linolenic oils are relatively slow to saponify. Rubbing a little sunflower or safflower oil onto the hands provides pretty good protection from lye splashes. The same holds true for the face and arms if the complexion allows it. Do not use so much oil that your hands become slippery.

9. Many people would prefer not to wear glasses when making lye and soap. What practice might protect the eyes from chemical burns without the use of glasses?

Anyone who objects to wearing glasses when making lye and soap should be encouraged to go into some other line of work.

10. Suppose that as you were weighing the lye for your soap, a drop of lye fell on the pan of your balance. What effect would this have on the accuracy or uncertainty of your lye weight?

As long as the lye is on the balance, whether inside or outside the weighing bottle, it remains part of the tare weight. Such an incident has no effect on either the accuracy or uncertainty of your lye weight.

If the lye had landed on the countertop, your soap would have contained one less drop than was registered by the balance. This would introduce an error of -1 drop without affecting the uncertainty. You could correct this error by continuing to weigh your lye until you reach the target weight, recording the weight registered by the balance, and then adding one more drop of lye to your soap. The accuracy of this correction would depend on how consistent your drop sizes are, but it would be easier than starting over.

Chapter 5, Section 5.3

1. How many pounds of 500 ppt NaOH should be used for an oil blend consisting of 20 lb of olive oil, 40 lb of palm oil, and 22 lb of coconut oil?

23.78 lb of lye should be used.

2. How many ounces of 500 ppt NaOH should be used for an oil blend consisting of 20 oz of olive oil, 40 oz of palm oil, and 22 oz of coconut oil?

23.78 oz of lye should be used.

3. How many grams of 500 ppt NaOH should be used for an oil blend consisting of 100 g of olive oil, 250 g of palm oil, and 150 g of coconut oil?

146.5 g of lye should be used.

4. How many grams of 500 ppt NaOH should be used for an oil blend consisting of 1000 g of olive oil, 2500 g of palm oil, and 1500 g of coconut oil?

1465 g of lye should be used.

5. What would be the recommended alkali ratio for an oil blend consisting of 280 g of coconut oil and 280 g of palm oil?

Coconut oil has a recommended alkali ratio of 176 ppt, so we need 49.28 g of NaOH for the coconut oil. Palm oil has a recommended alkali ratio of 135 ppt, so we need 37.80 g of NaOH for the palm oil. We need 87.08 g of NaOH for 560.00 g of oil, so the recommended alkali ratio is 155.5 ppt.

Chapter 5, Section 5.4

1. What is the one-duck formula for a blend of 2 lb olive oil, 3 lb palm oil, and 1 lb coconut oil?

$Palm_{500}Olive_{333}Coconut_{167}Lye_{280}Aq_{140}$

2. What is the one-duck formula for a blend of 140 g of coconut oil, 140 g of palm oil, 195 g of olive oil, and 25 g of castor oil?

$Olive_{390}Coconut_{280}Palm_{280}Castor_{50}Lye_{288}Aq_{144}$

3. What is the one-duck formula for a blend of 16 oz of palm kernel oil, 19 oz of palm oil, 6 oz of olive oil, and 10 oz of hempseed oil?

$Palm_{373}PalmKernel_{314}Hemp_{196}Olive_{117}Lye_{286}Aq_{143}$

4. The recommended alkali ratio of palm oil is 135. What would be the one-duck formula for a coconut/olive blend with the same recommended alkali ratio?

A very little algebra is needed here. Let x be the ppt of coconut oil:

0.176 x + 0.131 (1000-x) = 0.135

Solving for x, we find that the fraction of coconut oil is 89 ppt. The formula is then $Olive_{911}Coconut_{89}Lye_{270}Aq_{135}$.

5. Imagine a coconut/olive blend for which alkali required by the coconut oil is equal to that required by the olive oil. What would be the one-duck formula for this blend?

Let x be the ppt of coconut oil:

0.176 x = 0.131 (1000-x)

Solving for x, we find that the fraction of coconut oil is 427 ppt. The formula is $Olive_{573}Coconut_{427}Lye_{300}Aq_{150}$.

Chapter 6

1. One duck of raw Delight produces 9.25 bars from a cavity mold. How many kilograms of oil, lye, and water should be used to produce 144 bars from a set of these molds?

We use Equation 6-1 (X = 144, Y = 1, Z = 9.25) to calculate an answer of 15.568 ducks. For this you would need 15.568 kg of oil, 4.483 kg of lye, and 2.242 kg of water. You could weigh 15.568 kg of pre-mixed oil in three portions using a gram balance. Alternatively, you could weigh 6.072 kg of olive oil, 4.359 kg each of coconut and palm oils, and 0.778 kg of castor oil using a gram balance.

2. Soap from a slab mold is to be cut into 12 bars. When 1.2 ducks of raw Delight was used, the total weight of finished bars was 41.93 oz. If you would like the bars to weigh 4 oz, how much raw soap should you use next time?

We use Equation 6-2 (W = 4, X = 12, Y = 1.2, Z = 41.93) to calculate an answer of 1.374 ducks. Since you would like to produce 48 oz of finished soap, you should use 1.374 ducks next time. For this you would need 1373.7 g of oil, 395.6 g of lye, and 197.8 g of water. You could weigh 1373.7 g of pre-mixed oil using a decigram balance. Alternatively, you could weigh 535.7 g of olive oil, 384.6 g each of coconut and palm oils, and 68.7 g of castor oil using a decigram balance.

3. You find that you have 927 g of olive oil, which you are phasing out in favor of high-oleic canola oil. You would like to use up all of this olive oil to make one last batch of Delight. How much coconut, palm, and castor oil should you use to make this batch?

We use Equation 6-4 (X = 927, Y = 390) to calculate an answer of 2.377 ducks. Since you don't want to desperately scrape every last drop of olive oil, round this down to 2.3 ducks. You would then need 897.0 g of olive oil, 644.0 g each of coconut and palm oils, and 115.0 g of castor oil.

4. 17.3 ducks of raw soap produced 44 lb of finished soap. How many ducks would be needed to produce 40 lb of soap using the same mold?

We use Equation 6-3 (X = 40, Y = 17.3, Z = 44) to calculate an answer of 15.7 ducks.

5. Delight has a recommended alkali ratio of 144. Suppose that you used a decagram balance like the BCS 40 to weigh the ingredients for 9 ducks of Delight. What would be the uncertainty in the actual alkali ratio?

9 ducks of Delight would call for 2592 g of 500 ppt NaOH. The BCS 40, however, will register 2590 g and we'll know that the actual weight is between 2580 and 2600 g. These limits correspond to alkali ratios of 143.3 and 144.4 ppt, respectively. The uncertainty in the alkali ratio would be ±0.6 ppt.

6. Delight has a recommended alkali ratio of 144. Suppose that you used a decagram balance like the BCS 40 to weigh the ingredients for 1 duck of Delight. What would be the uncertainty in the actual alkali ratio?

1 duck of Delight would call for 288 g of 500 ppt NaOH. The BCS 40, however, will register 290 g and we'll know that the actual weight is between 280 and 300 g. These limits correspond to alkali ratios of 140 and 150 ppt, respectively. The uncertainty in the alkali ratio would be ±5 ppt. If we happened to be at the upper end of that range, we would run the risk of producing a soap containing excess alkali.

7. What would be the recommended alkali ratio for an oil blend consisting of 390 g of olive oil and 50 g of castor oil?

Olive oil has a recommended alkali ratio of 131 ppt, so we need 51.09 g of NaOH for the olive oil. Castor oil has a recommended alkali ratio of 125 ppt, so we need 6.25 g of NaOH for the castor oil. We need 57.34 g of NaOH for 440.00 g of oil, so the recommended alkali ratio is 130.3 ppt.

8. Suppose that you have a 3-duck jug of Delight and you wish to make one experimental bar of soap. The oil in the jug is cloudy but pourable, and you hate to go to the trouble of heating the whole jug. Instead, you pour 100 g of oil into a smaller bottle and heat it to the recommended temperature. Why should this action be considered a mistake?

The cloudiness in the jug means that some of the oil components have crystallized. Since palm and coconut oils have higher melting points than olive and castor oils, we may assume that the solid component of our Delight contains a greater proportion of the higher-melting oils. Let us suppose the worst: that the solid portion consists entirely of coconut and palm oils, and the liquid portion of olive and castor oils. The recommended alkali ratio for $Coconut_{280}Palm_{280}$ would be 156 ppt; that for $Olive_{390}Castor_{50}$ would be 130 ppt (see previous problem). The liquid oil used to make the experimental bar would require far less lye than the solid oil remaining in the bottle.

9. What is the smallest batch of lye that should be weighed and mixed using a decagram balance like the BCS 40?

According to Table 6-3 (page 97), the relative uncertainty of a 190 g batch using a centigram balance would be ±0.05 ppt, that for a 500 g batch using a decigram balance would be ±0.2 ppt, and that for a 2500 g batch using a gram balance would be ±0.4 ppt. If we would like to keep the relative uncertainty below ±0.4 ppt, the weight of NaOH should be kept above 25,000 g. This is within the capacity of the BCS 40 and would produce enough lye for about 1785 bars of soap. To mix this lye, we should use a container with a volume of about 50 liters (13 gallons).

10. What is the smallest batch of oil that should be weighed and mixed using a decagram balance like the BCS 40?

According to Table 6-4 (page 99), the relative uncertainty of a 3000 g batch using a gram balance would be ±0.3 ppt. If we would like to keep the relative uncertainty below ±0.3 ppt, the total oil weight should be kept above 33,333 g, or 33.3 ducks. This is within the capacity of the BCS 40 and would produce enough oil for about 333 bars of soap. To mix this oil, we should use a container with a volume of about 40 liters (10 gallons).

Chapter 7

1. What are the chemical and structural formulas of pentane, octane, and hexadecane?

You should be able to reproduce any of the alkane formulas or structural formulas given in Table 7-1 (page 129). The name of each alkane tells you how many carbon atoms it contains. We count to twenty as follows: meth, eth, prop, but, pent, hex, hept, oct, non, dec, undec, dodec, tridec, tetradec, pentadec, hexadec, heptadec, octadec, nonadec, eicos. If the number of carbon atoms in a linear alkane is n, the number of hydrogen atoms is $2n + 2$. The structural formula consists of a kinky line with $n - 1$ segments.

2. Describe the electrical charge distribution for the water molecule. What are the charges on the oxygen atom, the hydrogen atoms, and the molecule as a whole?

The oxygen atom has a charge between 0 and -1 (partially negative), and the hydrogen atoms have charges between 0 and +½ (partially positive). The OH bond is consequently described as polar. Since the charge on each hydrogen atom is exactly half that of the oxygen atom, the molecule has a net charge of 0.

3. Describe the electrical charge distribution for the ethane molecule. What are the charges on the carbon atoms, the hydrogen atoms, and the molecule as a whole?

The charges on the carbon and hydrogen atoms are very small compared to the atomic charges in the water molecule. The CH bond is consequently described as non-polar. As with water, however, the total charge on the molecule is 0.

4. What are the differences between a proton and a hydrogen atom?

A hydrogen atom consists of two parts: a positive proton and a negative electron. In a molecule, the hydrogen atom shares its electron with the remainder of the molecule. When a proton leaves a molecule, it relinquishes its electron, carries with it a +1 charge, and leaves a -1 charge on the remainder of the molecule.

5. What are the differences between a proton and a hydronium ion?

A hydronium ion is just a proton attached to a water molecule. Often, chemists will use the terms interchangeably with the understanding that a proton in aqueous solution is always attached either to an acid or to a water molecule.

6. Why are alkanes described as hydrophobic?

This poetic description (water-fearing) describes the apparent reluctance of alkanes to dissolve in water. In actuality, this occurs simply because water molecules are more attracted to one another than they are to non-polar molecules. The term *lipophilic* (fat-loving) is another poetic term used as a synonym for *hydrophobic*.

7. What is the difference between an OH bond and a hydrogen bond?

A water molecule is held together by polar, covalent bonds between each hydrogen atom and the central oxygen atom. These OH bonds are made up of the electrons shared between atoms of the same molecule. A hydrogen bond is the attractive force between a hydrogen atom on one molecule and an oxygen atom on another.

8. When water ionizes, which ion is the cation and which is the anion?

The hydronium ion is a cation. The hydroxide ion is an anion.

9. What is the difference between a colloidal suspension and an emulsion?

An emulsion is a colloidal suspension of one liquid in another. While emulsions are the most common kind of colloidal suspension found in cosmetics, we also find suspensions of solids in liquids (*sols*), liquids in solids (*gels*), and gases in liquids (*foams*). Examples of sols are colloidal oatmeal and paint. Gelatin and cheese are gels, and whipped cream is a foam.

10. What is the difference between a chemical formula and a chemical equation?

A formula consists of typographical representations of the atoms in a molecule or ion. NaOH, H_2O, and OH^- are chemical formulas. An equation consists of two sets of formulas separated by an equal sign or an arrow. The number of each kind of atom on one side of the equation must be equal to that on the other. Furthermore, the total charge on one side must equal that on the other.

$$H_2O = H^+ + OH^-$$

In this equation there are two hydrogen atoms and one oxygen atom on either side of the equal sign. Since the charge on H^+ is equal and opposite to that on OH^-, the total charge on either side is zero.

Chapter 8

1. What are the conjugate bases of citric acid and acetic acid?
What are the conjugate acids of hydroxide ion and ammonia?
What are the conjugate acids of water and ammonium ion?

The conjugate base of citric acid is citrate ion. The conjugate
base of acetic acid is acetate ion. The conjugate acid of hydroxide ion is water. The conjugate acid of ammonia is ammonium ion. The conjugate acid of water is hydronium ion.
Ammonium ion does not have a conjugate acid—its conjugate base is ammonia.

2. Write balanced chemical equations for the following reactions. Acetic acid reacts with sodium hydroxide. Citric acid
reacts with ammonia. Ammonium acetate reacts with potassium hydroxide.

$$HAce + NaOH = NaAce + H_2O$$
$$H_3Cit + 3\,NH_3 = (NH_4)_3Cit$$
$$(NH_4)Ace + KOH = KAce + (NH_4)OH$$

This last reaction could also be written:

$$(NH_4)Ace + KOH = KAce + NH_3 + H_2O$$

3. Describe the sequence of events that occur when sodium acetate dissolves in water.

The sodium ion separates from the acetate ion. The sodium ion
is surrounded by water molecules, each orienting its partially negative oxygen toward the positive sodium ion. The
acetate ion is also surrounded by water molecules, each orienting its partially positive hydrogen atoms toward the negative acetate ion. Chemists simply say that sodium acetate
ionizes when it dissolves in water. Because the ionization
is complete (no unionized sodium acetate remains), sodium
acetate is described as a strong electrolyte.

4. Describe the sequence of events that occur when acetic acid dissolves in water.

The hydrogen ion separates from the acetate ion and attaches to a water molecule, forming a hydronium ion. The hydronium ion is surrounded by water molecules, each orienting its partially negative oxygen toward the positive hydronium ion. The acetate ion is also surrounded by water molecules, each orienting its partially positive hydrogen atoms toward the negative acetate ion. Chemists simply say that acetic acid ionizes when it dissolves in water. Because the ionization is partial (some unionized acetic acid remains), acetic acid is described as a weak acid.

5. Describe the sequence of events that occur when acetic acid reacts with sodium hydroxide.

The acetic acid ionizes into hydrogen and acetate ions, each surrounded by water molecules. The hydrogen ion quickly attaches to one of the water molecules, forming a hydronium ion. Sodium hydroxide ionizes into sodium and hydroxide ions, each surrounded by water molecules. Eventually, the hydronium and hydroxide ions meet up, pass the proton from one to the other, and become two water molecules. The sodium and acetate ions remain ionized unless the water evaporates, in which case they recombine to produce solid sodium acetate.

6. Nitric acid is a strong acid with formula HNO_3. Write a balanced equation for the reaction of nitric acid with sodium hydroxide.

$$HNO_3 + NaOH = NaNO_3 + H_2O$$

$NaNO_3$ is called sodium nitrate.

7. Sulfuric acid is a strong acid with formula H_2SO_4. Write a balanced equation for the reaction of sulfuric acid with sodium hydroxide.

Like citric acid, sulfuric acid may give up one or two of its protons. There are thus two possible reactions, depending on the amount of sodium hydroxide provided:

$$H_2SO_4 + NaOH = NaHSO_4 + H_2O$$

$$H_2SO_4 + 2\,NaOH = Na_2SO_4 + 2\,H_2O$$

$NaHSO_4$ and Na_2SO_4 are called sodium hydrogen sulfate and sodium sulfate, respectively.

8. Calcium hydroxide (slaked lime) is used in canning and pickling. It has the formula $Ca(OH)_2$ and from this one may infer that it gives up two hydroxide ions upon dissociation. Write the balanced equation for the reaction of calcium hydroxide with acetic acid.

$$Ca(OH)_2 + 2\,HAce = CaAce_2 + 2\,H_2O$$

$CaAce_2$ is called calcium acetate.

9. A 1 ppt solution of NaOH in water has a pH of 12.4. What is the pH of a 0.1 ppt solution of NaOH in water?

Each step down the pH scale represents a ten-fold increase in the hydronium ion concentration and a ten-fold decrease in the hydroxide ion concentration. Since NaOH is a strong base, it is completely ionized, and a ten-fold decrease in concentration would bring us one step down the pH scale. The pH of a 0.1 ppt NaOH solution is 11.4.

10. Hydrochloric acid, HCl, is a strong acid. A 1 ppt solution of HCl in water has a pH of 1.56. What is the pH of a 0.01 ppt solution of HCl in water?

Each step up the pH scale represents a ten-fold decrease in the hydronium ion concentration. Since HCl is a strong acid, it is completely ionized. Thus, the concentration of hydronium in a 0.01 ppt solution is one-hundredth that in a 1 ppt solution. The pH is consequently 3.56, two steps up the pH scale.

Chapter 9

1. How many grams of citric acid are needed to react completely with 10 grams of sodium hydroxide?

$$? \text{ g } H_3Cit = 10.00 \text{ g } NaOH\left(\frac{1 \text{ mol } NaOH}{40.00 \text{ g } NaOH}\right)$$
$$\left(\frac{1 \text{ mol } H_3Cit}{3 \text{ mol } NaOH}\right)\left(\frac{192.12 \text{ g } H_3Cit}{1 \text{ mol } H_3Cit}\right)$$
$$= 16.01 \text{ g } H_3Cit$$

2. When 10 grams of sodium hydroxide react with excess citric acid, how many grams of sodium citrate are produced?

$$? \text{ g Na}_3\text{Cit} = 10.00 \text{ g NaOH}\left(\frac{1 \text{ mol NaOH}}{40.00 \text{ g NaOH}}\right)$$
$$\left(\frac{1 \text{ mol Na}_3\text{Cit}}{3 \text{ mol NaOH}}\right)\left(\frac{258.06 \text{ g Na}_3\text{Cit}}{1 \text{ mol Na}_3\text{Cit}}\right)$$
$$= 21.51 \text{ g Na}_3\text{Cit}$$

3. How many grams of sodium citrate can be produced from 10 grams of sodium hydroxide and excess citric acid?

From the previous problem, we know that we have enough sodium hydroxide to make 21.505 grams of sodium citrate. We now ask, "How many grams of sodium citrate can be produced from 10 grams of citric acid and excess sodium hydroxide?"

$$? \text{ g Na}_3\text{Cit} = 10.00 \text{ g H}_3\text{Cit}\left(\frac{1 \text{ mol H}_3\text{Cit}}{192.12 \text{ g H}_3\text{Cit}}\right)$$
$$\left(\frac{1 \text{ mol Na}_3\text{Cit}}{1 \text{ mol H}_3\text{Cit}}\right)\left(\frac{258.06 \text{ g Na}_3\text{Cit}}{1 \text{ mol Na}_3\text{Cit}}\right)$$
$$= 13.43 \text{ g Na}_3\text{Cit}$$

We have enough citric acid to make 13.432 grams of sodium citrate. In other words, we don't have enough citric acid to make more than 13.432 grams of sodium citrate. Consequently, 13.432 grams of sodium citrate will be produced and there will be excess, unreacted sodium hydroxide. We say that citric acid is the *limiting reagent* (the one that runs out first). One could ask, "How many grams of sodium hydroxide are needed to react completely with 10 grams of citric acid?"

4. How many grams of sodium hydroxide are needed to react completely with 10 grams of citric acid? How many grams of water would be produced?

6.246 grams of sodium hydroxide are needed. 2.814 grams of water are produced. Thus, if 10 grams of sodium hydroxide are added to 10 grams of citric acid, the products will be 13.432 grams of sodium citrate (see the previous problem), 2.814 grams of water, and 3.754 grams of leftover, unreacted sodium hydroxide. Note that the total weight of the reactants is the same as that of the products.

5. How many grams of 50 ppt ammonium hydroxide are needed to react completely with 10 grams of citric acid?

$$? \text{ g base} = 10.00 \; g\,H_3Cit\left(\frac{1 \; mol\,H_3Cit}{192.12 \; g\,H_3Cit}\right)$$
$$\left(\frac{3 \; mol\,NH_4OH}{1 \; mol\,H_3Cit}\right)\left(\frac{35.05 \; g\,NH_4OH}{1 \; mol\,NH_4OH}\right)\left(\frac{1000 \text{ g base}}{50 \; g\,NH_4OH}\right)$$
$$= 109.5 \text{ g base}$$

6. How many grams of 500 ppt sodium hydroxide are needed to react completely with 100 grams of 50 ppt acetic acid?

$$? \text{ g base} = 100 \; g\,acid\left(\frac{50 \; g\,HAce}{1000 \; g\,acid}\right)\left(\frac{1 \; mol\,HAce}{60.06 \; g\,HAce}\right)$$
$$\left(\frac{1 \; mol\,NaOH}{1 \; mol\,HAce}\right)\left(\frac{40.00 \; g\,NaOH}{1 \; mol\,NaOH}\right)\left(\frac{1000 \text{ g base}}{500 \; g\,NaOH}\right)$$
$$= 6.66 \text{ g base}$$

7. How many grams of 5 ppt potassium hydroxide are needed to react completely with 1000 grams of 1 ppt citric acid?

$$? \text{ g base} = 1000 \; g\,acid\left(\frac{1 \; g\,H_3Cit}{1000 \; g\,acid}\right)\left(\frac{1 \; mol\,H_3Cit}{192.12 \; g\,H_3Cit}\right)$$
$$\left(\frac{3 \; mol\,KOH}{1 \; mol\,H_3Cit}\right)\left(\frac{56.11 \; g\,KOH}{1 \; mol\,KOH}\right)\left(\frac{1000 \text{ g base}}{5 \; g\,KOH}\right)$$
$$= 175.2 \text{ g base}$$

8. What is the pH of a 5 ppt solution of potassium hydroxide in water?

$$? \text{ mol OH}^- = 1 \; L\left(\frac{1000 \; g\,soln}{1 \; L}\right)\left(\frac{5 \; g\,KOH}{1000 \; g\,soln}\right)\left(\frac{1 \; mol\,KOH}{56.11 \; g\,KOH}\right)$$
$$\left(\frac{1 \text{ mol OH}^-}{1 \; mol\,KOH}\right)$$
$$= 0.089 \text{ mol OH}^-$$
$$\text{pOH} = -log(0.089) = 1.05$$
$$\text{pH} = 14 - 1.05 = 12.95$$

9. Nitric acid is a strong acid with a molecular weight of 63.01 g/mol. What is the molarity of a 1 ppt solution of HNO_3 in water? What is its pH?

$$? \text{ mol H}^+ = 1 \, L \left(\frac{1000 \, \cancel{g \, acid}}{1 \, \cancel{L}} \right) \left(\frac{1 \, \cancel{g \, HNO_3}}{1000 \, \cancel{g \, acid}} \right) \left(\frac{1 \, \cancel{mol \, HNO_3}}{63.01 \, \cancel{g \, HNO_3}} \right)$$

$$\left(\frac{1 \text{ mol H}^+}{1 \, \cancel{mol \, HNO_3}} \right)$$

$$= 0.016 \text{ mol H}^+$$

$$\text{pH} = -log(0.016) = 1.80$$

10. When 10 grams of 50 ppt sodium hydroxide reacts with 10 grams of 50 ppt acetic acid, is the resulting solution acidic or alkaline?

$$? \text{ g acid} = 10.00 \, \cancel{g \, base} \left(\frac{50 \, \cancel{g \, NaOH}}{1000 \, \cancel{g \, base}} \right) \left(\frac{1 \, \cancel{mol \, NaOH}}{40.00 \, \cancel{g \, NaOH}} \right)$$

$$\left(\frac{1 \, \cancel{mol \, HAce}}{1 \, \cancel{mol \, NaOH}} \right) \left(\frac{60.06 \, \cancel{g \, HAce}}{1 \, \cancel{mol \, HAce}} \right) \left(\frac{1000 \text{ g acid}}{50 \, \cancel{g \, HAce}} \right)$$

$$= 15.02 \text{ g acid}$$

There is enough base to react with 15 grams of acid, but only 10 grams of acid are available. Consequently, the acid will be completely consumed and there will be excess base. The resulting solution will be alkaline.

Chapter 10

1. Write balanced chemical equations for the following reactions. Stearic acid reacts with sodium hydroxide. Ricinoleic acid reacts with ammonia. Sodium palmitate reacts with acetic acid. Potassium linoleate reacts with citric acid. Oleic acid reacts with acetic acid.

$$\text{HStr} + \text{NaOH} = \text{NaStr} + \text{H}_2\text{O}$$
$$\text{HRic} + \text{NH}_3 = (\text{NH}_4)\text{Ric}$$
$$\text{NaPlm} + \text{HAce} = \text{NaAce} + \text{HPlm}$$
$$3 \, \text{KLin} + \text{H}_3\text{Cit} = \text{Na}_3\text{Cit} + 3 \, \text{HLin}$$

Oleic acid does not react with acetic acid, since both of them are acids.

2. Use the balanced equations of the previous problem to answer the following stoichiometric questions: How many grams of sodium hydroxide are required to react completely with 1000 g of stearic acid? How many grams of 500 ppt citric acid are required to react completely with 1000 g of potassium linoleate?

Note that, unlike the example problem, this question asks for grams of NaOH, not grams of lye.

$$? \text{ g NaOH} = 1000 \, g \, HStr \left(\frac{1 \, mol \, HStr}{284.48 \, g \, HStr} \right) \left(\frac{1 \, mol \, NaOH}{1 \, mol \, HStr} \right)$$
$$\left(\frac{40.00 \text{ g NaOH}}{1 \, mol \, NaOH} \right)$$
$$= 140.6 \text{ g NaOH}$$

For the second problem we need the molecular weight of potassium linoleate. This could be computed by adding up all the atomic weights, but there is a shortcut. We note that potassium linoleate is just linoleic acid with a missing hydrogen and an extra potassium atom. Thus the molecular weight is simply:

280.46 - 1.01 + 39.10 = 318.55 g/mol

$$? \text{ g acid} = 1000 \, g \, KLin \left(\frac{1 \, mol \, KLin}{318.55 \, g \, KLin} \right) \left(\frac{1 \, mol \, H_3Cit}{3 \, mol \, KLin} \right)$$
$$\left(\frac{192.12 \, g \, H_3Cit}{1 \, mol \, H_3Cit} \right) \left(\frac{2 \text{ g acid}}{1 \, g \, H_3Cit} \right)$$
$$= 402.1 \text{ g acid}$$

3. Without consulting any of the figures in this chapter, draw structural formulas for the following fatty acids: C14:0, C18:1, C18:2, C18:0-OH.

Check your answers using the tables in the chapter.

4. What is the molecular weight of the fatty acid C20:0?

This fatty acid has 20 carbon atoms. 18 of the carbons carry 2
hydrogen atoms each. The alpha (acidic) carbon has only 1
hydrogen and the omega carbon has 3. Thus, the formula is
$C_{19}H_{39}COOH$, or $C_{20}H_{40}O_2$. Its molecular weight is:

$20(12.01) + 40(1.01) + 2(16.00) = 312.6$ g/mol.

This acid is called arachidic acid and is found in peanut oil.

5. What is the molecular weight of the fatty acid C22:1?

This fatty acid has 22 carbon atoms. 18 of the carbons carry
2 hydrogen atoms each. The alpha (acidic) carbon has only
1 hydrogen and the omega carbon has 3. The two remaining carbons carry 1 hydrogen each. Thus, the formula is
$C_{21}H_{41}COOH$, or $C_{22}H_{42}O_2$. Its molecular weight is:

$22(12.01) + 42(1.01) + 2(16.00) = 338.64$ g/mol.

This acid is called erucic acid and is found in rapeseed oil.

6. Draw the structural formula of C22:6. This omega-3 fatty
acid has its double bonds at carbon atoms 4, 7, 10, 13, 16,
and 19, counting from the alpha carbon. Why do you suppose
it is called an omega-3 fatty acid?

cervonic acid

328.49 g/mol $C_{22}H_{32}O_2$, docosahexaenoic acid

Cervonic acid is found in fish oils. The final double bond is
on the third carbon from the omega carbon, hence omega-3.

7. How many grams of sodium hydroxide are needed to react
completely with 1000 grams of palmitic acid?

$$? \text{ g NaOH} = 1000 \text{ g HPlm}\left(\frac{1 \text{ mol HPlm}}{256.42 \text{ g HPlm}}\right)$$
$$\left(\frac{1 \text{ mol NaOH}}{1 \text{ mol HPlm}}\right)\left(\frac{40.00 \text{ g NaOH}}{1 \text{ mol NaOH}}\right)$$
$$= 156.0 \text{ g NaOH}$$

8. How many grams of 50 ppt acetic acid are needed to convert 1000 grams of sodium stearate into stearic acid?

$$? \text{ g acid} = 1000 \text{ g NaStr} \left(\frac{1 \text{ mol NaStr}}{306.47 \text{ g NaStr}} \right) \left(\frac{1 \text{ mol HAce}}{1 \text{ mol NaStr}} \right)$$

$$\left(\frac{60.06 \text{ g HAce}}{1 \text{ mol HAce}} \right) \left(\frac{1000 \text{ g acid}}{50 \text{ g HAce}} \right)$$

$$= 3919 \text{ g acid}$$

9. When 10 grams of 10 ppt KPlm are added to 10 grams of 50 ppt HAce, is the resulting solution acidic or alkaline?

It takes 1 mol of HAce to neutralize 1 mol of KPlm. We ask the stoichiometric question, "How many grams of 50 ppt HAce are required to neutralize 10 grams of 10 ppt KPlm?" The answer is 0.407 g. We have more than this, so the solution is acidic.

10. Suppose that you start with 10 grams of NaOle. You wish to add enough acid to convert half of the NaOle to HOle. How many grams of 50 ppt H_3Cit should you add?

It takes 1 mol of H_3Cit to neutralize 3 mol of NaOle. We ask, "How many grams of 50 ppt H_3Cit are required to neutralize 5 grams (half) of NaOle?" The answer is 21.04 g.

Chapter 11

1. Draw the structural formulas for methyl acetate and iso-propyl acetate and calculate the molecular weight for each.

methyl acetate   74.07 g/mol, $C_3H_6O_2$, MthAce

isopropyl acetate   102.13 g/mol, $C_5H_{10}O_2$, IprAce

2. Draw the structural formula for lauryl laurate and calculate its molecular weight. Search the Internet for a manufacturer who uses lauryl laurate in a product. Why do you suspect this particular compound was chosen for this particular application?

lauryl laurate

368.64 g/mol $C_{24}H_{48}O_2$, dodecyl dodecanoate

Lauryl laurate has a melting point very close to body temperature. For this reason it is often used in creams, lotions, and lipsticks when the desired effect is that the product melts onto the skin.

3. Of the compounds glyceryl monoacetate, glyceryl diacetate, and glyceryl triacetate, which do you expect to be most soluble in water and which least?

Glyceryl monoacetate has two free hydroxyl groups with which it may engage in hydrogen bonding, and we may expect it to be the most soluble of the three. Glyceryl diacetate has one free hydroxyl group. Glyceryl triacetate (triacetin) has no free hydroxyl groups, and we may expect it to be the least soluble of the three.

4. How many grams of NaOH would be required to react completely with 1000 grams of glyceryl monoacetate?

One mole of NaOH reacts with each mole of the monoglyceride:

$$NaOH + GlyAce(OH)_2 = Gly(OH)_3 + NaAce$$

$$? \text{ g NaOH} = 1000 \text{ } g\text{ } GlyAce(OH)_2 \left(\frac{1 \text{ } mol \text{ } GlyAce(OH)_2}{134.13 \text{ } g \text{ } GlyAce(OH)_2} \right)$$

$$\left(\frac{1 \text{ } mol \text{ } NaOH}{1 \text{ } mol \text{ } GlyAce(OH)_2} \right) \left(\frac{40.00 \text{ g NaOH}}{1 \text{ } mol \text{ } NaOH} \right)$$

$$= 298 \text{ g NaOH}$$

5. How many grams of NaOH would be required to react completely with 1000 grams of glyceryl diacetate?

Two moles of NaOH react with each mole of the diglyceride:

$$2 \text{ NaOH} + GlyAce_2OH = Gly(OH)_3 + 2 \text{ NaAce}$$

In addition, the molecular weight of the diglyceride is bigger than that of the monoglyceride. The answer is 454 g.

6. How many grams of NaOH would be required to react completely with 1000 grams of glyceryl triacetate?

Three moles of NaOH react with each mole of the triglyceride:

$$3 \text{ NaOH} + GlyAce_3 = Gly(OH)_3 + 3 \text{ NaAce}$$

The answer is 550 g.

7. Imagine that 1000 grams of glyceryl triacetate react completely with the stoichiometric quantity of 500 ppt NaOH, as determined in the previous problem. What percentage of the total weight of products will be made up of glycerol?

We have already determined that this would require 550 g of NaOH, and hence 1100 g of lye.

$$? \text{ g Gly(OH)}_3 = 1000 \text{ g } \cancel{GlyAce_3}\left(\frac{1 \text{ mol } \cancel{GlyAce_3}}{218.21 \text{ g } \cancel{GlyAce_3}}\right)$$
$$\left(\frac{1 \text{ mol } \cancel{Gly(OH)_3}}{1 \text{ mol } \cancel{GlyAce_3}}\right)\left(\frac{92.05 \text{ g Gly(OH)}_3}{1 \text{ mol } \cancel{Gly(OH)_3}}\right)$$
$$= 422 \text{ g Gly(OH)}_3$$

This will result in 422 g of glycerol. A similar calculation would show that 1128 g of sodium acetate will be produced. Since water did not appear in the reaction, 550 g of water remains among the products. The total weight of the products is the same as that of the reactants:

1000 g + 1100 g = 422 g + 1128 g + 550 g = 2100 g

Glycerol makes up 20% of the total, water makes up 26%, and the remaining 54% is made up of sodium acetate.

8. What do you suppose would happen if less than the stoichiometric quantity of 500 ppt NaOH were added to 1000 g of glyceryl triacetate?

The sodium hydroxide would be consumed. We expect the products to include glycerol, sodium acetate, and glyceryl tri-, di-, and monoacetate.

9. What do you suppose would happen if more than the stoichiometric quantity of 500 ppt NaOH were added to 1000 g of glyceryl triacetate?

The glyceryl triacetate would be consumed. We expect the products to include glycerol, sodium acetate, and sodium hydroxide.

10. How many grams of 500 ppt NaOH would be required to react completely with 1 gram of eugenol?

$$\text{NaOH} + \text{HEug} = \text{NaEug} + \text{H}_2\text{O}$$
$$? \text{ g Lye} = 1.00 \text{ g } \cancel{HEug}\left(\frac{1 \text{ mol } \cancel{HEug}}{164.20 \text{ g } \cancel{HEug}}\right)\left(\frac{1 \text{ mol } \cancel{NaOH}}{1 \text{ mol } \cancel{HEug}}\right)$$

$$\left(\frac{40.00 \; \cancel{g \; NaOH}}{1 \; \cancel{mol \; NaOH}}\right)\left(\frac{1000 \; g \; Lye}{500 \; \cancel{g \; NaOH}}\right)$$
$$= 0.49 \; g \; Lye$$

Chapter 12

1. Given the triacylglyceride compositions of Table 12-1 (page 208), what are the percentages of palmitic, oleic, stearic, and linoleic acids in olive oil?

⅓(23%)+ ⅓(4%)+ ⅓(2%)+ ⅓(2%)+ ⅔(3%)=12.33% palmitic acid

⅔(23%)+ ⅔(8%)+(45%)+ ⅓(4%)+ ⅔(10%)+ ⅓(1%)+ ⅓(2%)
+ ⅓(3%)=75.67% oleic acid

⅓(8%)+ ⅓(2%)=3.33% stearic acid

⅓(4%)+ ⅓(10%)+ ⅔(1%)+ ⅔(1%)=6.67% linoleic acid

2. Given the triacylglyceride compositions of Table 12-1 (page 208), what are the percentages of palmitic, oleic, stearic, and linoleic acids in almond kernel oil?

6.67% palmitic acid, 67.67% oleic acid, 0.67% stearic acid, and 23.00% linoleic acid.

3. Given the triacylglyceride compositions of Table 12-1 (page 208), what are the percentages of palmitic, oleic, stearic, and linoleic acids in apricot kernel oil?

3.67% palmitic acid, 60.67% oleic acid, 0.33% stearic acid, and 34.33% linoleic acid.

4. The percentages of fatty acids calculated in the previous three questions differ from those listed in Table 12-2 (page 210). Why?

The calculations were for the specific oils given in Table 12-1. The composition of an oil varies seasonally and geographically; these variations are reflected in the ranges of Table 12-2.

5. What are the saponification value and sodium saponification value of triolein?

Triolein is glyceryl trioleate. Its molecular weight is:

92.05 g/mol + 3(282.46 g/mol) - 3(18.02 g/mol) = 885.37 g/mol

Its sv and ssv are 190 ppt and 136 ppt, respectively. These may be compared to the ranges for olive oil: 184–196 ppt and 131–140 ppt.

6. What are the saponification value and sodium saponification value of tripalmitin?

Tripalmitin is glyceryl tripalmitate. Its molecular weight is:
92.05 g/mol + 3(256.42 g/mol) - 3(18.02 g/mol) = 807.25 g/mol
Its sv and ssv are 209 ppt and 149 ppt, respectively. These may be compared to the ranges for palm oil: 190–209 ppt and 135–149 ppt.

7. Compare the saponification values of triolein and tristearin.

Triolein is glyceryl trioleate, and tristearin is glyceryl tristearate. Their svs are 190 ppt and 189 ppt, respectively. They are very close to one another because their fatty acids are the same length and have nearly the same molecular weights.

8. Compare the saponification values of trilaurin and tristearin.

Trilaurin is glyceryl trilaurate and tristearin is glyceryl tristearate. Their svs are 263 ppt and 189 ppt, respectively. Trilaurin has a much larger sv than tristearin because lauric acid is much shorter (and lighter) than stearic acid.

9. What are the saponification values for each of the triacylglycerides of Table 12-1 (page 208)?

TAG	MW (g/mol)	SV (ppt)
GlyPlmOleOle	859.33	196
GlyStrOleOle	887.39	190
GlyOleOleOle	885.37	190
GlyPlmOleLin	857.33	196
GlyOleOleLin	883.37	191
GlyPlmLinLin	855.33	197
GlyOleLinLin	881.37	191
GlyPlmStrOle	861.35	195
GlyPlmPlmOle	833.29	202
GlyLinLinLin	879.37	191

10. Given the triacylglyceride compositions of Table 12-1 (page 208) and the saponification values calculated in the previous question, what is the saponification value of olive oil?

Oil	SV (ppt)	SSV (ppt)
Olive	192	137
Almond Kernel	192	137
Apricot Kernel	191	136

11. Which contains more glycerol, a bar of soap made from 100% coconut oil, or one made from 100% olive oil?

The amount of glycerol produced is proportional to the amount of NaOH used. Since the ssv of coconut oil is higher than that of olive oil, its fully saponified soap will contain more glycerol than one made from olive oil.

12. What assumptions were made in the calculations of Section 12.5?

We have assumed that the oil contains only triacylglycerides, that all of the NaOH is consumed, that no mono- or diacyl-glycerides are produced, and that none of the water has evaporated. The glycerol concentration of the soap will be lower than expected if the oil contains unsaponifiable material, if unreacted NaOH remains, or if some of the oil is only partially saponified. It will be higher than expected if some of the water evaporates.

Chapter 13

1. Soap labels sometimes list as ingredients sodium tallowate, sodium cocoate, sodium palmate, or sodium palm kernelate. How do these differ from soaps like sodium stearate and sodium laurate?

These descriptions actually refer to mixtures of soap compounds. Sodium tallowate describes those soaps produced from the saponification of tallow (chiefly sodium stearate and sodium palmitate). Sodium cocoate describes those soaps produced from the saponification of coconut oil (chiefly sodium laurate). Sodium palmate contains chiefly sodium palmitate. Sodium palm kernelate, like sodium cocoate, contains chiefly sodium laurate.

2. Soap labels sometimes list as ingredients coconut acid and tallow acid. What do you suppose these are?

Coconut acid is the mixture of fatty acids (mostly lauric acid) produced by adding acid to coconut oil soap. Tallow acid is the mixture of fatty acids (mostly stearic and palmitic acids) produced by adding acid to tallow soap. When we acidified olive oil soap in Section 10.2 (page 179), we actually produced a mixture of fatty acids more properly described as olive acid.

Makers of commodity soap add these acids to finished soap to lower the pH. These same acids are produced during the curing of a superfatted cold-process soap.

3. Sodium laureth sulfate (cas 9004-82-4) is a popular detergent. Search for information on this compound and draw its structural formula. What makes it an effective detergent?

This is actually a family of detergents with alkyl chains of variable length. Shown here is sodium laureth-2 sulfate. You can count 12 carbon atoms on the right (lauryl), followed by two 2-carbon subunits (ethyl). Members of the family differ in the number of ethyl groups.

Sodium laureth sulfate has the same ionic head group as sodium lauryl sulfate. Its non-polar tail is longer than that of sodium lauryl sulfate, and it contains one or more oxygen atoms. Its detergent properties follow from the combination of an ionic head and a greasy, alkyl tail.

4. Sodium lauroyl isethionate (cas 7381-1-3) is a popular detergent for solid cleansing bars. Search for information on this compound and draw its structural formula. What makes it an effective detergent?

This is an ester of lauric acid and sodium 2-hydroxyethane sulfonate. You can count 12 carbon atoms on the right (lauryl), followed by a 2-carbon subunit (ethyl). The double-bonded oxygen marks the end of the lauric acid moiety.

Sodium lauroyl isethionate has an ionic head group similar to that of sodium lauryl sulfate, but with one fewer oxygen atoms. Its non-polar tail is two carbons longer than that of sodium lauryl sulfate. Its detergent properties follow from the combination of an ionic head and a greasy, alkyl tail.

5. Cocamidopropyl betaine (CAS 86438-79-1) is a popular detergent for solid cleansing bars. Search for information on this compound and draw its structural formula. What makes it an effective detergent?

This is an unusual detergent because its ionic head group contains neither sodium nor sulfur.

Its detergent properties follow from the combination of an ionic head and a greasy, alkyl tail.

6. A recent television ad claims that the cleansing system in a Dove bar is fundamentally different from soap. Examine the ingredients list on a Dove beauty bar and classify each ingredient as detergent, soap, fatty acid, or other.

I examined the label for the Dove Sensitive-Skin, Unscented Beauty Bar. Detergents: sodium lauroyl isethionate, sodium isethionate, cocamidopropyl betaine, sodium C14-C16 olefin sulfonate. Soaps: sodium tallowate, sodium palmitate, sodium stearate, sodium cocoate, sodium palm kernelate. Fatty acids: stearic acid, lauric acid. The label also lists tetrasodium EDTA and tetrasodium etidronate (metal chelators), water, sodium chloride (salt), titanium dioxide (colorant), and maltol (scent, antioxidant).

7. Ivory Soap's slogan, "99-44/100% Pure," follows from an 1882 analysis by chemist W. M. Habirshaw, who found the soap to be 72.53 percent "fatty anhydrides," 9.28 percent "soda combined," and 17.63 percent "water by difference." Examine the ingredients list on an Ivory Soap bar and classify each ingredient as detergent, soap, fatty acid, or other.

Soap: sodium tallowate and/or sodium palmate, sodium cocoate and/or sodium palm kernelate. Fatty acids: coconut acid, palm kernel acid, tallow acid, palm acid. Other: water, glycerin, sodium chloride (salt), fragrance, tetrasodium EDTA (metal chelator).

8. Palmolive Soap was originally named for the oils used to make it. Examine the ingredients list on a Palmolive Soap bar and classify each ingredient as detergent, soap, fatty acid, or other.

I examined the label for Palmolive Soap Classic Scent. Soap: sodium tallowate, sodium cocoate and/or sodium palm kernelate. Fatty acids: hydrogenated tallow acid, coconut acid. Other: water, glycerin, fragrance, sodium chloride (salt), titanium dioxide (colorant), pentasodium pentetate (metal chelator), pentaerythrital tetra-di-t-butyl hydroxyhydrocinnamate (antioxidant), D&C green No. 5, D&C yellow No. 10 (colorants). Note that sodium olivate and sodium palmate are not listed.

9. Liquid soap may be made by substituting potassium hydroxide for sodium hydroxide. Commodity liquid "soaps," however, are more often made with detergents than soaps. Examine the ingredients list on several bottles of liquid soap, and find examples that are predominantly soap or predominantly detergent.

Murphy Oil Soap is primarily a tall oil soap. Dr. Bronner's Magic Peppermint Soap is predominantly a coconut and olive oil soap. Dial Antibacterial Hand Soap contains predominantly sodium laureth sulfate and ammonium lauryl sulfate.

10. Many email chain letters and websites malign sodium lauryl sulfate as a toxin and a carcinogen. One website even goes so far as to misquote, misinterpret, and fabricate portions of an extensive review of the properties of sodium lauryl sulfate [60]. A copy of the original review may be obtained by interlibrary loan. Summarize in your own words the Discussion and Conclusion sections of this review.

The Discussion comprises four paragraphs, not reproduced here to encourage you to read the original. The Conclusion:

> Sodium Lauryl Sulfate and Ammonium Lauryl Sulfate appear to be safe in formulations designed for discontinuous, brief use followed by thorough rinsing from the surface of the skin. In products intended for prolonged contact with skin, concentrations should not exceed 1%.

Chapter 14

1. A bar of $Palm_{1000}Lye_{286}Aq_{286}$ initially weighed 116.36 g. After curing for several weeks, it weighed 93.25 g. What were the initial and final moisture concentrations?

The total weight of the formula is 1572 g. The lye provides 143 g of water and another 286 g are added explicitly, for a total of 429 g. The initial moisture concentration is then $1000(429/1572) = 272.9$ ppt. Curing removes 23.11 g of the original 116.36 g, for a loss of $1000(23.11/116.36) = 198.6$ ppt. The final moisture concentration is then $272.9 - 198.6 = 74.3$ ppt, rounded off to 74 ppt. This bar appears in Section 21.2 (page 297).

2. A bar of $Coconut_{1000}Lye_{348}Aq_{174}$ initially weighed 118.03 g. After curing for several weeks, it weighed 101.47 g. What were the initial and final moisture concentrations?

The total weight of the formula is 1522 g. The lye provides 174 g of water and another 174 g are added explicitly, for a total of 348 g. The initial moisture concentration is then $1000(348/1522) = 228.7$ ppt. Curing removes 16.56 g of the original 118.03 g, for a loss of $1000(16.56/118.03) = 140.3$ ppt. The final moisture concentration is then $228.7 - 140.3 = 88.4$ ppt, rounded off to 88 ppt. This bar appears in Section 21.3 (page 298).

3. In Example 14-1, the moisture concentrations of samples A and B are lower than those computed from the formula. Why? How would you test your hypothesis?

We might suppose that the soap lost some moisture during saponification, even though it was sealed in a plastic bag. To test this hypothesis, we could record the weight of a raw soap, including the mold and plastic bag. After saponification, we could reweigh the soap, including the mold and bag, to determine whether the weight had changed.

Sample B lost less moisture than Sample A. We might suppose that Sample B, which cooled on the countertop, might have picked up some moisture from the air. To test this hypothesis, we could place a potholder or Styrofoam block onto the balance as part of the tare weight. We could then place the hot sample onto the balance and monitor its weight while cooling.

Chapter 15

1. A soap whose alkali ratio exceeds its saponification value is initially found to be excessively alkaline, as expected. After some time, however, it is retested and found to be tongue neutral. Formulate a hypothesis for this decrease in alkalinity. How would you test this hypothesis?

We might suppose that carbon dioxide in the air slowly neutralizes excess sodium hydroxide in an excessively alkaline soap. To test this hypothesis, we could repeat Example 15-1 (page 250) but take steps to protect the soaps from carbon dioxide. We might seal them in plastic bags, but this would have the unintended effect of preventing moisture loss. A better solution would be to place them in an airtight box, slowly purged with a stream of dry nitrogen gas.

2. It takes 3.63 g of 5 ppt H_3Cit to titrate a 1.61 g sample to the phenolphthalein endpoint. What is its total alkali?

$$TA = 3.123 \left(\frac{3.63}{1.61}\right) \text{ppt NaOH}$$
$$= 7.0 \text{ ppt NaOH}$$

A sample from the bottom of the same bar had a TA of 6.6 ppt NaOH. This alkaline bar provided one point on the graph of Example 15-1.

3. It takes 0.26 g of 5 ppt H_3Cit to titrate a 1.27 g soap sample to the phenolphthalein endpoint. What is its total alkali?

0.6 ppt NaOH.

4. For a soap that does not turn ethanolic phenolphthalein pink, we can determine the alkali "shortage" as a *negative* total alkali. We titrate a sample with an alkaline standard like 5 ppt KOH until the solution turns pink. Derive an equation to calculate total alkali from the quantity of soap and the amount and concentration of the standard.

$$? \text{ g NaOH} = -1000 \text{ g soap}\left(\frac{\text{Y.YY g standard}}{1.XX \text{ g soap}}\right)\left(\frac{\text{Z.ZZ g KOH}}{1000 \text{ g standard}}\right)$$
$$\left(\frac{1 \text{ mol KOH}}{56.11 \text{ g KOH}}\right)\left(\frac{1 \text{ mol NaOH}}{1 \text{ mol KOH}}\right)\left(\frac{40.00 \text{ g NaOH}}{1 \text{ mol NaOH}}\right)$$
$$\text{TA} = -0.713\left(\frac{\text{(Y.YY)(Z.ZZ)}}{1.XX}\right) \text{ppt NaOH}$$

Here Z.ZZ is the actual concentration of the KOH standard.

5. It takes 0.37 g of 4.18 ppt KOH to titrate a 1.22 g soap sample to the phenolphthalein endpoint. What is its total alkali?

-0.9 ppt NaOH.

6. Reference [56] lists the pH of Zest Aqua soap as 9.89 and that of Johnson's Baby soap as 11.90. Should the more alkaline soap be considered harsher?

The reference reports that the irritation index of Johnson's Baby soap (3.199) is lower than that of Zest Aqua soap (4.999). The most irritating soap in this study was Camay Gala (5.284), with a pH of 10.36. The least irritating soap was Johnson's Baby soap with oatmeal (2.799), with a pH of 12.35. This illustrates the difficulty of promoting a dogmatic value for the proper pH of soap.

7. Why do you suppose that the total alkali test is performed in ethanol rather than water?

In aqueous solution, there is a complex equilibrium between water, soaps, and fatty acids (which differ in their pK_a values). Consequently, the pink color of phenolphthalein fades gradually when acid is added to a dilute aqueous soap solution. In contrast, ethanol does not donate or accept protons as water does. The pink color of ethanolic phenolphthalein fades rapidly once excess hydroxide has been neutralized by acid.

Chapter 16

1. 10.23 g of a compromised lye requires 15.46 g of 500 ppt citric acid to reach the endpoint. How much sodium hydroxide is required to bring 2519 g of this lye up to 500 ppt?

The concentration of the compromised lye is 472 ppt NaOH. To bring it up to 500 ppt, we need to add $2519(0.056) = 141$ g of NaOH.

2. 9.97 g of a compromised caustic soda requires 28.55 g of 500 ppt citric acid to reach the endpoint. How much water is required to produce a 500 ppt NaOH solution from 25.7 kg of this caustic soda?

The caustic soda has a concentration of 894 ppt NaOH. We need $25.7(0.789) = 20.3$ kg of water to make up our standard lye.

3. In cleaning up the soap lab, white crystals are found under the balance. Are they more likely to be sodium hydroxide or sodium carbonate?

Sodium hydroxide is extremely hygroscopic. In all but the driest climate, it will absorb water from the air, leaving a caustic puddle rather than solid crystals. Over time, however, carbon dioxide may react with the puddle, leaving crystals of sodium carbonate. The crystals under the balance are more likely to be sodium carbonate than sodium hydroxide.

Chapter 17

1. It took 3.50 g of 4.72 ppt KOH to titrate 1.17 g of an unknown oil to the phenolphthalein endpoint. What was its acid value?

14 ppt KOH.

2. An unknown oil has an AV of 6 ppt KOH. Express the FFA "as lauric acid," "as palmitic acid," and "as oleic acid." How might you decide which expression would be most suitable?

The FFA would be expressed "21 ppt as lauric acid," "27 ppt as palmitic acid," or "30 ppt as oleic acid." To determine which was most suitable, you could measure the saponification value of the oil, as described in Chapter 18. An sv greater than 210 ppt KOH would indicate a lauric oil. While palmitic oils tend to melt at a higher temperature than oleic ones, specialized tests would be needed to definitively distinguish one from the other. An academic or industrial laboratory could distinguish them by iodine value, nuclear magnetic resonance spectroscopy, or infrared spectroscopy.

3. We have used the AV to characterize oils, but it may also be used for pure acids. Calculate the AV for pure oleic acid. Hint: What is the FFA of pure oleic acid?

Pure oleic acid must be 1000 ppt oleic acid. Rearranging Equation 17-2 (page 264), we have:

AV = (1000/5.035) ppt KOH = 199 ppt KOH.

4. Derive an equation relating AV to FFA "as stearic acid."

Substituting the molecular weight of stearic acid for one of those in Equation 17-2 (page 264), we have:

FFA = 5.070 (AV) ppt as stearic acid.

Chapter 18

1. It takes 13.05 g and 4.01 g of 500 ppt H_3Cit to titrate the blank and soap solutions, respectively, for a 20.05 g sample of tallow. What are the sv and ssv for this oil?

197.5 ppt KOH and 140.8 ppt NaOH.

2. An oil is known to contain free fatty acids. How will this affect the determination of sv and ssv?

Because the free fatty acids might cause the oil to absorb more than the usual amount of moisture from the air, the measured saponification values might be slightly less than those for pristine oil. The measured saponification values, however, would be correct for the rancid oil. The free fatty acids would simply react quickly with the KOH while the oil reacted slowly. Fast or slow, the amount of acid would be the same as if the oil were pristine. Thus, the measured saponification values correctly tell us how much alkali is needed to turn the oil into soap.

3. sv and AV have the same units. How do they differ from one another?

The difference between sv and AV is simply a matter of the speed of the reaction with alkali. Free fatty acids react immediately with alkali; oils must be cooked for several hours.

4. It takes 13.05 g and 10.23 g of 500 ppt H_3Cit to titrate the blank and soap solutions, respectively, for a 19.97 g sample of hemp oil. What are the sv and ssv for this oil?

61.9 ppt KOH and 44.1 ppt NaOH. These values are nowhere near the values for hemp oil listed in Appendix B. Linoleic and linolenic oils react very slowly with alkali. To speed up the reaction, the AOCS method calls for the oil sample to be boiled in ethanolic KOH, not simply heated. To prevent the loss of ethanol, a *reflux condenser* returns the evaporated ethanol to the boiling flask. Such a setup costs a few hundred dollars.

There are, however, some workarounds. It is possible to measure the saponification values for oil blends containing oils that would ordinarily be slow to react. The soap produced from the faster oils speeds up saponification of the slow ones. It is also possible to use the procedure of Section 12.4 (page 215) to measure the ssv for single-oil soaps containing 1 ppt clove oil, as was done in Section 13.5 (page 233). Either of these methods is appropriate for occasional analyses without the expense of specialized glassware.

5. Pure coconut oil may be used to make a soap that is effective even in salt water. Its tabulated ssv ranges from 176–189 ppt NaOH. What is the lye discount for $Coconut_{1000}Lye_{352}Aq_{176}$?

This is a trick question. The lye discount depends on the actual sv, which is not given in this problem. The sv might be as low as 176 ppt NaOH, in which case the AR is 100% of the ssv and the lye discount is 0%. It might be as high as 189 ppt NaOH, in which case the AR is 93% of the ssv and the lye discount is 7%.

6. The average ssv for coconut oil is 183 ppt NaOH. A soapmaker without knowledge of the actual ssv for the oil at hand might apply a 5% lye discount. Under what circumstances might this practice lead to the production of excessively alkaline soap?

The soapmaker would use an AR that is 95% of the average ssv, or 174 ppt NaOH. This would be lower than the lowest value in the ssv range. The soap is sure to be tongue neutral.

7. The average ssv for emu oil is 137 ppt NaOH. A soapmaker without knowledge of the actual ssv for the oil at hand might apply a 5% lye discount. Under what circumstances might this practice lead to the production of excessively alkaline soap?

The soapmaker would use an AR that is 95% of the average ssv, or 130 ppt NaOH. This would be higher than the lowest value in the ssv range. If the oil at hand happened to have an ssv between 124 and 129 ppt, the soap would be excessively alkaline.

8. Why is it necessary to measure the sv for every oil you buy?

Another trick question. If you use an AR at or below the lowest sv in the range, you are assured of producing tongue-neutral soap. If, however, you have a batch of oil that does not behave as expected, you might measure the ssv as part of the troubleshooting process. You might also want to know the actual ssv if you are studying the effects of lye discounting or superfatting.

9. Imagine that after receiving a new batch of palm kernel oil, you start producing excessively alkaline soap. It takes 14.12 g and 4.67 g of 500 ppt H_3Cit to titrate the blank and soap solutions, respectively, for a 21.07 g sample of this oil. What might the problem be?

The ssv for this oil is 140 ppt NaOH. This is in range for palm oil, not palm kernel oil. The oil is likely mislabeled.

Appendix B

Saponification Values

You would think that as important a term as *saponification value* would be used consistently by soapmakers universally. Sadly, this is not the case. The technical literature defines it to be the number of milligrams of KOH required to saponify 1 gram of an oil completely. Older books have used the acronym SAP, but modern books have generally settled on the acronym sv. The choice of KOH is entirely natural, since KOH is the alkali used to make the measurement, as detailed in Chapter 18. But the handcrafted soap literature is concerned predominantly with solid soap made using NaOH as the alkali. The handcrafted soapmaking community would be well served by a term for what would have been the saponification value for NaOH, but neither the technical nor the handcrafted literature has provided one. That being the case, I have introduced the *sodium saponification value,* with acronym ssv. The sodium saponification value is defined as the number of milligrams of NaOH required to saponify 1 gram of an oil completely.[1]

With that out of the way, there remains a problem with tabulating saponification values of either stripe. The amount of alkali required for complete saponification depends on the particular alkali (NaOH or KOH) and on the oil in question. It will be different for coconut oil than for olive oil. But since the composition of a given kind of oil may vary seasonally and geographically, the amount of alkali required for complete saponification may be slightly different even from one batch of olive oil to another. Soapmaking books generally report only average saponification values, which may be higher or lower than that for the oil actually sitting in your bottle.

The American Oil Chemists' Society publishes a book that gives the maximum and minimum saponification values for an

---

1. Since 1000 milligrams equals 1 gram, *milligrams per gram* is identical to *parts per thousand.*

enormous number of oils [80]. The sv of olive oil, for example, may be as low as 184 ppt or as high as 196 ppt. Unless your vendor measures the sv for every lot of olive oil shipped, you have no way of knowing whether your oil is at the top, the bottom, or in the middle of this range. Some soapmakers claim that the tabulated saponification values in one book are "better" than those in another, but the truth is that no single saponification value is appropriate for every bottle of olive oil. The only way to know the sv of an oil is to measure it.

Makers of handcrafted soap generally cope with the uncertainty in the sv by discounting a tabulated value. To apply a 5 percent discount, one multiplies the tabulated sv by 0.95. Certainly soapmakers have been making wonderful soap with this practice for decades, and I am not about to claim that it is wrong. But using the methods of this book, you can do better than that. You can actually measure the sv or ssv of an oil using the methods of Chapter 18. This removes the uncertainty and allows you to choose the appropriate amount of alkali without fear.

For the early chapters of the book, however, we need some guidance in choosing the amount of alkali until we learn to measure saponification values. And we need a term for the amount of alkali *actually used* to make soap. I have adopted a term introduced by Robert McDaniel in his book, *Essentially Soap* [54]. The alkali ratio, or AR, is defined as the number parts of alkali (KOH or NaOH) used to make soap from 1000 parts of an oil. The sv is the AR required to completely saponify an oil with KOH. The ssv is the AR required to completely saponify an oil with NaOH. The AR may be chosen to be higher or lower than the sv or ssv. A given bottle of oil *has* a saponification value, though it may be unknown to you until you measure it. That same oil does not *have* an alkali ratio—the alkali ratio is the amount of alkali *you decided to use* to make soap.

An analogous situation arises in driving a car. Each road has a speed limit, which may be unknown to you until you see a sign. You must drive your car at some speed whether or not you know the speed limit. You are free to drive as fast or as slow as you wish, but there are consequences to driving faster than the speed limit. The alkali ratio is analogous to the speed you have chosen; the saponification value is analogous to the speed limit. Just as a particular road *has* a speed limit, a particular oil *has* a saponification value. When you do not know the speed limit, you make an educated guess when you decide how fast to drive. When you do not know the saponification value, you have to make an educated guess when you decide how much alkali to use.

To arrive at the recommended values of Table 4-1 (page 65), I started with the saponification value at the bottom of the range for each oil, as given in reference [80], and multiplied each of these values by the ratio of the molecular weights of NaOH and KOH, (40.00/56.11), or 0.7129. A soapmaker using these alkali ratios is assured that the amount of NaOH actually used will not exceed that required for complete saponification.

Fats and oils are commonly classified as saturated, monounsaturated, and polyunsaturated, depending on the number of double bonds present in the fatty acid acyl groups. The degree of saturation is often expressed as the iodine value (IV). While the method of determining the IV is beyond the scope of this book, its interpretation is relatively straightforward. The higher the IV of a fat or oil, the more double bonds are present in the fatty acid acyl groups. Saturated fats have a low IV; polyunsaturated fats, a high one. Fats and oils with similar SVs and IVs can be expected to have similar properties. The following tables can assist in finding oils that may be substituted for one another.

Table B-1. Saturated Fats and Oils

Description	SV (ppt)	SSV (ppt)	IV (ppt)
Lauric Oils			
Babassu Palm Oil	245–256	174–182	10–18
Buffalo Milk Butter	225–235	160–168	28–32
Butterfat	210–232	149–165	26–40
Coconut Oil	248–265	176–189	5–13
Cohune Nut Oil	251–260	178–185	9–14
Palm Kernel Oil	230–254	163–181	14–21
Palmitic Oils			
Baobab Seed Oil	133–195	94–139	55–96
Borneo Tallow	189–200	134–143	29–38
Cocoa Butter	192–200	136–143	32–40
Dhupa (Malabar) Fat	187–192	133–137	36–43
Emu Oil	175–210	124–150	40–80
Kanya Tallow	188–194	134–138	37–47
Kokum Butter	192–192	136–137	33–37
Lard (Pork Fat)	192–203	136–145	45–70
Malabar (Dhupa) Fat	187–192	133–137	36–43
Mango Seed Oil	188–195	134–139	39–48
Palm Oil	190–209	135–149	49–55
Palm Stearin	193–205	137–146	48–48
Sal (Shorea) Fat	175–192	124–137	31–45
Sheanut Butter	178–198	126–141	52–66
Shorea (Sal) Fat	175–192	124–137	31–45
Tallow (Beef Fat)	190–200	135–143	33–47

Data derived from reference [80]. Fats and oils are listed
alphabetically within families.

Table B-2. Monounsaturated Fats and Oils

Description	SV (ppt)	SSV (ppt)	IV (ppt)
Oleic Oils			
Almond Kernel Oil	188–200	134–143	89–101
Apricot Kernel Oil	185–199	131–142	97–110
Avocado Oil	177–198	126–141	85–90
Canola (Rapeseed) Oil	182–193	129–138	110–126
Domba (Tamanu) Fat	192–201	136–143	82–98
Filbert (Hazelnut) Oil	188–197	134–140	83–90
Groundnut (Peanut) Oil	187–196	133–140	86–107
Hazelnut (Filbert) Oil	188–197	134–140	83–90
Karanja (Pongam) Oil	177–193	126–138	81–96
Margosa (Neem) Oil	195–204	139–145	68–71
Meadowfoam Seed Oil	168–168	119–120	86–91
Neem (Margosa) Oil	195–204	139–145	68–71
Olive Oil	184–196	131–140	75–94
Palm Olein	194–202	138–144	56–56
Peach Kernel Oil	189–194	134–138	94–110
Peanut (Groundnut) Oil	187–196	133–140	86–107
Pecan Nut Oil	190–198	135–141	100–106
Pistachio Nut Oil	189–195	134–139	84–96
Pongam (Karanja) Oil	177–193	126–138	81–96
Rapeseed (Canola) Oil	182–193	129–138	110–126
Rice Bran Oil	181–189	129–135	92–108
Tamanu (Domba) Fat	192–201	136–143	82–98
Teaseed Oil	188–196	134–140	80–92
Ricinoleic Oils			
Castor Oil	176–187	125–133	81–91
Cervonic Oils			
Cod Liver Oil	180–192	128–137	142–176

Table B-3. Polyunsaturated Fats and Oils

Description	SV (ppt)	SSV (ppt)	IV (ppt)
Linoleic Oils			
Cherry Kernel Oil	190–198	135–141	110–118
Coffee Bean Oil (Raw)	184–195	131–139	100–100
Coffee Bean Oil (Roasted)	165–195	117–139	78–96
Corn (Maize) Oil	187–195	133–139	107–135
Cottonseed Oil	189–198	134–141	96–115
Evening Primrose Oil	193–198	137–141	147–155
Grapefruit Seed Oil	178–197	126–140	92–106
Grape Seed Oil	188–194	134–138	130–138
Maize (Corn) Oil	187–195	133–139	107–135
Poppyseed Oil	188–196	134–140	132–146
Pumpkin Seed Oil	174–203	124–145	103–133
Safflower Seed Oil	186–198	132–141	136–148
Sesame Seed Oil	187–195	133–139	104–120
Soybean Oil	189–195	134–139	118–139
Sunflower Seed Oil	188–194	134–138	118–145
Wheat Germ Oil	179–217	127–155	100–128
Linolenic Oils			
Blackcurrant Oil	185–195	131–139	173–182
Borage Oil (Dwarf)	190–196	135–140	148–151
Borage Oil	189–192	134–137	141–160
Cameline Oil	180–190	128–135	127–155
Candlenut (Kukui) Oil	188–202	134–144	136–167
Flaxseed (Linseed) Oil	188–196	134–140	170–203
Hempseed Oil	190–195	135–139	145–166
Kukui (Candlenut) Oil	188–202	134–144	136–167
Linseed (Flaxseed) Oil	188–196	134–140	170–203
Perilla Oil	188–197	134–140	192–208
Walnut Oil	189–197	134–140	138–162

Appendix C

Vendors

Any list of vendors runs the risk of becoming quickly out of date. Nevertheless, a list that is out of date is often better than no list at all. At the time of publication all of these merchants were active and the links to their websites current. Each of them has a complete entry in the *References* (page 398), including address and phone number.

Alcohol
- [15], www.GrainProcessing.com
- [19], www.Luxco.com
- [27], www.Pharmco-Prod.com
- [36], www.ShoppersVinyard.com
- [44], www.WineChateau.com

Alkalis, NaOH, KOH
- [1], www.AAA-Chemicals.com
- [2], www.BoyerCorporation.com
- [5], www.CertifiedLye.com
- [39], www.SnowdriftFarm.com

Balances, Scales
- [26], www.OldWillKnottScales.com

Colors and Scents
- [3], www.BrambleBerry.com
- [4], www.CamdenGrey.com
- [6], www.ChemistryStore.com
- [10], www.EssentialWholesale.com
- [17], www.Lebermuth.com
- [18], www.LotionCrafter.com
- [20], www.TheSage.com
- [25], www.OilsByNature.com
- [28], www.PineMeadows.net
- [39], www.SnowdriftFarm.com
- [42], www.WholesaleSuppliesPlus.com

Fats and Oils

- [3], www.BrambleBerry.com
- [4], www.CamdenGrey.com
- [6], www.ChemistryStore.com
- [7], www.SoapersChoice.com
- [14], www.GloryBeeFoods.com
- [22], www.MissionPeakSoap.com
- [10], www.EssentialWholesale.com
- [20], www.TheSage.com
- [25], www.OilsByNature.com
- [28], www.PineMeadows.net
- [35], www.ShayAndCompany.com
- [39], www.SnowdriftFarm.com
- [40], www.TayloredConcepts.com

Laboratory Supplies

- [9], www.Cynmar.com
- [16], www.Labelmaster.com
- [32], www.SafetyEmporium.com
- [33], www.ScienceCompany.com
- [34], www.ScienceLab.com

Lye Calculators

- [3], www.BrambleBerry.com
- [7], www.SoapersChoice.com
- [20], www.TheSage.com
- [28], www.PineMeadows.net
- [46], www.ScientificSoapmaking.com
- [39], www.SnowdriftFarm.com
- [47], www.SoapCalc.com
- [48], www.SoapMaker.ca
- [49], www.MillerSoap.com
- [50], www.FutureVenturesOnline.com

Molds, Cutters, Heaters, Equipment

- [11], www.ForCraftsSake.com
- [12], www.SoapNSupplies.com
- [22], www.MissionPeakSoap.com
- [41], www.UplandSoapFactory.com
- [43], www.SoapEquipment.com

Glossary

Accuracy

The difference between a measured value and either the true value or the target value. If your goal is to weigh out 173 g of oil and you actually weigh out 171 g of oil, you are accurate to within 2 g. If all of the digits of the measured value are correct, the measurement is said to be accurate.

Acid

A material that contributes H^+ to an aqueous solution. Acids taste sour and neutralize alkalis. Examples include acetic acid, the acid present in vinegar, and oleic acid, the major fatty acid in olive oil, and citric acid, the acid used in this book for analyzing alkaline materials.

Acid Value

The number of milligrams of KOH needed to neutralize 1 g of oil.

Alkali

A material that contributes OH^- to an aqueous solution. Alkalis taste bitter and neutralize acids. Examples include sodium hydroxide, the alkali used to make solid soap, and potassium hydroxide, the alkali used to make liquid soap. *Alkali* and *base* are synonyms.

Alkali Ratio

The number of grams of alkali used to saponify 1000 g of oil. In practice, the alkali ratio should not exceed the saponification value.

Alkanes

A class of non-polar hydrocarbons with the general formula C_nH_{2n+2}, where n is any integer. Alkanes are the principle components of petroleum and natural gas.

Anhydrous

Without water. Many substances contain water even when they appear as dry solids. Among these are citric acid and soap. Hydrates of these may be converted to anhydrates by drying them in an oven.

Anion

An ion with a negative electrical charge. As a mnemonic, remember that *anion* and *negative* both contain the letter *n*.

Atomic Weight

The weight of one mole of an element.

Base

A material that accepts H^+ from an acid. In aqueous solution, the most prominent base is the hydroxide ion, OH^-, which becomes water when it accepts H^+ from an acid. Bases taste bitter and neutralize acids. Examples include sodium hydroxide, the alkali used to make solid soap, and potassium hydroxide, the alkali used to make liquid soap. *Base* and *alkali* are synonyms.

Batch Code

A code that uniquely identifies each batch of soap. One bar of a large batch is labeled with the batch code and reserved for testing and evaluation. The batch code should also appear on the notebook page that describes the ingredients and method used to produce the soap. It should be possible to exactly replicate any batch of soap from its batch code and notebook entry.

Beaker

A container with straight walls. A beaker often has a pouring lip that makes it convenient for dissolving solids and pouring the solution into another container. A Pyrex measuring cup may be substituted when beakers are unavailable.

Boldface Italics

The first time a word from the glossary appears in this book, it is set in boldface italics.

Capacity

The maximum weight that a balance can register.

Cation

An ion with a positive electrical charge. As a mnemonic, remember that the *t* in *cation* looks like a plus sign.

Centigram Balance

A balance with a readability of 0.01 g. A centigram balance with a capacity of 200.00 g may conveniently be used to make 1 or 2 bars of soap.

Cold-process Soap

Soap produced by mixing fats, oils, alkali, and water at concentrations such that the alkali is completely consumed by the saponification reaction. Colorants, scents, and preservatives are added before the soap is poured into the mold, where the bulk of the saponification reaction takes place.

Commodity Soap

Soap produced at very low cost by very large companies. Commodity soap is generally produced by saponifying fats and oils at high temperature. Any alkali is removed from the soap before blending it with colorants, scents, fatty acids, and preservatives.

Conjugate Acid

The molecule or ion that results when a base accepts H^+ from an acid. Water is the conjugate acid of hydroxide ion. Ammonium ion is the conjugate acid of ammonia.

Conjugate Base

The molecule or ion that remains when an acid gives up H^+ to a base. Hydroxide ion is the conjugate base of water. Ammonia is the conjugate base of ammonium ion.

Covalent Bond

A bond between atoms in which the bonding electrons are shared. If they are shared equally, the bond is non-polar; if not, the bond is polar.

Decigram Balance

A balance with a readability of 0.1 g. A decigram balance with a capacity of 2000.0 g may conveniently be used to make between 2 and 20 bars of soap.

Delight

A blend of olive, palm, coconut, and castor oils:
$Olive_{390}Coconut_{280}Palm_{280}Castor_{50}$

Deliquescent

A deliquescent material absorbs so much humidity from the air that it dissolves in the water absorbed. Sodium and potassium hydroxides are deliquescent.

Double Bond

Carbon atoms always share four bonds with neighboring atoms, oxygen atoms two bonds, and hydrogen atoms one. When there are not enough neighboring atoms to satisfy each atom with single bonds, some neighbors will share a double bond. For soapmakers there are two double bonds of interest. All fatty acids have a double bond between the alpha carbon and one of its oxygen neighbors. This is what causes the proton on the other oxygen to become acidic. In addition, unsaturated fatty acids have at least one double bond between carbon atoms in the interior of the carbon chain.

Dreaded Orange Spots

Orange or brown spots that appear on soap at some point after saponification is complete. They are caused by the oxidation of unsaturated fatty acids in the presence of trace metals. They may be controlled by reducing the amount of unsaturated oils, adding an antioxidant, or adding a chelating agent.

Duck

A duck is that amount of raw soap produced from 1000 g of oil. One duck of raw soap will become approximately ten bars of finished soap. The exact number of bars per duck, however, depends on the desired bar weight, on the oils used, on losses incurred while mixing and pouring the raw soap, and on losses incurred while cutting and curing the finished soap. By measuring raw soap in ducks, we can predict the quantity needed to produce a desired number of bars of soap.

Electrolyte

A compound that ionizes in aqueous solution. The positive ion, or *cation,* separates from the negative ion, or *anion.* Because ions carry charges, electrolyte solutions conduct electricity. Electrolytes are considered *strong* if the ionization is complete and *weak* if it is incomplete.

Endpoint

The point in a titration where the indicator changes color.

Erlenmeyer Flask

A container with a wide base and narrow neck. An Erlenmeyer flask is particularly suited to mixing solutions by swirling rather than stirring. A jar with a lid may be substituted when Erlenmeyer flasks are unavailable.

Error

The difference between a measured value and the true or intended value of a quantity. If you intend to weigh 100.00 g of a material, but actually weigh 100.05 g, you have made an error of +0.05 g.

Ester

A compound resulting from the combination of an organic acid with an alcohol.

Fatty Acid

An organic acid derived from the saponification of a fat or oil. Fatty acid molecules have a hydrophilic, acidic head group at one end, and a hydrophobic, hydrocarbon tail at the other. When neutralized with a base, fatty acids turn into soaps.

Fixed Oil

An oil that does not readily vaporize at room temperature. The boiling point of a fixed oil is much higher than that of water.

Gram Balance

A balance with a readability of 1 gram. A gram balance with a capacity of 7000 g may conveniently be used to make between 24 and 60 bars of soap.

Handcrafted Soap

Soap produced in small batches, usually less than 100 pounds. The most popular methods involve mixing fats, oils, alkali, and water at concentrations such that the alkali is completely consumed by the saponification reaction.

Hotdog

A fraction in which the numerator (top) is equal or equivalent to the denominator (bottom). In some sense, the top and bottom of a hotdog are the same, so a hotdog is numerically equal to 1 (one, unity). Hotdogs are called *unit factors* in many books.

Hot-process Soap

Soap produced by mixing fats, oils, alkali, and water at concentrations such that the alkali is completely consumed by the saponification reaction, which takes place in a heated container. Colorants, scents, and preservatives may be added before or after saponification is complete, but before the soap is pressed into the mold.

In the commodity soap industry, *hot process* refers to a process in which oil is heated with an excess of alkali. The soap floats to the top, leaving the glycerine behind in the spent lye. The fully saponified soap is removed, dried, mixed with colors and scents, and then pressed into bars.

Hydrocarbon

A molecule or moiety that contains only carbon and hydrogen. Hydrocarbons are non-polar and insoluble in water.

Hydrogen Bond

A bond between two molecules, each of which contains an OH bond.

Hygroscopic

A hygroscopic material absorbs humidity from the air.

Indicator

A substance that changes color in the presence of another substance. Phenolphthalein, for example, is colorless in acidic solutions and pink in alkaline ones.

Ionic Bond

A bond in which the bonding electrons are not shared. One atom or group of atoms holds all of the electrons that would have constituted a covalent bond if the electrons *had* been shared. The atom or group of atoms is called a negative ion, or *anion*. The atom or group of atoms that does not hold the bonding electrons is called a positive ion, or *cation*. The ionic "bond" is simply the mutual attraction between the oppositely charged cation and anion. A molecule with at least one ionic bond is deemed an ionic molecule.

Lye

An alkali, or, more commonly, an alkaline solution. In common usage, *lye* is used as a synonym for sodium hydroxide, but in this book it refers specifically to an aqueous sodium hydroxide solution with a concentration of 500 ppt.

Lye Discount

The practice of using less lye than is required for complete saponification. The result is that unsaponified oil or partially saponified oil remains in the finished soap.

Miscible

Mixable. Water and ethanol are miscible. Water and oil are immiscible.

Moiety

A recognizable part of a molecule. Acid and alcohol moieties, for example, may be identified in an ester. Fatty acid and glycerol moieties may be identified in a fat.

Molarity

A unit of concentration, mol/L. A 0.1 M solution is said to be "tenth molar" or to have a molarity of 0.1.

Mole

The amount of material containing the same number of atoms or molecules as there is in 12.00 grams of ^{12}C.

Molecular Model

A figure that shows the three-dimensional structure of a molecule. In this book, negatively charged atoms are shown in dark colors, positively charged atoms in light colors, and neutral atoms in medium colors.

Molecular Weight

The weight of one mole of a compound.

Neat Soap

A liquid-crystalline phase of soap, known in the handcrafted soapmaking community as "gel phase."

Non-polar Bond

A bond between two atoms that share electrical charge equally. A compound that contains only non-polar bonds is described as a non-polar compound.

Parts per Thousand (ppt)

The number of parts of one thing in 1000 parts of something else. For example, when we say that a soap contains 1 ppt residual alkali, we mean that there is 1 gram of alkali in 1000 g of soap. 1 ppt is 0.1%.

Percent

The number of parts of one thing in 100 parts of something else. For example, when we say that an oil blend is 25% olive oil by weight, we mean that there are 25 g of olive oil in 100 g of mixed oil. 1% is 10 ppt.

pH

The negative logarithm of the hydronium molarity. Acidic solutions have a low pH, alkaline solutions a high pH. pH = 14 - pOH.

Pipet

A fancy name for a medicine dropper. Modern disposable pipets are molded from a single piece of plastic and are particularly convenient for dispensing harsh chemicals.

pKa

A constant that characterizes the strength of an acid. Strong acids have a small pK_a (0–2); Weak acids have a high pK_a (3–10). When a solution contains an equal number of moles of an acid and its conjugate base, the pH is equal to pK_a.

pOH

The negative logarithm of the hydroxide molarity. Acidic solutions have a high pOH, alkaline solutions a low pOH. pOH = 14 - pH.

Polar Bond

A bond between two atoms that share electrical charge unequally. A compound that contains at least one polar bond is described as a polar compound.

Precision

A measure of the repeatability of a measurement. If, for example, I measure the saponification value of an oil twice, I might find it to be 197 ppt the first time and 192 ppt the second. My best estimate of the saponification value would be the average, 194.5 ppt. The precision is half the difference between the maximum and minimum values, or ±2.5 ppt. The precision should be rounded to a single digit, and I would express this saponification value as 195±3 ppt. A more sophisticated measure of precision is to be found in the standard deviation, σ_{n-1}, which may be calculated using a scientific calculator.

Primary Standard

A substance, usually a solution, whose concentration is known with confidence. Because high-purity citric acid is available to soapmakers, a 500 ppt citric acid solution is used as a primary standard in this book.

Proton

A hydrogen atom that may be transferred from an acid to a base. This is in contrast to hydrogen atoms, sometimes in the same molecules, that are not easily transferred.

Readability

The smallest incremental weight that a balance can register. If it can read 10.1 g, the readability is 0.1 g. If it can read 10.01 g, the readability is 0.01 g. The readability of a balance is also referred to as its resolution. The readability of a balance is usually assumed to be equal to the uncertainty in the weights it registers.

Relative Error

The error of a measured value divided by the actual value. Relative error is often expressed in percent or parts per thousand. An accurate value has a small relative error.

Relative Uncertainty

The uncertainty of a measured value divided by the measured value itself. Relative uncertainty is often expressed in percent or parts per thousand. A certain value has a small relative uncertainty.

Saponification

The chemical reaction by which oil is turned into soap. Three moles of alkali react with each mole of oil to produce three moles of soap and one mole of glycerol.

Saponification Value (SV)

The number of milligrams of KOH needed to saponify 1 g of oil *completely*. Whereas the alkali ratio is the actual ratio of alkali to oil in a given formula, the saponification value is the maximum value of the alkali ratio that may be used without producing an excessively alkaline soap.

Saturated Fat or Fatty Acid

A fat or fatty acid in which each of the interior carbon atoms is bonded to two hydrogen atoms and the terminal carbon atom is bonded to three hydrogen atoms. Since each carbon atom participates in four bonds, a saturated molecule has as many hydrogen atoms as can possibly fit on its carbon chain. Saturated fats may occur naturally, or they may be produced from unsaturated fats by reacting them with hydrogen gas in a process called *hydrogenation*.

Seizing

A condition in which raw soap thickens so rapidly that it can be poured only with difficulty. Seizing can prevent soap ingredients from being thoroughly mixed before the soap is poured into the mold. In extreme cases, the soap solidifies in the mixing container.

Soap Curd

A mixed solid soap phase. As many as three kinds of soap crystal may be present in ordinary bar soap.

Soap Formula

A kind of formula that gives the relative amounts of each ingredient in parts per thousand parts of oil. One form gives the relative amounts of oil, sodium hydroxide, and water. The other gives the relative amounts of oil and lye, where lye is assumed to be 500 ppt NaOH.

Sodium Saponification Value (SSV)

The number of milligrams of NaOH needed to saponify 1 g of oil *completely*. Whereas the alkali ratio is the actual ratio of alkali to oil in a given formula, the sodium saponification value is the maximum value of the alkali ratio that may be used without producing an excessively alkaline soap.

Stoichiometric Coefficient

The number in front of each participant in a balanced chemical equation.

Strong Acid/Base/Electrolyte

A strong acid, base, salt, or electrolyte is one that ionizes *completely* in aqueous solution. Sodium hydroxide is a strong base. Sodium chloride is a strong electrolyte.

Stoichiometry

The method used to answer questions like, "How many grams of A are required to react completely with a given weight of B?"

Structural Formula

A kind of formula that provides an easily drawn notation for the structure of a molecule. In the absence of other symbols, each line in the formula represents a carbon-carbon bond.

Superfatting

The practice of adding more than the stoichiometric quantity of fat or oil to the soap pot. The presumption is that the finished soap will contain unsaponified oil with desirable properties.

Titration

A procedure for measuring the amount of a substance by adding a solution with a known concentration (a standard) until a recognizable event occurs—usually a change in the color of an indicator.

Tongue Neutral

A term used to describe a soap that does not sting the tongue when it is tasted. A tongue-neutral soap registers a pH between 8 and 10 when tested with pH paper. For precise analytical work, a tongue-neutral soap has a total alkali of 0 ppt NaOH.

Total Alkali (TA)

The excess alkalinity of a soap expressed as milligrams of NaOH per gram of soap. A TA of 0 ppt is defined as tongue neutral. An ethanolic solution of a soap with a positive

TA turns phenolphthalein pink; one with a negative TA does not.

Trace

The point in the soapmaking process at which the soap surface no longer heals itself when disturbed. This corresponds to a viscosity of about 500 cP.

Triacylglyceride (TAG)

An ester of three fatty acids with glycerol.

Uncertainty

The magnitude of the last digit used to express a measured value. When a weight is given as 173 g, it is assumed to be between 172 g and 174 g, and the uncertainty is expressed as ± 1 g. When a weight is given as 173.2 g, it is assumed to be between 173.1 g and 173.3 g, and its uncertainty is ± 0.1 g.

Unsaturated Fat or Fatty Acid

A fat or fatty acid in which two or more interior carbon atoms are bonded to only one hydrogen atom each. Since each carbon atom participates in four bonds, an unsaturated molecule has fewer hydrogen atoms than the maximum number possible. Two consecutive carbon atoms share a double bond to make up for the bonds to the missing hydrogen atoms. Molecules with one carbon double bond are monounsaturated and those with more than one are polyunsaturated.

Volatile

Chemists endow the word *volatile* with a very specific meaning. A volatile substance is simply one that evaporates easily, nothing more, nothing less. It has nothing to do with being flammable, unstable, or explosive. Gasoline and butane are volatile, but so are water, ammonia, and vanilla. Volatile substances tend to have low molecular weight or weak intermolecular forces. Water and ammonia fall into the first category, gasoline and vanilla into the second.

Weak Acid/Base/Electrolyte

A weak acid, base, salt, or electrolyte is one that ionizes *incompletely* in aqueous solution. Ammonium hydroxide is a weak base. All fatty acids are weak acids.

Weighing Analytically

When weighing something analytically, it is not important to hit the weight target exactly. Whatever the weight turns out to be, however, you should record all of the digits of that weight.

Weighing Synthetically

When weighing something synthetically, it is very important to hit the weight target as closely as possible. Whether or not you hit the target exactly, you should record all of the digits of that weight.

Yield

The yield is calculated by dividing the weight of material that comes out of a procedure by the total weight of materials that went into it. In making soap, for example, the weight of the finished soap is divided by the total weight of its ingredients. The yield is generally expressed as a percent. A high soap yield would indicate that the raw soap was thin when poured, a low yield that it was thick.

References

Vendors

[1] AAA Chemicals, 601 Oakdale Street, Shoreacres, TX 77571.
www.AAA-Chemicals.com, accessed June 8, 2007.
Sodium and potassium hydroxides

[2] Boyer Corporation, P.O. Box 10, La Grange, IL 60525, Phone:
(800) 323-3040.
www.BoyerCorporation.com, accessed June 8, 2007.
Sodium and potassium hydroxides

[3] Bramble Berry, 2138 Humboldt St., Bellingham, WA 98225,
Phone: (877) 627-7883.
www.BrambleBerry.com, accessed July 4, 2007.
Fats and oils, general soapmaking supplies, lye calculator

[4] Camden-Grey Essential Oils, 3579 NW 82 Ave., Doral, FL
33122, Phone: (305) 500-9630.
www.CamdenGrey.com, accessed July 4, 2007.
Fats, oils, essential oils, lye

[5] Certified Lye, PO Box 133, Spring Valley, CA 91976, Phone:
(619) 548-2378.
www.CertifiedLye.com, accessed June 11, 2007.
Sodium hydroxide

[6] The Chemistry Store, 1133 Walter Price Street, Cayce, SC
29033, Phone: (800) 224-1430.
www.ChemistryStore.com, accessed July 4, 2007.
Fats and oils, additives

[7] Columbus Foods, 730 N. Albany Avenue, Chicago, IL 60612,
Phone: (800) 322-6457.
www.SoapersChoice.com, accessed May 27, 2007.
Fats and oils, lye calculator

[8] Consolidated Plastics, 8181 Darrow Road, Twinsburg, OH
44087, Phone: (800) 362-1000.
www.ConsolidatedPlastics.com, accessed March 20, 2008.
Plastic jugs, pails, drums, spigots, and drum taps

[9] Cynmar Corporation, 21709 Route 4 North, P.O. Box 530, Carlinville, IL 62626, Phone: (800) 223-3517.
www.Cynmar.com, accessed May 27, 2007.
Fats and oils

[10] Essential Wholesale, 8850 SE Herbert Ct, Clackamas, OR 97015, Phone: (503) 722-7557.
www.EssentialWholesale.com, accessed May 27, 2007.
Essential oils, cosmetic supplies

[11] For Crafts Sake, 601 Oakdale Street, Shoreacres, TX 77571.
www.ForCraftsSake.com, accessed June 8, 2007.
Molds and soap cutting equipment

[12] Gaily Rebecca Soaps.
www.SoapnSupplies.com, accessed June 11, 2007.
ProForm molds and presses

[13] General Electric.
www.geHousewares.com, accessed March 8, 2008
Roaster ovens

[14] Glory Bee Foods, Inc., 120 N. Seneca Rd, Eugene, OR 97402, Phone: (800) 456-7923.
www.GloryBeeFoods.com, accessed July 1, 2007.
A full line of soapmaking supplies and equipment, particularly bulk oils

[15] Grain Processing Corporation, 1600 Oregon Street, Muscatine, IA 52761-1494, Phone: (563) 264-4265.
www.GrainProcessing.com, accessed Dec 1, 2007.
Grain alcohol and SDA alcohol

[16] Labelmaster, Phone: (800) 621-5808.
www.Labelmaster.com, accessed May 28, 2007.
Chemical labels

[17] Lebermuth, Phone: (800) 648-1123.
www.Lebermuth.com, accessed July 4, 2007.
Essential oils, fragrances

[18] Lotion Crafter, 532 Point Lawrence Road, Olga, WA 98279, Phone: (360) 376-8008.
www.LotionCrafter.com, accessed May 27, 2007.
Additives, cosmetic supplies

[19] Luxco, 5050 Kemper Avenue, St. Louis, MO 63139, Phone: (314) 772-2626.
www.Luxco.com, accessed Dec 1, 2007.

Makers of Everclear grain alcohol

[20] Majestic Mountain Sage, 918 West 700 North Ste 104, Logan, UT 84321.
www.TheSage.com, accessed July 4, 2007.
Fats and oils, general soapmaking supplies, lye calculator

[21] Mallinckrodt Baker, Phillipsburg, NJ.
www.MallBaker.com, accessed March 8, 2008.
A global chemical company. Use their search box to find information on *Saf-T-Data Labeling*.

[22] Mission Peak Soap, P.O. Box 2086, Fremont, CA 94536, Phone: (510) 795-1326.
www.MissionPeakSoap.com, accessed June 30, 2007.
Fats and oils

[23] Mission Restaurant Supply, 1126 S. St. Mary's, San Antonio, TX 78210, Phone: (800) 319-0690.
www.MissionRS.com, accessed April 8, 2008.
Restaurant supplies, stick blenders

[24] Norcross Corporation, 225 Newtonville Avenue, Newton, MA 02458, Phone: (617) 969-7020.
www.Viscosity.com, accessed February 28, 2010.
Restaurant supplies, stick blenders

[25] Oils by Nature, 30300 Solon Industrial Parkway Suite E, Solon, OH 44139, Phone: (440) 498-1180.
www.OilsByNature.com, accessed July 4, 2007.
Fats, oils, essential oils

[26] Old Will Knott Scales, Professional Retail Service, 1738 S Van Buren St, Enid, OK 73703, Phone: (866) 867-5400.
www.OldWillKnottScales.com, accessed July 1, 2007.
Balances

[27] Pharmco-AAPER, 1101 Isaac Shelby Drive, Shelbyville, KY 40065, Phone: (800) 456-1017.
www.Pharmco-Prod.com, accessed Dec 1, 2007.
Grain alcohol and SDA alcohol

[28] Pine Meadows, 860 N. 1430 W., Orem, UT 84057, Phone: (801) 221-0483.
www.PineMeadows.net/, accessed July 4, 2007.
Fats and oils, general soapmaking supplies, lye calculator

[29] Radio Shack.
www.RadioShack.com, accessed March 8, 2008.
Electronic gadgets, including infrared thermometers

[30] Restaurant Equipment World, 2413 Forsyth Road, Orlando, FL 32807, Phone: (800) 821-9153.
www.RestaurantEquipment.net/, accessed April 8, 2008.
Restaurant supplies, stick blenders, immersion blenders

[31] Rival Products.
www.RivalProducts.com, accessed March 8, 2008.
Roaster ovens

[32] Safety Emporium, Phone: (856) 449-8956.
www.SafetyEmporium.com, accessed May 24, 2008.
Chemical labels and safety equipment

[33] Science Company, 95 Lincoln St., Denver, CO 80203, Phone: (800) 372-6726.
www.ScienceCompany.com, accessed January 29, 2008.
Chemicals, laboratory equipment

[34] Science Lab, 14025 Smith Rd., Houston, TX 77396, Phone: (800) 901-7247.
www.ScienceLab.com, accessed July 6, 2007.
Chemicals, laboratory equipment

[35] Shay & Company, 7941 S.E. Steele Street, Suite # 2, Portland, OR 97206, Phone: (877) 293-5035.
www.ShayAndCompany.com, accessed June 30, 2007.
Fats and oils

[36] Shoppers Vineyard, 875 Bloomfield Avenue, Clifton, NJ 07012, Phone: 973) (916-0707.
www.ShoppersVineyard.com, accessed December 1, 2007.
Grain alcohol

[37] Sigma-Aldrich Chemicals, 3050 Spruce Street, Saint Louis, MO 63103.
www.SigmaAldrich.com, accessed March 6, 2010.
Fine chemicals

[38] Smart Home.
www.SmartHome.com, accessed March 8, 2008.
Home automation, including digital timer switches

[39] Snowdrift Farm, 2750 S. 4th Ave., Suites 107/108, Tucson, AZ 85713, Phone: (888) 999-6950.
www.SnowdriftFarm.com, accessed July 4, 2007.
Fats and oils, lye, essential oils, lye calculator

[40] Taylored Concepts, 12021 Plano Road Suite#190, Dallas, TX 75243, Phone: (866) 322-9944.
www.TayloredConcepts.com, accessed July 4, 2007.

Fats and oils, additives

[41] Upland Soap Factory, 213 Flynn Branch Road, Marshall, NC 28753, Phone: (828) 649-0303.
www.UplandSoapFactory.com, accessed July 1, 2007.
Soap molds

[42] Wholesale Supplies Plus, 10035 Broadview Rd, Broadview Heights, OH 44147, Phone: (800) 359-0944.
www.WholesaleSuppliesPlus.com, accessed July 8, 2007.
Waxes, additives, colors, essential oils

[43] Willow Way, 5697 East 300 North, Greenfield, IN 46140, Phone: (317) 467-8645.
www.SoapEquipment.com, accessed July 9, 2007.
Large-scale soap equipment

[44] Wine Chateau, 160 Durham Ave., Metuchen, NJ 08840, Phone: (800) 946-3190.
www.WineChateau.com, accessed December 1, 2007.
Grain alcohol

Safety and Hygiene

[45] *Occupational Health and Safety* (OSHA), 2004.

Lye Calculators

[46] *Lye-On*, Kevin M. Dunn, www.ScientificSoapmaking.com, 2009.
This is a spreadsheet developed as a supplement to *Scientific Soapmaking*.

[47] *SoapCalc*, BRL Enterprises, Inc, www.SoapCalc.com, 2007.
This is an online calculator with many options. Your formulas may be stored as cookies on your computer.

[48] *SoapMaker*, Woodman Designs, 1080 Brooke Valley Rd., Perth, Ontario K7H 3C6, www.SoapMaker.ca/, 2007.
This is a powerful calculator that includes pricing and inventory management. A 30-day trial version may be downloaded for free, after which a licence must be purchased.

[49] *Soapmaking Recipe Template*, Millers Homemade Soap Pages, www.MillerSoap.com, 2007.
This website contains an Excel spreadsheet by Chris Mathes.

[50] *Soapsheet*, Soul Gazer Sundries, Bossier City, LA 71111, Phone: (318)470-0171, www.FutureVenturesOnline.com, 2007.
This website contains an updated variation of the Chris Mathes Excel spreadsheet.

Handcrafted Soap Books

[51] Ann Bramson, *Soap: Making it, Enjoying It*, 1972, ISBN 0-911104-57-7.

[52] Susan Cavitch, *The Soapmaker's Companion*, 1997, ISBN 0-88266-965-6.

[53] Marie Gale, *Soap & Cosmetic Labeling*, Cinnabar Press, Broadbent, OR, 2007, ISBN 978-0-9795945-0-2.

[54] Robert McDaniel, *Essentially Soap*, Krause Publications, Iola, WI, 2000, 125 pp., ISBN 0-87341-832-8.
This is the book that introduced INS to the handcrafted soap community.

[55] Anne Watson, *Smart Soapmaking*, 2007, ISBN 978-0-938497-42-4.

Journal Articles

[56] Sayed Abbas, Jessica Goldberg, and Michael Massaro, "Personal Cleanser Technology and Clinical Performance", *Dermatologic Therapy*, 2004, 17, pp. 35-42.

[57] R. Ahmad, R. Kahn, M. Naushahi, M. Iqbal, and G. Kahn, "Saponification Catalysts", *Pakistan Journal of Science and Industrial Research*, 1997, 40, (1-4), pp. 44-46.

[58] "ASTM D460-91(2005) Standard Test Methods for Sampling and Chemical Analysis of Soaps and Soap Products", ASTM International, West Conshohocken, PA, www.astm.org, 2005.

[59] Marcellin Berthelot, "On the Compounds of Glycerine with Acids", *Quarterly Journal of the Chemical Society of London*, 1855, VII, pp. 282-286.

[60] Karl Beyer, "Final Report on the Safety of Sodium Lauryl Sulfate and Ammonium Lauryl Sulfate", *International Journal of Toxicology*, 1983, 2, (7), pp. 127-181.

[61] E. Caley, "The Stockholm Papyrus", *Journal of Chemical Education*, 1927, 3, pp. 992-999.

[62] R. H. Ferguson, F. B. Rosevear, and R. C. Stillman, "Solid Soap Phases", *Industrial and Engineering Chemistry*, 1943, 35, (9), pp. 1005-1012.

[63] Mark Flair, William Setzer, "An Olfactory Indicator for Acid Base Titrations", *Journal of Chemical Education*, 1990, 67, 9, pp. 795-796.

[64] J. R. Kanicky, A. F. Poniatowski, N. R. Mehta, and D. O. Shah, "Cooperativity among Molecules at Interfaces in Relation to Various Technological Processes: Effect of Chain Length on the pK_a of Fatty Acid Salt Solutions", *Langmuir*, 2000, 16, (1), pp. 172-177.

[65] J. R. Kanicky and D. O. Shah, "Effect of Degree, Type, and Position of Unsaturation on the pK_a of Long Chain Fatty Acids", *Journal of Colloid and Interface Science*, 2002, 256, pp. 201-207.

[66] R. S. Lanigan and T. A. Yamarik, "Final Report on the Safety Assessment of BHT", *International Journal of Toxicology*, 2002, 21, (2), pp. 19–94.

[67] R. S. Lanigan and T. A. Yamarik, "Final Report on the Safety Assessment of EDTA, Calcium Disodium EDTA, Diammonium EDTA, Dipotassium EDTA, Disodium EDTA, TEA-EDTA, Tetrasodium EDTA, Tripotassium EDTA, Trisodium EDTA, HEDTA, and Trisodium HEDTA", *International Journal of Toxicology*, 2002, 21, (2), pp. 95–142.

[68] "Final Report of the Safety Assessment of Lithium Stearate, Aluminum Distearate, Aluminum Stearate, Aluminum Tristearate, Ammonium Stearate, Calcium Stearate, Magnesium Stearate, Potassium Stearate, Sodium Stearate, and Zinc Stearate", *International Journal of Toxicology*, 1982, 1, 2, 143-177.

[69] Russell Moore, "The Relation of Cocoanut Oil to the Various Methods of Butter Analysis", *Journal of the American Chemical Society*, 1885, VII, pp. 188-193.

[70] Richard Ramette, "Gravimetric Titrations: In Support of Weight Titration Techniques", *Journal of Chemical Education*, 2004, 81, 12, p. 1715.

[71] Naoki Watabe, Yoshikazu Tokuoka, and Norimichi Kawashima, "Influence of Synthetic Perfumes on Stability of O/W Emulsion in Sodium Dodecyl

Sulfate-n-Dodecane-Water Ternary Systems", *Colloid Polymer Science*, 2008, 286, pp. 769-776.

Books

[72] *Official Methods and Practices of the AOCS*, American Oil Chemists' Society, Champaign, IL, 2003.

A very large and expensive book of methods for measuring just about anything that can be measured for oils, soaps, and detergents.

[73] William Brannt, *A Practical Treatise on the Manufacture of Soap and Candles*, Henry Carey Baird, Philadelphia, 1888.

Page 90 lists saponification values used to characterize oils, but they are not mentioned in the discussion of the cold process.

[74] Jean-Antoine Chaptal, *Chemistry Applied to Arts and Manufactures*, Richard Phillips, London, 1807.

Volume IV, pages 370-372 contain a chapter on "soaps formed without heat."

[75] Michel Eugène Chevreul, *A Chemical Study of Oils and Fats of Animal Origin*, American Oil Chemists' Society, Champaign, IL, 2009, ISBN 9782953324402.

English translation of the 1823 classic, *Recherches Chimiques sur les Corps Gras d'Origine Animale*. In this work, Chevreul elucidated the chemical nature of oils, identified and named glycerin and several fatty acids, and articulated the stoichiometric hypothesis of saponification.

[76] *Solubilization in Surfactant Aggregates*, Edited by Sherril Christian and John Scamehorn, Marcel Dekker, New York, NY, 1995, ISBN 0824790995.

Everything you ever wanted to know about micelles.

[77] J. Davidsohn, E. Better, and A. Davidsohn, *Soap Manufacture*, Interscience Publishers, New York, NY, 1953, I.

This book contains a section on catalysts for saponification on pages 36-37.

[78] William B. Dick, *Encyclopedia Of Practical Receipts And Processes*, Dick and Fitzgerald, New York, NY, 1872, ISBN 0824790995.

This book describes trace in cold-process soap.

[79] *Dictionary.com Unabridged (v1.1)*, Random House, www. Dictionary.com, accessed April 13, 2008.

[80] *Physical and Chemical Characteristics of Oils, Fats, and Waxes*, Second, Edited by David Firestone, American Oil Chemists' Society, Champaign, IL, 2006, ISBN 9781893997998.
The title says everything. Data is given for just about any oil, fat, or wax.

[81] Claudius Galenus, *Opera Omnia*, Georg Olms Verlag, 2001.
Kuhn Book X, page 569 and Book XII, page 589 are cited.

[82] Philip Kurten, *The Art of Manufacturing Soaps*, Lindsay and Blackiston, Philadelphia, 1854.
The state of the art in 1854. This book describes the cold process as a recent innovation, placing its invention between 1839 and 1844. A table of alkali ratios for the cold process appears on page 114.

[83] Campbell Morfit, *Chemistry Applied to the Manufacture of Soap and Candles*, Carey and Hart, Philadelphia, 1847.
The state of the art in 1847. Pages 227-233 describe "extemporaneous" (cold-process) soaps as alternatives to mainstream boiled soaps. The process given here is more detailed than that provided by Chaptal forty years earlier.

[84] Drew Myers, *Surfaces, Interfaces, and Colloids*, Second, Wiley-VCH, New York, NY, 1999, ISBN 0471330604.
Everything you ever wanted to know about emulsions, colloids, and surfactants.

[85] Antonio Neto and Silvio Salinas, *The Physics of Lyotropic Liquid Crystals*, Oxford University Press, Oxford, 2005, ISBN 0198525508.
Everything you ever wanted to know about lyotropic liquid crystals, including neat soap.

[86] *The Complete Technology Book on Soaps*, National Institute of Industrial Research, Asia Pacific Business Press, Delhi, 2004, ISBN 8178330512.
This book focuses mainly on commodity soapmaking, but has some information on soap formulations and analytical techniques.

[87] Thomas Osborne, *The Harleian Miscellany*, Osborne, 1745, IV.

Osborne summarizes the contents of a pamphlet entitled *A Short and True Relation, Concerning the Soap Business,* a contemporary account of the Westminster soap monopoly of 1631. Page 180 is cited.

[88] Adolph Ott, *The Art of Manufacturing Soap and Candles,* Lindsay and Blackiston, Philadelphia, 1867.

This book describes the cold process and the phenomenon we would recognize as trace (page 101).

[89] Alexander Petrov, *The Lyotropic State of Matter,* Gordon and Breach Science Publishers, Amsterdam, 1999, ISBN 905699638X.

This book explores the physics and chemistry of lyotropic liquid crystals, of which neat soap is an example.

[90] Pliny, *Natural History,* Harvard University Press, Cambridge, 1962, ISBN 0674993888.

An encyclopedia of the first century AD. Book XXVIII, page li is cited.

[91] William Price, *The English Patents of Monopoly,* Harvard University Press, Cambridge, 1913.

This book includes a full account of the Westminster soap monopoly of 1631. Pages 119-128 are cited.

[92] *Mappae Clavicula,* Edited by Cyril Smith and John Hawthorne, American Philosophical Society, Philadelphia, 1974, ISBN 0871696444.

This is a medieval collection of trade secrets for painters and artisans. Item 280 is cited.

[93] Alexander Watt, *The Art of Soap-Making,* Crosby Lockwood and Son, London, 1896.

This book notes that the introduction of solid sodium hydroxide onto the market may make the cold process more viable than it had been (page 81). The cited patent description is from page 2.

[94] E. T. Webb, *Soap and Glycerine Manufacture,* Davis Brothers, London, 1927, 224 pp.

A very good book for the soap chemist of the day. Unlike many commodity soap writers, he is not dismissive of the cold process. His description of trace appears on page 116.

Molecular Models

Molecular models for this book and its cover were generated using four computer programs. First, the molecular geometries were optimized at the PM3 level of theory using the Ghemical program. Second, Lowdin atomic charges were calculated at the HF/3-21G level of theory using the Gamess program. Third, the Jmol program was used to construct models with atoms colored according to charge. Finally, the POV-Ray program was used to render the graphics. Websites for these programs were current as of May 21, 2008.

[95] Gamess, www.msg.ameslab.gov/gamess/gamess.html, accessed May 21, 2008.

[96] Ghemical, www.bioinformatics.org/ghemical/, accessed May 21, 2008.

[97] Jmol, www.jmol.org, accessed May 21, 2008.

[98] POV-Ray, www.povray.org, accessed May 21, 2008.

Software

[99] GNU Image Manipulation Program, www.gimp.org, accessed May 21, 2008.

The GIMP is a program for manipulating and analyzing images. It was used to measure color density of soaps in the study of DOS.

About the Author

Kevin Dunn is the Elliott Professor of Chemistry at Hampden-Sydney College. He holds a BS degree from the University of Chicago and a PhD from the University of Texas at Austin. He appears on the Learning Channel's *Mysteries of Magic* and the History Channel's *Modern Marvels*. He lives in central Virginia with his wife and several cats.

[100] Kevin M. Dunn, *Caveman Chemistry*, Universal Publishers, 2003, ISBN 1581125666.

[101] Kevin M. Dunn, "The Dreaded Orange Spot", *Journal of the Handcrafted Soap Makers Guild*, Winter 2005/2006.

[102] Kevin M. Dunn, "A Brief Introduction to Chemistry", *Journal of the Handcrafted Soap Makers Guild*, 2006.

[103] Kevin M. Dunn, "Superfatting and the Lye Discount", *Journal of the Handcrafted Soap Makers Guild*, 2007-2.

[104] Kevin M. Dunn, "The Water Discount", *Journal of the Handcrafted Soap Makers Guild*, 2008-2.

[105] Kevin M. Dunn, John Campbell, Andrew Basinger, Tyler Bowman, "How Time and Temperature Affect the Soap-making Process", *Journal of the Handcrafted Soap Makers Guild*, 2009-2.

Colophon

Scientific Soapmaking was composed in DocBook and typeset via JadeTeX using a custom stylesheet. The interior fonts are Schola, Pagella, Heros, and Chorus from the TeX-Gyre font family. The cover font is Fletcher Gothic.

[106] Art Parts/Ron and Joe, Inc., PO Box 6547, Santa Ana, CA 92706, Phone: (714) 834-9166, www.RonAndJoe.com, accessed July 14, 2007.
Clip art

[107] Comprehensive TeX Archive Network, www.CTAN.org, accessed March 10, 2010.
JadeTeX, XyMTeX, TeX-Gyre fonts

[108] DocBook, www.DocBook.org, accessed March 10, 2010.

[109] OpenJade, www.OpenJade.Sourceforge.net/, accessed March 10, 2010.

Index

CPSIA information can be obtained at www.ICGtesting.com
Printed in the USA
LVOW08s0236301014

411214LV00001B/47/P